Instructor's Resource Manual

PRABHA RAMAKRISHNAN
North Carolina State University

Instructor Notes on ConcepTest Questions

CORNELIUS BENNHOLD
The George Washington University

—

GERALD FELDMAN
The George Washington University

PHYSICS
for Scientists and Engineers
THIRD EDITION

FISHBANE | GASIOROWICZ | THORNTON

PEARSON
Prentice Hall

Upper Saddle River, NJ 07458

Associate Editor: Christian Botting
Senior Editor: Erik Fahlgren
Editor-in-Chief, Science: John Challice
Vice President of Production & Manufacturing: David W. Riccardi
Executive Managing Editor: Kathleen Schiaparelli
Assistant Managing Editor: Becca Richter
Production Editor: Elizabeth Klug
Supplement Cover Management/Design: Paul Gourhan
Supplement Cover Designer: Christopher Kossa
Manufacturing Buyer: Ilene Kahn

© 2005 Pearson Education, Inc.
Pearson Prentice Hall
Pearson Education, Inc.
Upper Saddle River, NJ 07458

The author and publisher of this book have used their best efforts in preparing this book. These efforts include the development, research, and testing of the theories and programs to determine their effectiveness. The author and publisher make no warranty of any kind, expressed or implied, with regard to these programs or the documentation contained in this book. The author and publisher shall not be liable in any event for incidental or consequential damages in connection with, or arising out of, the furnishing, performance, or use of these programs.

Printed in the United States of America

10 9 8 7 6 5 4 3 2 1

ISBN 0-13-141738-X

Pearson Education Ltd., *London*
Pearson Education Australia Pty. Ltd., *Sydney*
Pearson Education Singapore, Pte. Ltd.
Pearson Education North Asia Ltd., *Hong Kong*
Pearson Education Canada, Inc., *Toronto*
Pearson Educación de Mexico, S.A. de C.V.
Pearson Education—Japan, *Tokyo*
Pearson Education Malaysia, Pte. Ltd.

Instructor's Resource Manual

PRABHA RAMAKRISHNAN
North Carolina State University

PHYSICS
for Scientists and Engineers
THIRD EDITION

FISHBANE | GASIOROWICZ | THORNTON

Instructor's Resource Manual

to accompany *Physics for Scientists and Engineers 3rd edition,* **by Paul M. Fishbane, Stephen G. Gasiorowicz, and Stephen T. Thornton**

Table of Contents

Introduction to the Instructor's Resource Manual

In writing the *Instructor's Resource Manual for Physics for Scientists and Engineers*, third edition, by Paul Fishbane, Stephen Gasiorowicz, and Stephen Thornton, I have those instructors in mind who are new to teaching physics or this particular course. I hope that experienced instructors will find this manual useful as well. I have had the opportunity to teach the so-called *physics for poets* course to liberal arts students, the algebra-based course for non-engineering science majors, and the calculus-based course for the engineering majors. I have taught physics at a Community College as well as at a major Research University. This manual draws heavily from my many years of experience in these different situations. Obviously, teaching styles vary, and so I hope you will use the material in this manual to suit your particular style.

The majority of students in this course will be aspiring engineers who will come in with the view that physics is a hard subject to master. Many would not have had any physics in high school. In two semesters, we try to cram in as much material as we can and expect the students to achieve a certain level of mastery. It is no wonder that they have this built-in fear of the subject. It is hence very important that we as instructors, address this fear from the very beginning. Physics is a very logical subject. It is certainly not just a course with a bunch of formulae that students can plug numbers into. A lot will depend on our approach to teaching, how well prepared we are, and how interesting we can make the class. So the more structured the class is, the more successful we will be in easing students' anxieties and fears.

Demonstrations and visual aids will stimulate students' interest in the subject matter. Try to relate the concepts to a particular field of engineering, wherever possible. This always helps students to realize why they are enrolled in this class. Show them why they need a good foundation in physics if they want to be nuclear engineers, chemical engineers, aeronautical engineers, civil engineers, computer science engineers, etc. Discussing the connection between the topics in the textbook and the cutting edge research in these areas will help maintain students' interest in the subject matter. It is very important that we do not reduce the class to a mere discussion of what students perceive as physics that has nothing to do with the present-day world.

Course Organization and Structure

As mentioned earlier, how successful your semester is will depend on how you structure the course and how organized you are. Providing students with a syllabus that includes reading assignments, homework assignments, test dates, and grading scheme will ensure that students learn to structure their studies around this syllabus.

Quite often we tend to forget how difficult it is to keep one's interest on task for the full 50 minutes. To keep the students' attention from wandering, minimize the time spent on lecturing and try to vary the format of the class. Discussion of the previous day's material, a quick quiz at the beginning or end of class, five minutes to address concerns regarding homework assignments, a demonstration to introduce the next topic, cooperative learning through group problem solving could all be used at various times during the class to maintain a level of interest that is conducive to learning. Encourage students to be active learners by encouraging participation in class.

How often we have heard the litany that problem solving is very hard. To demystify this task, be sure to solve problems in a structured and systematic way in class every time you work an example on the board. If possible, schedule an hour of problem-solving sessions each week when you can make yourself available to help students. Better yet, have it in a classroom where you can encourage students to work in groups and you can circulate around as a facilitator. Homework assignments ensure that students learn to work problems on their own, and it also provides you with some valuable feedback. Finding time to grade problems is not always easy. However, for students to value the homework assignments and to ensure that they are an effective learning tool, consider grading at least part of the assignment each week. There are several on-line homework delivery systems available that take away the grading chore from your busy schedule. Consider using one of these if possible.

Quizzes and tests are important for two reasons. First, they encourage students to not get behind in the course. Second, they provide the necessary feedback to you and the students. You, as the instructor, will be able to evaluate your students on a regular basis. The students, for their part, will know how they are performing in class and accordingly modify their approach to the course.

Quizzes need not take up too much of class time. A quick quiz at the beginning or end of the class followed by a discussion of the correct answers will help students clarify questions they may have on the material covered in the previous class. It will encourage them to attend class regularly and keep up with the reading assignments before each class. As an option or in addition to in-class quizzes, consider giving a web quiz before each class. Use the Just in Time teaching method (see reference on page xxi, preface to the textbook) to get feedback on students understanding (or lack thereof) of the material discussed in the previous class.

Three to four tests per semester and a final exam is standard practice for most physics courses. While we may feel that tests take up valuable class time, it helps to keep students on track during the semester. If you are responsible for the tests, consider including a good mixture of conceptual questions and problems. To de-emphasize memorization of formulas, consider providing a formula sheet. Some instructors allow students to bring an index card instead. However, it is hard to monitor the content of these cards. In some large departments where there are multiple sections of the same course, the tests are written by one faculty member (or a committee) and administered at a common time to all the students. If such is the case, it might be good to have an idea of the kind of test given in your department to ensure that you have covered the required material and done so on time for the test. There will always be students who will miss a test and need to make it up at a later date. Makeup test policy should be clearly outlined in the syllabus and consistently applied through the semester.

How the course is graded will depend on the different components to the course as well as departmental practices. Whatever the grading scheme, it is very important that it is clearly stated in the syllabus and explained to students at the beginning of the semester. If changes are to be made midway through the semester, these should be consistently applied to all students in the class. See the suggested grading scale included in the sample syllabus.

Sample schedules

Most departments offer either three 50-minute meetings or two 75-minute meetings per week for 15 weeks. The sample schedules given below address both of these options. Time is allowed for three tests per semester or two tests per quarter. The final exam is a comprehensive one, and it is assumed that there is a separate time period allotted for the exam at the end of the semester or quarter. Note that the second semester covers more material than the first one. Hence, you will find the schedule to be very tight. If you decide to omit certain topics, try not to exclude relativity and quantum physics.

SCHEDULE FOR A TWO-SEMESTER COURSE: FIRST SEMESTER Mechanics, Oscillations and Wave Motion, Fluids, and Thermodynamics		
Chapter	No. of 50-min. lectures (3/week)	No. of 75-min. lectures (2/week)
Ch. 1	1	1
Ch. 2	2	1.5
Ch.3	2	1
Ch. 4	2	1
Ch. 5	2	1.5
Test 1	1	1
Ch. 6	2	1
Ch. 7	2	1.5
Ch. 8	2.5	1.5
Ch. 9	2	1.5
Ch. 10	2.5	1.5
Test 2	1	1
Ch. 11	2	1.5
Ch. 12	1.5	1
Ch. 13	2	1
Ch. 14	2	1.5
Ch. 15	1.5	1
Test 3	1	1
Ch. 16	2.5	2
Ch. 17	2	1
Ch. 18	2	1.5
Ch. 19	2.5	2
Ch. 20	2.5	1.5
Review	1.5	1
TOTAL	**45**	**30**

SCHEDULE FOR A TWO-SEMESTER COURSE: SECOND SEMESTER Electricity and Magnetism, Optics, Modern Physics, and Quantum Mechanics		
Chapter	No. of 50-min. lectures (3/week)	No. of 75-min. lectures (2/week)
Ch. 21	2	1
Ch. 22	1.5	1
Ch. 23	1	1
Ch. 24	1.5	1
Ch. 25	1.5	1
Ch. 26	1.5	1
Ch. 27	2	1
Test 1	1	1
Ch. 28	2	1.5
Ch. 29	2	1
Ch. 30	2	1
Ch. 31	1.5	1
Ch. 32	2	1.5
Ch. 33	1.5	1
Test 2	1	1
Ch. 34	1.5	1
Ch. 35	1.5	1
Ch. 36	1.5	1
Ch. 37	1.5	1
Ch. 38	2	1
Ch. 39	2	1
Test 3	1	1
Ch. 40	1.5	1
Ch. 41	1.5	1
Ch. 42	1.5	1
Ch. 43	2	1.5
Ch. 44	2	1.5
Ch. 45	1.5	1
TOTAL	**45**	**30**

The schedule for the quarter system, as you can see, is not as balanced over the three quarters. This is unavoidable if you do not wish to split major topics between quarters. A second option (which is not my preference) would be to switch wave mechanics and thermodynamics and move fluids to the third quarter.

SCHEDULE FOR A THREE-QUARTER COURSE: FIRST QUARTER Mechanics, Oscillations and Wave Motion, and Fluids		
Chapter	No. of 50-min. lectures (3/week)	No. of 75-min. lectures (2/week)
Ch. 1	1	1
Ch. 2	2	1
Ch. 3	1.5	1
Ch. 4	1.5	1
Ch. 5	2	1
Ch. 6	1.5	1
Ch. 7	1.5	1
Test 1	1	1
Ch. 8	2	1
Ch. 9	2	1.5
Ch. 10	2	1.5
Ch. 11	2	1
Test 2	1	1
Ch. 12	1.5	1
Ch. 13	2	1.5
Ch. 14	2	1
Ch. 15	1.5	1
Ch. 16	2	1.5
TOTAL	30	20

SCHEDULE FOR A THREE-QUARTER COURSE: SECOND QUARTER Thermodynamics, Electricity and Magnetism		
Chapter	No. of 50-min. lectures (3/week)	No. of 75-min. lectures (2/week)
Ch. 17	1	1
Ch. 18	1.5	1.5
Ch. 19	2	1
Ch. 20	2	1.5
Ch. 21	1.5	1
Ch. 22	1.5	1
Ch. 23	1.5	1
Test 1	1	1
Ch. 24	1.5	1
Ch. 25	2	1
Ch. 26	1.5	1
Ch. 27	2	1
Ch. 28	1.5	1
Ch. 29	1.5	1
Test 2	1	1
Ch. 30	2	1
Ch. 31	1.5	1
Ch. 32	1.5	1
Ch. 33	2	1
TOTAL	30	20

SCHEDULE FOR A THREE-QUARTER COURSE: THIRD QUARTER Optics, Modern Physics, and Quantum Mechanics		
Chapter	No. of 50-min. lectures (3/week)	No. of 75-min. lectures (2/week)
Ch. 34	2.5	1.5
Ch. 35	2	1
Ch. 36	2	1.5
Ch. 37	2.5	1.5
Ch. 38	2	1.5
Test 1	1	1
Ch. 39	2.5	1.5
Ch. 40	2.5	1.5
Ch. 41	2	1.5
Ch. 42	2.5	1.5
Ch. 43	2.5	2
Test 2	1	1
Ch. 44	2.5	1.5
Ch. 45	2.5	1.5
TOTAL	30	20

On the next page I have included a sample syllabus for Fall 2004. Note that it includes all of the pertinent information regarding class policies, attendance, reading and homework assignments, grading, test dates and makeup test policies.

Instructor:
  Office: *Phone:*   *E-mail:*
  Office hours: 11:30–1:00 MW, 2:00–4:00 TH or by appointment

Text:

- The *prerequisite* for PY 205 is MA 141 with a grade of *C* or better.
- **Attendance**: University policy requires that attendance be taken in each class. More importantly, keep in mind that attending classes regularly and participating in class discussions is essential to your success in this class.
- **Homework:** The *homework grade* will be determined from the online homework assignments at WebAssign (http://webassign.ncsu.edu/student.html). The first required assignment, *Introduction to Webassign*, is an orientation to the system. Assignments are of two kinds: questions and problems. Questions will be based on material to be covered and will be due one hour before class. No extensions will be given on these. Problems are due one class date after the completion of the material. Extensions to problem assignments will not be given without valid reasons. **Check due dates for each assignment.**
- **Extra Credit**: Weekly extra credit assignments will be posted on Webassign as well. While these are optional, keep in mind that these will be used to determine your final grade at the end of the semester.
- **Quizzes**: You can expect an average of two quizzes per week and these will be on material covered in the previous class. There will be no makeup quizzes. The lowest quiz grade will be dropped.
- **Tests**: Test dates are indicated on the schedule. Makeup tests will not be given without prior permission. *Practice tests* from previous (regular) semesters are available online on the course homepage.
- The *final average* in the course is computed as follows:

Three tests	40%	(10% lowest, 15% each other two)
Quizzes	10%	(includes in-class work as well)
Laboratory	10%	
Homework	15%	
Final Exam	25%	
	100%	

- **Labs**: Even-numbered lab sections begin on August 23, and odd-numbered lab sections begin on August 24. Take your lab manual and a calculator to the first lab. ***You must receive a score of 50% or better in lab in order to pass the course.*** For additional lab information go to http://www.physics.ncsu.edu/courses/pylabs/.
- The *Physics Tutorial Center* (132 Withers) offers a variety of tutoring services on a walk-in basis. The PTC will be open Monday through Friday. The hours are posted online at http://www.physics.ncsu.edu:8380/ptc/.
- If you have any special needs regarding this course, please see me as soon as possible.
- University policies regarding academic integrity and accommodations of students with disabilities may be found at http://www.fis.ncsu.edu/ncsulegal/41.03-codeof.htm and http://ncsu.edu/provost/offices/affirm_action/dss/.

Weekly Schedule

Week	Date	Chapter & Section	Suggested Problems
1	Aug.16	Chap. 1: 1–6 Chap. 2: 1–6	**1:** **2:**
2	Aug. 23	Chap. 3: 1–6 Chap. 4: 1–3	**3:** **4:**
3	Aug. 30	Chap. 4: 4–6 Chap. 5: 1–5	**4:** **5:**
4	**Sept. 8 (wed)**	**Test 1**	
	Sept. 10	Chap. 6: 1–2	**6:**
5	Sept. 13	Chap. 6: 3–6 Chap. 7: 1–4	**6:** **7:**
6	Sept. 20	Chap. 8: 8–6 Chap. 9: 1	**8:** **9:**
7	Sept. 27	Chap. 9: 2–6 Chap. 10: 1–4	**9:** **10:**
8	Oct. 4	Chap. 10: 5–7	**10:**
	Oct. 6	**Test 2**	
9	Oct. 11	Chap. 11: 1–4 Chap. 12: 1–4	**11:** **12:**
10	Oct. 18	Chap. 12: 4–5 Chap. 13: 1–8 Chap. 14: 1–2	**12:** **13:** **14:**
11	Oct. 25	Chap. 14: 3–8 Chap. 15: 1–5	**14:** **15:**
12	**Nov. 1**	**Test 3**	
	Nov. 3 (Wed)	Chap. 16: 1–6	**16:**
13	Nov. 8	Chap. 16: 7–8 Chap. 17: 1–4 Chap. 18: 1–3	**16:** **17:** **18:**
14	Nov. 15	Chap. 18: 4–8 Chap. 19: 1–2	**18:** **19:**
15	Nov. 22	Chap. 19: 3–6 Chap. 20: 1–4	**19:** **20:**
16	Nov. 29	Chap. 20: 5–7 Review	**20:**
	Dec. 6	**FINAL EXAM**	

Special Dates:

Monday, September 6: Holiday/no classes

Thursday–Friday, October 7–8: Fall break

Thursday–Friday, November 25–26: Thanksgiving holiday

Teaching Resources

Supplementary Materials

As an instructor, it is important that you familiarize yourself with all of the available supplementary materials and use them at every opportunity. Besides this *Instructor's Resource Manual*, the authors and publishers of *Physics for Scientists and Engineers*, 3rd edition, have provided several additional resources as supplementary material. The *Instructor's Solutions Manual* (**Vol. I: 0-13-039157-3** and **Vol. II: 0-13-144741-6**) by *Jerry Shi* of Pasadena College, has detailed worked solutions to all end-of-chapter problems and answers to even-numbered "Understanding the Concepts" questions. Close to 3000 multiple-choice, short answer, and true/false questions can be found in the *Test Item File* (**0-13-039158-1**). These questions are referenced to the appropriate text sections and ranked by difficulty level for the users' convenience. Over 400 full-color transparencies of images from the text are compiled in a *Transparency Pack* (**0-13-039166-2**). Organized by chapter, the *Instructor's Resource CD-ROM Package* (**0-13-039150-6**) is a comprehensive package that has electronic versions of the above-mentioned resources. In addition, the CD-ROM package includes *TestGen.* which, in the authors' words, is "a powerful dual-platform, fully networkable software program for creating tests."

Prentice Hall has its own online homework system. To register and use this resource see *The PH GradeAssist Instructor's Quick Start Guide* (**0-13-141740-1**).

Besides these supplements that are directly connected to the textbook, there are additional resources that are invaluable to every instructor, new or experienced. See pages xxi–xxiii of the preface to the textbook for a complete listing and brief description of these resources.

Don't forget to visit the companion website to the textbook (http://physics.prenhall.com/fishbane). This website is intended for both the instructor and the students. Familiarize yourself with the resources to be found on this site and urge your students to use them as well.

Demonstration Resources

Demonstrations should form an integral part of any course. A good demonstration can get the concept across to students far more easily than words can. Try to involve the students as often as possible and get them to predict the outcome as well as explain what they observe. The demonstrations that I have suggested in each chapter of this manual are based on my experience as a faculty member of the department of Physics at North Carolina State University. I am fortunate in that we have a very active demo section that is well maintained and is continually updated. Don't hesitate to ask your colleagues for their favorite demos, try some new ones on your own, and refer to the well-tested resources listed below.

Edge, R.D., *String and Sticky Tape Experiments*. College Park, MD: American Association of Physics Teachers, 1981.

Ehrlich, R., *Turning the World Inside Out and 174 Other Simple Physics Demonstrations*. Princeton, NJ: Princeton University Press, 1990.

Ehrlich, R., *Why Toast Lands Jelly-Side Down:Zen and the Art of Physics Demonstrations*. Princeton, NJ: Princeton University Press, 1997.

Frier, G.D., and F.J. Anderson, *A Demonstration Handbook for Physic*. College Park, MD: American Association of Physics Teachers, 1981.

Mamola, K.C., editor, *Apparatus for Teaching Physics*, College Park, MD: American Association of Physics Teachers.

Meiners, H., editor, *Physics Demonstration Experiments*. New York: The Ronald Press Company, 1970.

Physics Education Resources

At first glance, this long list can be intimidating. Even if you are not overly interested in this area of research, use these resources to get an idea of what does and what does not work when teaching introductory physics.

Arons, A.B., "Cultivating the Capacity for Formal Reasoning," *Am.J.Phys*. (September 1976), p. 834 – 838.

Arons, A.B., *A Guide to Introductory Physics Teaching*, (John Wiley & Sons, Inc., New York, NY, 1990).

Arons, A.B., *Homework and Test Questions for Introductory Physics Teaching*, (John Wiley & Sons Inc., New York, NY, 1994).

Beatty, I.D., and Gerace, W.J., "Probing Physics Students' Conceptual Knowledge Structures through Term Association," *Am.J.Phys*. (July 2002), p. 750 – 758.

Chabay, R., and Sherwood, B., "Bringing Atoms into First-Year Physics," *Am.J.Phys*. (December 1999), p. 1045 – 1050.

Chabay, R., and Sherwood, B., *Matter and Interactions: Modern Mechanics*, (John Wiley & Sons Inc., New York, NY, 2002).

Chabay, R., and Sherwood, B., *Matter and Interactions: Electric and Magnetic Interactions*, (John Wiley & Sons Inc., New York, NY, 2002).

Champagne, A., Klopfer, L., and Anderson, J., "Factors Influencing the Learning of Classical Mechanics," *Am J.Phys*. (December 1980), 1074 – 1079.

Chi, M.T.H., Feltovich, P.J., and Glaser, R., "Categorization and Representation of Physics Problems by Experts and Novices," *Cognitive Science* 5 (1981), p. 121 – 152.

Clement, J., "Using Bridging Analogies and Anchoring Intuitions to Deal with Students' Preconceptions in Physics," *Jour.Res.Sci.Teaching* 30:10, (1993), p. 1241 – 1257.

Crouch, C.H., and Mazur, E., "Ten Years of Experience and Results," *Am.J.Phys*. (September 2001), p. 970 – 977.

Ehrlich, R., "How Do We Know if We Are Doing a Good Job in Physics Teaching?," *Am.J.Phys*. (January 2002), p. 24 – 9.

Elby, A., "Helping Physics Students Learn How to Learn," *Am.J.Phys*. Suppl. (July 2001), p. S54 – S64.

Halloun, I.A, and Hestenes, D., "The Initial Knowledge State of College Physics Students," *Am J Phys.* (November 1985), p. 1043 – 1055.

Hammer, D., "Two Approaches to Learning Physics," *The Physics Teacher* (December 1989), p. 664 – 670.

Hammer, D., "Student Resources for Learning Introductory Physics," *Am J Phys.* (July 2000), p. S52 – S59.

Kim, E., and Pak, S., "Students do not Overcome Conceptual Difficulties after Solving 1000 Traditional Problems," *Am.J.Phys.* (July 2002), p. 759 – 765.

McDermott, L.C., "What We Teach and What is Learned. Closing the Gap," *Am J Phys.* (April 1991), p. 301 – 315.

McDermott, L.C., "Physics Education Research–The Key to Student Learning," *Am.J.Phys.* (November 2001), p. 1127–1137.

McDermott, L.C., and Redish, E.F., "Resource Letter: PER 1: Physics Education Research," *Am.J.Phy.* (September 1999), p. 755 – 767.

McKeechie, W.J., and Gibbs, G., *Teaching Tips : Strategies, Research, and Theory for College and University Teachers*, 10th Edition, (Houghton Mifflin, Boston, MA, 1999).

Mestre, J, "Learning and Instruction in Pre-College Physical Science," *Physics. Today* (September 1991), p. 56 – 62.

Moore, T., and Schroeder, D., *Six Ideas that Shaped Physics*, (WCB/McGraw-Hill, Columbus, OH, 2003).

Redish, Edward F., "Implications of Cognitive Studies for Teaching Physics," *Am.J.Phys.* (September 1994), p. 796 – 803.

Redish, E.F., "Millikan Lecture 1998: Building a Science of Teaching Physics," *Am.J.Phys.* (July 1999), p.562 – 573.

Redish, E.F., *Teaching Physics with the Physics Suite*, (John Wiley & Sons Inc., New York, NY, 2003).

Reif, F., "Teaching Problem Solving–A Scientific Approach," *The Physics Teacher* (May 1981), p. 310 – 316.

Reif, F., and Scott, L.A., "Teaching Scientific Thinking Skills: Students and Computers Coaching Each other," *Am.J.Phys.* (September 1999), p. 819 – 831.

Reif, F., "Scientific Approaches to Science Education," *Physics Today* (November 1986), p. 11.

Swartz, C.E., and Miner, T.D., *Teaching Introductory Physics : A Sourcebook*, (Springer Verlag, New York, NY, 1996).

Tobias, S., and Raphael, J., *The Hidden Curriculum: Faculty-Made Tests in Science*, 2 vols., (Plenum, New York, NY, 1997).

Van Heuvelen, A., "Learning to Think Like a Physicist: A Review of Research-Based Instructional Strategies," *Am.J.Phys.* 59, (1991), p. 891 – 897.

Van Heuvelen, A., "The Workplace, Student Minds, and Physics Learning Systems," *Am.J.Phys.* (November 2001), p. 1139 – 1146.

Physics Organizations

Consider becoming a member of the American Association of Physics Teachers (AAPT), which caters to two-year and four-year colleges as well as research universities. The association publishes *The Physics Teacher* and *The American Journal of Physics*. (http://www.aapt.org)

American Institute of Physics (http://www.aip.org) publishes *Physics Today*.

American Physical Society (www.aps.org) publishes the *Physics Review* journals.

Materials and Equipment

The materials for the demonstrations suggested in this resource manual can be obtained from the companies listed below.

Arbor Scientific (http://www.arborsci.com/)

Carolina Science and Math (www.carolina .com)

Central Scientific (http://www.sargentwelch.com)

Edmund Scientific (http://www.edsci.com)

Educational Innovations, Inc. (http://www.teachersource.com)

Fisher Scientific (https://www1.fishersci.com/index.jsp)

Klinger Educational Products Corporation (http://www.KlingerEducational.com)

Learning Technologies, Inc. (http://www.starlab.com)

Pasco Scientific (www.pasco.com)

Physics Academic Software (http://www.webassign.net/pasnew/)

Sargent-Welch (http://www.sargentwelch.com)

Vernier Software and Technology (http://www.vernier.com)

Ztek Company – for multimedia products (http://www.ztek.com/)

Organization of the IRM

This *Instructor's Resource Manual* is organized by chapters from the textbook. Each chapter in the manual starts with an outline, a summary of the major ideas discussed in the textbook, and a list of major concepts, followed by a brief paragraph on teaching suggestions and demonstrations. The manual then discusses, by sections, the important aspects that need to be emphasized, points out typical student misconceptions, and offers suggestions for demonstrations. Each chapter of the resource manual also has a list of transparency acetates, Physlet Illustrations, Physlet Explorations, Physlet Problems, appropriate selections from the student edition of *Ranking Task Physics*, and a list of end-of-chapter problems with solutions in the *Student Study Guide*. The chapters end with a selection of articles (from physics journals) on the topics covered in that particular chapter.

I would like to thank Christian Botting and Elizabeth Klug of Prentice Hall for their help, support, and encouragement while writing this manual.

Prabha Ramakrishnan
Department of Physics
North Carolina State University
pkramakr@ncsu.edu
June 2004

Chapter 1: Tooling Up

Outline

1-1   Background
1-2   Fundamental Physical Quantities and Their Units
1-3   Accuracy and Significant Figures
1-4   Dimensional Analysis
1-5   Estimates
1-6   Scalars and Vectors

Summary

Chapter 1 is an overview of the nature of physics and the tools needed to understand the physical laws discussed in the rest of the textbook. It discusses the **fundamental physical quantities** of length, mass and time and their **units**. The conversion from one system of units to another is illustrated. The importance of accuracy in measurements and **significant figures** is shown. **Dimensional analysis** and **order of magnitudes** are discussed. The last section of this chapter is devoted to the understanding of **vectors, vector addition** and **subtraction** and how to break up vectors into **components**.

Major Concepts

- Background
    - Descriptive and predictive theories
    - Scientific method
    - Hypothesis
    - Scales

- Representation of numbers
    - Powers of ten
    - Standard scientific notation

- Fundamental physical quantities
    - Length, time and mass
    - SI system of units: meter, second and kilogram
    - cgs system
    - British engineering system
    - Unit prefixes

- Units and unit conversions
    - Fundamental units
    - Derived units
    - Conversion from one system to another

- Uncertainty in measurement
    - Uncertainty
    - Percentage uncertainty
    - Significant figures

- Dimensional analysis
  - o Three primary dimensions
  - o Matching dimensions
  - o Deriving relations between physical quantities

- Estimates
  - o Order of magnitude

- Scalars and vectors
  - o Definition of scalars
  - o Definition of vectors
  - o Displacement vector
  - o Addition and subtraction of vectors
  - o Resultant vector
  - o Commutative rule for vector addition of vectors
  - o Null vector
  - o Scalar multiplication of a vector
  - o Unit vector
  - o Components of a vector

Teaching Suggestions and Demonstrations

While many teachers prefer to skip the introductory chapter, it is worth the time spent if only to show the students the importance of understanding the basics in order to appreciate the physical laws they will be introduced to throughout the rest of the course. This is a good opportunity to stress the concept of **units**, **accuracy in measurement** of physical quantities and the basics of **vector mathematics**.

Sections 1-1 – 1-3

Not much time needs to be devoted to the concept of the **scientific method** except to point out the basic differences between hypothesis and predictive and descriptive theories. The idea of the scale of things will help students to relate to the behavior of things (in the physical world) from an atomic as well as universal point of view. Most students will be familiar with the three **fundamental quantities** of length, mass, and time. However, they need to be made aware of the order of magnitude of these quantities, which are shown in the corresponding tables. **Unit prefixes** is another aspect that students will tend to ignore unless mention is made of this in the class. **Conversion of units** is always a stumbling block to a fair number of students as is the need to keep track of significant figures. Tell students that the number of digits displayed on their calculators has nothing to do with the accuracy of the answer.

> ⮕ **DEMO**   *The Powers of Ten* is a ten-minute video film from Ztek Company that shows the scale of things starting from our own backyard and going "out to the edges of the universe and in to the micro world of cells, molecules, and atoms". This is a good film that never fails to grab the students' attention.

Sections 1-4 – 1-5

Dimensional analysis is useful when checking the validity of an equation as well as when deriving relations between physical quantities. It also is a very helpful tool when a student is not sure of the units for a particular physical quantity in a calculation. Worked example 1-6 is a good exercise to go over in class. While it is not necessary to spend a great deal of class time on **estimating** exercises, it is a good idea to stress the importance of checking the order of magnitude of an answer to see if it is indeed a reasonable value.

Section 1-6

A sound understanding of **vectors** and their mathematical manipulations is absolutely essential if the student is to grasp two- and three-dimensional physics. This chapter introduces just the displacement vector. However, tell the students to expect many more vector physical quantities as the semester progresses. In finding **components of vectors**, students will associate the cosine factor with the *x*-component of the vector. They will fail to recognize that this will depend on the angle used. They will also not notice the difference between using angles measured counterclockwise from the positive *x*-axis and those measured clockwise from the negative *x*-axis. It might be well worth the time spent in reminding them of the sign of the components based on the quadrant in which the vector is located.

> ⊃ **DEMO** Use meter sticks of varying lengths to introduce vectors and vector addition/subtraction. These can be easily built by attaching small triangular pieces of light weight wood to one end of the stick. This will be the head of the vector and the other end will serve as the tail. To make it more visible to the entire class, paint the meter stick in two different and bright colors at 10-cm intervals. If you use a white board, make these meter sticks magnetic by attaching magnetic strips to their underside.
> This then becomes an easy tool to illustrate addition and subtraction of vectors by the head-to-tail or the parallelogram method.

> ⊃ **DEMO** *Video Encyclopedia of Physics Demonstrations* Disc (by The Education Group) is a laser disc that shows how vectors can be broken down into components along the coordinate axes.

Textbook Resource Information

Transparency Acetates

Fig. 1-13	Addition of two vectors by graphical method
Fig. 1-14	Adding three vectors
Fig. 1-16	Negative of a vector
Fig. 1-17	Vector difference
Fig. 1-20	Position vector and resultant of two displacements
Fig. 1-21	Components of a vector in two-dimensional representation
Fig. 1-25	Components of a vector in three-dimensional representation

Physlet Physics Illustrations

1.1	Introduction to Physlets
1.2	Animations, Units and Measurements
3.1	Vector Decomposition

Physlet Physics Explorations

1.1	Click-Drag To Get Position
1.2	Input Data Numbers
3.1	Addition of Displacement Vectors

Physlet Physics Problems

1.1   Measurements
3.1   Vector Components
3.2   Addition of Two Vectors

End of Chapter Problems with Solutions in the *Student Study Guide*

5, 13, 19, 31, 53, 61

Suggested Readings

Allie, S., Buffler, A., Campbell, B., Lubben, F., Evangelinos, D., Psillos, D., and Valassiades, O., "Teaching Measurement in the Introductory Physics Laboratory," *The Physics Teacher* (October 2003), p. 394 – 401.

Bergquist, J., Jefferts, S., and Wineland, D., "Time Measurement at the Millennium," *Physics Today* (March 2001), p. 37 – 42.

Black, H.S., "Vector Toy," *The Physics Teacher* (September 1998), p. 375.

Carlson, J.E., "Fermi Problems on Gasoline Consumption," *The Physics Teacher* (May 1997), p. 308 – 309.

Friberg, J., "Numbers and Measures in the Earliest Written Records," *Scientific American* (February 1984), p. 110.

Gardner, M., "Physics Tricks of the Month: Estimating Height," *The Physics Teacher* (September 2001), p. 370.

Goodwin, I., "Washington Briefings: One Too Many Mishaps on Voyages to Mars," *Physics Today* (January 2000), p. 47.

Goth, G.W., "Dimensional Analysis by Computer," *The Physics Teacher* (February 1986), p. 75 – 76.

Graham, A., "The U.S. Metric Association," *The Physics Teacher* (September 2001), p. 378.

Hillger, D., "Metric Units and Postage Stamps," *The Physics Teacher* (November 1999), p. 507 – 510.

Keeports, D., "Addressing Physical Intuition – A First Day Event," *The Physics Teacher* (May 2000), p. 318 – 319.

Larson, R.F., "Measuring Displacement Vectors with the GPS," *The Physics Teacher* (March 1998), p. 161.

Nguyen, N., and Meltzer, D.E., "Initial Understanding of Vector Concepts Among Students in Introductory Physics Courses", *Am. J. Phys.* (June 2003), p. 630 – 638.

Romano, J.D., "Supermarket Physics," *The Physics Teacher* (December 1996), p. 562 – 563.

Romer, R., "Units—SI-Only, or Multicultural Diversity?," *Am. J. Phys.* (January 1999), p. 13 – 16. (Also see several related articles in the June 1999 issue).

Wheeler, D., and Charoenkul, N., "Whole Vectors", *The Physics Teacher* (May 1998), p. 274 – 275.

Wheeler, D., and Mazur, E., "The Great Thermometer Challenge," *The Physics Teacher* (April 2000), p. 235.

Notes and Ideas

Preparation time: *Estimated:* _____   *Actual:* _____

Class time spent on material: *Estimated:* _____   *Actual:* _____

Related laboratory activities:

Demonstration materials:

Notes for next time:

Chapter 2: Straight-Line Motion

Outline

Summary

One-dimensional kinematics is the study of motion in a straight line. Chapter 2 gives a working definition of the main concepts of one-dimensional kinematics; namely, **displacement**, **speed**, **velocity** and **acceleration**. The emphasis is on motion with constant acceleration. The kinematic **equations of motion** are derived and **motion graphs** are discussed. The chapter also treats **free fall motion,** which is one-dimensional vertical motion under the influence of the gravitational force. Finally, **displacement**, **velocity** and **acceleration** are discussed using the calculus of integration.

Major Concepts

- Displacement
    - Distance and displacement
    - Position vector
    - Displacement vector
    - Net displacement
    - Distance-time graph

- Velocity
    - Speed and average speed
    - Difference between speed and velocity
    - Average and instantaneous velocity
    - Motion graph

- Acceleration
    - Average and instantaneous acceleration
    - Kinematic equation for constant acceleration motion

- Freely falling objects
    - Acceleration due to gravity
    - Free fall
    - Equations of motion for freely falling objects

- Integration and motion in one dimension
    - Displacement as time integral of velocity
    - Velocity as time integral of acceleration
    - Equations of motion using integration

Teaching Suggestions and Demonstrations

You will find that students are familiar with words such as **speed** and **acceleration** because of their experiences with driving a car. However, they will not be aware of the more formal physics definitions of these terms or the differences between **speed** and **velocity** or **distance** and **displacement**. Hence they have a lot of misconceptions. It will be a good idea to take the time to lay the groundwork for understanding **two-** and **three-dimensional** motion. This is also the first time they will have a chance to learn **problem-solving methods**, which are an integral part of any physics course.

Sections 2-1 – 2-3

Students who have had physics in high school will be familiar with **speed** and **velocity** or **distance** and **displacement**. However, the majority of the students will not have had physics prior to this class. Since they were introduced to vectors in Chapter 1, discuss the difference between these quantities in terms of **scalars** and **vectors**. The concept of the **position vector** is a difficult one for most students. Use the vector meter sticks to show them the **position vectors** and the **displacement** vector due to the change in the position of an object.

Emphasize that **displacement** is the change in the position of an object and not the actual distance covered. Take the example of a typical day in the life of one of your students. Ask them to estimate how much they walk and/or drive in a day from the time they get up in the morning to the time they go to bed at night. Then ask them what their **displacement** would be for such a day. They will then see that the **displacement** is zero while the distance covered is not.

The difference between **speed** and **velocity** will have to be explained with examples. Take the case of a person running laps around a track. Ask the students to determine the **speed** and the **velocity** given the number of laps covered in a given time.

In discussing **acceleration**, be sure to spend a little time on the units. This can be confusing since the denominator has two time units.

Motion graphs are a source of confusion and frustration. Students have a hard time visualizing **negative velocity** or **negative acceleration** as well as change in the direction of motion as represented on a graph. They will need lots of practice in interpreting **motion graphs**. While they have been introduced to the concepts of slope and tangent to a curve in calculus, don't be surprised if most of the students fail to make the connection here when studying **displacement** vs. **time** or **velocity** vs. **time** graphs.

➲ **DEMO** Use the vector meter sticks described in Chapter 1 of this manual to show that the displacement vector is the subtraction of two position vectors.

➲ **DEMO** A motion detector (from Pasco or Vernier Software) is a good way to show, in real time, the position, velocity and acceleration versus time of a student volunteer moving in front of the motion detector. Have a student walk toward and away from the detector. You can either show the graphs directly on the monitor screen or save them for later use. Make sure the path the student will walk is clear, so no one trips. The motion detector is very small, so care must be taken to not damage it.

Section 2-4

Students will have a difficult time with the concepts of **constant velocity** and **constant acceleration**. Quite often they will confuse one with the other. Use the familiar example of driving a car on the highway with the cruise control activated to discuss constant velocity. Use one of the demos listed here to clarify the difference between **constant velocity** and **constant acceleration**.

Some people prefer to skip the derivations of the **kinematic equations** for **constant acceleration**. This is a question of philosophy and availability of class time. If you decide to skip the derivations, be sure to discuss the fact that these equations are derived from the basic definitions of **displacement**, **velocity** and **acceleration**. Students will have a difficult time interpreting the problems and assigning symbols to the various values given in a problem. They will need plenty of practice, and the textbook has sufficient worked examples. In **solving problems**, students will benefit greatly from sketching the situation however simple it may be. Unfortunately, they will be reluctant to do this.

➲ **DEMO** Use Pasco air track and gliders. The track should be set and leveled before use. Turn on the power for the air supply and adjust the flow until the carts just start to rise on the jets of air. The carts will move with constant velocity. You can have two students help you to measure the time taken for the glider to cover equal distances. This is an excellent demonstration for showing constant velocity. You will find that the blower is a little loud, so you will have to talk over it.

➲ **DEMO** Use the same set up as above. Raise the air track by placing aluminum blocks under a single leg of the air track. The glider will move down the incline with constant acceleration. You can show that the velocity is not constant by having two students measure the time taken to cover equal distances as the glider moves down the incline. Alternately, a motion detector can be used to measure acceleration with the Pasco Dynamic Carts.

Section 2-5

Making the transition from **constant acceleration** motion in the horizontal direction to **free fall** will be fairly easy. There are two points that will confuse most students with regard to the value and direction of g. You will have many students claim that g will be zero at the very top of a vertical motion since the velocity goes to zero there. Remind them that acceleration is the change in velocity (direction as well as magnitude). So, if the velocity is 10 m/s just before it reaches the very top and it is 10 m/s a moment later on its way down, then the acceleration is (-10-10)/2, which is a non-zero quantity.

Students will also have to be constantly reminded that the g vector is always in the downward direction regardless of the direction of motion of the object in **free fall**.

➲ **DEMO** Simultaneously drop a book and a sheet of paper from the same height. The book falls much faster. Crumple the paper into a ball and repeat the experiment, and the two will reach the floor at almost the same time. Discuss the effect of air resistance on "light" objects that have a larger surface area.

➲ **DEMO** You could illustrate the same concept using the penny and feather equipment (from Central Scientific). Make sure the lead ball and feather are at one end of the tube, which is filled with air. Quickly bring the tube to a vertical position, and you will see the ball falling much faster than the feather. Now connect the tube to a vacuum pump. Once the air is pumped out, close the valve and disconnect the tube. Now repeat the experiment and you will find the ball and feather reaching the bottom simultaneously.

⊃ **DEMO** This is a simple demo to calculate the value of g by using the equation: $x = \frac{1}{2} g t^2$
Have one student hold a meter stick vertically. Have a second student hold his/her fingers (beside the 50-cm point) on either side of the stick as if ready to grab it. At some random time the first student drops the meter stick. The second student should try to grab the meter stick the instant he/she sees it being dropped. Measure the distance from the 50-cm mark to the point where it is caught. Use the equation to calculate g.
You could do this as a demo in front of the whole class or have students pair up and do it as an in-class activity. This can also be used to discuss reaction time of the student.

Section 2-6

This is a good time to show the students the application of calculus to situations in physics. Many of your students will be able to integrate a function with ease if the function uses x and y as the variables. However, the moment you give them an equation expressing **velocity** as a **function of time**, they will flounder when asked to find the **displacement**. This section also deals with the case of **non-constant acceleration** and discusses what happens when the **acceleration** is indeed constant.

Textbook Resource Information

Transparency Acetates

Fig. 2-2	Distance vs. time graph
Fig. 2-3	Position-time graph
Fig. 2-5	Slope of displacement-time graph
Fig. 2-9	Velocity-time and acceleration-time graphs
Fig. 2-19	Time sequence picture of a ball in free fall
Fig. 2-25	Displacement as area under velocity-time curve
Fig. 2-26	Velocity as area under acceleration-time curve

Physlet Physics Illustrations

2.1 Position and Displacement
2.3 Average and Instantaneous Velocity
2.4 Constant Acceleration
2.5 Motion on a Hill
2.6 Free Fall

Physlet Physics Explorations

2.1 Compare position vs. time and velocity vs. time graphs
2.2 Determine the correct graph
2.7 Determine the area under $a(t)$ and $v(t)$

Physlet Physics Problems

2.2 Analyzing motion

Ranking Task Exercises in Physics, Student Edition

End of Chapter Problems with Solutions in the *Student Study Guide*

9, 21, 35, 59, 65, 73

Suggested Readings

Aguirre, J.M., "Student Preconceptions about Vector Kinematics," *The Physics Teacher* (April 1988), p. 212 – 216.

Beichner, R.J., "Testing Student Interpretation of Kinematic Graphs," *Am. J. Phys.* (August 1994), p. 750 – 762.

Bowden, J., Dall'Alba, G., Martin, E., Laurillard, D., Marton, F., Masters, G., Ramsden, P., Stephanou, A., and Walsh, E., "Displacement, Velocity and Frames of Reference: Phenomenographic Studies of Students' Understanding and Some Implications for Teaching and Assessment," *Am. J. Phys.* (March 1992), p. 262 – 269.

Conderle, L., "Extending the Analysis of One-Dimensional Motion," *The Physics Teacher* (November 1999), p. 486 – 489.

Goldberg, F.M., and Anderson, J.H., "Student Difficulties with Graphical Representation of Negative Values of Velocity," *The Physics Teacher* (April 1989), p. 254 – 260.

Halloun, I.A., and Hestenes, D., "Common Sense Concepts about Motion," *Am. J. Phys.* (November 1985), p. 1056 – 1065.

Heller, P., Keith, R., and Anderson, S., "Teaching Problem Solving through Cooperative Grouping. Part I: Group versus Individual Problem Solving," *Am. J. Phys.* (July 1992), p. 627 – 636.

McClelland, J., "g-whizz," *The Physics Teacher* (March 2000), p. 150.

McDermott, L.C., Rosenquist, M.L., and van Zee, E.H., "Student Difficulties in Connecting Graphs and Physics: Examples from Kinematics," *Am. J. Phys.* (June 1987), p. 503 – 513.

Peters, P.C., "Even Honors Students have Conceptual Difficulties with Physics," *Am. J. Phys.* (June 1982), p. 501 – 508.

Singh, K., "The Flight of the Bagel," *The Physics Teacher* (October 2000), p. 432 – 433.

Thornton, R.K., and Sokoloff, D.R., "Learning Motion Concepts Using Real-Time Micro-Computer-Based Laboratory Tools," *Am. J. Phys.* (September 1990), p. 858 – 867.

Trowbridge, D.E., and McDermott, L.C., "Investigation of Student Understanding of the Concept of Velocity in One Dimension," *Am. J. Phys.* (December 1980), p. 1020 – 1028.

Trowbridge, D.E., and McDermott, L.C., "Investigation of Student Understanding of the Concept of Acceleration in One Dimension," *Am. J. Phys.* (March 1981), p. 242 – 253.

Notes and Ideas

Preparation time: *Estimated:* _____   *Actual:* _____

Class time spent on material: *Estimated:* _____   *Actual:* _____

Related laboratory activities:

Demonstration materials:

Notes for next time:

Chapter 3: Motion in Two and Three Dimensions

Outline

Summary

Chapter 2 dealt with the kinematics of **linear motion**. Now, in Chapter 3, these concepts are extended to motion in **two** and **three dimensions**. The **position, velocity** and **acceleration vectors** for **three-dimensional motion** are defined in terms of their components and, in particular, for the case of **constant acceleration** motion. This leads into the discussion of **projectile motion** in the absence of air resistance, as well as **circular motion**, which is motion in a plane. **Relative velocity** is discussed in the last section of the chapter.

Major Concepts

- Motion in two and three dimensions (in a plane and in space)
  - Position and displacement vectors
  - Velocity and acceleration
  - Graphical representation of trajectories

- Motion with constant acceleration
  - Plane of motion
  - x and y components of position vector
  - x and y components of velocity vector

- Projectile motion
  - Projectile motion as two independent motions in horizontal and vertical planes
  - Trajectory of projectile motion
  - Range
  - Flight time
  - Maximum height

- Uniform circular motion
  - Definition of the radian
  - Plane polar coordinates
  - Angular speed and its relation to linear speed
  - Period and frequency
  - Centripetal acceleration and its relation to angular velocity

- Relative motion
  - Frame of reference
  - Relative velocity

Teaching Suggestions and Demonstrations

Many of the topics covered in Chapter three are extensions of the ideas that were introduced in the previous chapter, with the exception of **circular motion** and **relative velocity**. This chapter also uses vectors extensively. The concept of treating **two-dimensional motion** as two independent motions in two perpendicular directions will baffle many students. Allow sufficient time to work examples in class. Also consider using simulations as demos or as in-class activities. There are plenty of these available, and these are listed under resources.

Sections 3-1 – 3-2

These two sections discuss the trajectory for motion in a plane. It may be helpful to quickly review vector addition. This will make it easy to understand what follows in this chapter. Stress the difference between **position vectors** and the actual trajectory of motion. Students will calculate the **acceleration** for a given situation where the speed (magnitude of **velocity**) changes without much difficulty. However, they will not as easily be able to visualize the **acceleration** vector for motion with directional change as well. Use the tail-to-head method of vector addition to show that the **displacement vector** is $\Delta \vec{r}$, and the **acceleration vector** is obtained by finding $\Delta \vec{v}$ as the difference between two **velocity vectors** for a small time interval Δt .

Figure 3-6 is a good one to show the **velocity** and **acceleration** vectors at a point on the trajectory of motion. Discuss the fact that the **speed** of the object changes because of the **acceleration** component parallel to the trajectory at that point, and the directional change is brought about by the component of the **acceleration** that is perpendicular to the path. These two will change in direction and magnitude as the object moves along its trajectory.

➲ **DEMO** Use the vector meter sticks described in Chapter 1 of this manual to show the displacement and acceleration vectors. Draw a random trajectory on the board. Pick two points Δt apart on the path. Use the vector meter sticks to represent v_1 and v_2. Show that $v_2 - v_1$ vector gives the direction of the acceleration vector.

Sections 3-3 – 3-4

Begin by discussing how the **kinematic equations** derived in Chapter 2 can be used in the x and y directions independent of each other. Then show what happens to these equations when there is **constant velocity** in the horizontal direction and **constant acceleration** g in the vertical direction. This particular section lends itself nicely to the use of examples from sports, especially when discussing **range** and **time of flight** of a **projectile**. Students will relate well to these examples.

The significance of Equation 3.39 will not be obvious to the students. You may have to elaborate on the fact that there will be two angles for which the range will be the same. Figure 3-9 clearly shows the **velocity** component changing in the downward direction and being constant in the horizontal direction. Discuss this in detail and point out that while v_y,=0, the object still has a **velocity** in the x direction, and this is what makes it go forward as it experiences **free fall** in the vertical direction.

Some of the difficulties encountered by students include using $a = g$ in the x direction motion, not recognizing that there will be an **acceleration** at the highest point of the trajectory, even though v_y,=0, and not knowing how to use the solution from the y direction motion to find the unknown in the x direction or (vice versa). Work as many examples of different situations as possible in class.

⊃ **DEMO** The Monkey and Hunter demonstration (from Pasco Scientific) shows that vertical and horizontal motion are two independent motions. A ball is launched from a cannon, and simultaneously the target is released from the magnet from which it is suspended. (A small piece of permanent magnet holds the target in place. When the ball is launched, this sends a pulse of current that disrupts the field). The horizontal motion is at constant velocity, and both objects have the same constant acceleration in their vertical motion. So by aiming directly at the target, you will successfully hit the target. It might be a good idea to set up the demo and have it aimed correctly before the start of class.

⊃ **DEMO** A Pasco projectile launcher can be used to test the range of the projectile for different angles of projection. This is a good demo to show that the maximum range can be obtained for a launching angle of $45°$.

⊃ **DEMO** Simultaneous ball drop. This can be either built or purchased from Central Scientific. Two balls are situated on a small platform. When the spring is released, one ball falls vertically down and the other is launched with a horizontal velocity.

Section 3-5

Most of your students will be familiar with the **radian** unit. But it might be a good idea to go over the conversion from **degrees** to **radians** to **revolution** and why the **radian** is a dimensionless quantity. Stress that in converting **linear velocity** to **angular velocity** and vice versa, ω has to be in rad/s. This would be a good place to remind them of **dimensional analysis** and why other units like deg/sec or rpm will not work.

Go back to Fig. 3-6 and discuss the fact that for **uniform circular motion** there is no **acceleration** in a direction parallel to the path of motion. Then show them Fig. 3-22, which clearly illustrates the existence of a **radial acceleration** for an object moving with **constant speed** in a circular path. Also emphasize that while the magnitude of the **position vector** $\vec{r}$, **velocity** $\vec{v}$ and **acceleration** $\vec{a}$ are constant, they are continually changing in direction.

Section 3-6

This will be the first time that most of your students are introduced to the formal definition of frame of reference. Start off the discussion with the demo described below. Then discuss the fact that all motion is **relative** and depends on the **reference frame** with respect to which it is described. Figure 3-28 and worked example 3-13 explain this concept very clearly.

⊃ **DEMO** Walk across the room at a steady rate. Toss a ball in a parabolic path at the start of your motion and catch the ball at the end of your motion. This might take a little practice. If done correctly, from your frame of reference the ball goes vertically up and then down. From the students' frame of reference the ball has a parabolic trajectory.

⊃ **DEMO** Alternately, stand on a platform with wheels. Have another person pull you with constant velocity to simulate a moving frame of reference. Toss a ball straight up and catch it. This demo should be done with great care. If the person pulling the platform jerks on it, you can fall back. For the same reason, it is best that a student does not perform the demo.

⊃ **DEMO** A battery operated toy tractor and a large sheet of paper are all you need for this simple but effective demonstration of relative velocity. The tractor is placed at an angle near one edge of the sheet of paper. Activate the tractor and pull the sheet of paper at a constant rate. This will simulate a running "river". Practice this before class so that you can get the tractor to end up on the other side of the river but at the same relative place it was to begin with.

Textbook Resource Information

Transparency Acetates

Fig. 3-2	Position and displacement vectors
Fig. 3-6	Velocity and acceleration vectors represented in terms of components
Fig. 3-8	Plane of motion for a projectile
Fig. 3-9	Horizontal and vertical components of velocity vector for a projectile
Fig. 3-12	Range and relative height of a projectile for different launch angles
Fig. 3-22	Computing direction of Δv
Fig. 3-23	Computing direction of Δv
Fig. 3-25	Instantaneous position, velocity and acceleration
Fig. 3-28	Velocity in two frames of reference

Physlet Physics Illustrations

3.1	Vector Decomposition
3.3	Direction of Velocity and Acceleration Vectors
3.4	Projectile Motion
3.5	Uniform Circular Motion and Acceleration
3.6	Circular and Noncircular Motion

Physlet Physics Explorations

3.4	Space probe with constant acceleration
3.5	Uphill and downhill projectile motion
3.6	Uniform circular motion

Physlet Physics Problems

3.3	Motion down an incline
3.5	Graphing position and velocity graphs
3.6	Analyzing two-dimensional motion
3.10	Relation between initial velocity and launch angle
3.15	Circular motion
3.17	Speed and acceleration in circular motion

Ranking Task Exercises in Physics, Student Edition

Page 47	Rifle shots – time to hit ground
Page 48	Toy trucks rolling off table

End of Chapter Problems with Solutions in the *Student Study Guide*

7, 23, 33, 45, 55, 67

Suggested Readings

Baugh, R.A., "Dynamics of Spear Throwing," *Am. J. Phys.* (April 2003), p. 345 – 350.

Brancazio, P., "The Physics of Kicking a Football," *The Physics Teacher* (October 1985), p. 403 – 407.

Brancazio, P., "Trajectory of a Fly Ball," *The Physics Teacher* (January 1985), p. 20 – 23.

Brown, R.A., "Maximizing the Range of a Projectile," *The Physics Teacher* (September 1992), p. 344 – 347.

Cordry, S., "Projectile Motion Model," *The Physics Teacher* (October 2003), p. 430 – 431.

DiLisi, G.A., and Rarick, R., "Monday Night Football: Physics Decides Controversial Call," *The Physics Teacher* (November 2003), p. 454 – 459.

Graham, A., "Websights: Football Physics," *The Physics Teacher* (October 2002), p. 447.

Pratt, J., "Figuring Physics: A Full Solution and a Challenging Problem," *The Physics Teacher* (April 2003), p. 220 – 221.

Price, R., and Romano, J., "Aim High and Go Far – Optimal Projectile Launch Angles Greater than 45°," *Am. J. Phys.* (February 1998), p. 109 – 113.

Robinett, R.W., "It's, Like, Relative Motion at the Mall," *The Physics Teacher* (March 2003), p. 140 – 143.

Van den Berg, W., and Burbank, A.R., "Sliding off a Roof: How Does the Landing Point Depend on the Steepness?," *The Physics Teacher* (February 2002), p. 84 – 85.

Notes and Ideas

Preparation time: *Estimated:* _____   *Actual:* _____

Class time spent on material: *Estimated:* _____   *Actual:* _____

Related laboratory activities:

Demonstration materials:

Notes for next time:

Chapter 4: Newton's Laws

Outline

Summary

Chapters 1 - 3 defined and explained vectors, displacement, velocity and acceleration — quantities that are essential in describing motion. Chapter 4 now looks at what causes this motion and how an object gets an acceleration. **Newton's three laws** of motion are discussed in detail. The use of **free-body diagrams** to solve problems is shown.

Major Concepts

- Newton's first law
    - Force and net force
    - First law of motion or law of inertia
    - Inertial frame
    - Some common forces
    - Reference frames

- Newton's second law of motion
    - Inertial mass
    - Force – acceleration equation
    - Newton's second law as seen from different inertial frames

- Newton's third law of motion
    - Equal action and reaction
    - Non-inertial frames
    - Pseudo force or non-inertial force

- Using Newton's law
    - Identifying forces
    - Free body diagrams
    - External and internal forces
    - Isolating the system
    - Problem-solving techniques

Teaching Suggestions and Demonstrations

Newton's laws of motion and their application to solving problems are some of the most important topics in the study of mechanics. Identifying **forces** acting on a system and representing these forces on a **free body-diagram** is essential to solving problems in dynamics. Students exhibit a remarkable reluctance to drawing **free-body diagrams** and they need to see the importance of doing so. They will also have to relearn vector addition in this chapter.

Sections 4-1 – 4-3

The difference between **force** and the effect of the **force** on an object is often not obvious to students. So begin by defining **force** and introduce the concept of **net force**. Remind them that **forces** are vectors and so all of the rules for vector addition and subtraction will apply here. They will also quite often add a **force vector** and an acceleration vector.

Newton's first law is best explained by breaking it into two parts – one for objects at rest and the other for objects moving at constant velocity. The statement of the **first law** of motion as given on page 89 will be familiar to most students. However, the idea of **inertial frames** in the context of the **first law** is not a common approach. Use examples similar to Example 4-2 to discuss **inertial frames**.

Section 4-1 includes a very nice discussion of some of the **common forces** that one will encounter in this course. The idea of **contact forces** and **forces at a distance** is also introduced. This sets the stage for identifying **forces** when solving problems later in the chapter.

➲ **DEMO** Suspend a steel ball (you can get one from Central Scientific) from a string tied to a horizontal rod, which is suspended across two other stands as shown. Tie two strings to the bottom of the ball. Pull on the bottom string very quickly to have it snap. Next, pull down on the second string below the ball very slowly and this will snap the string above the ball.

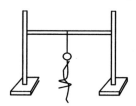

The next three demos are classic demonstrations of the concept of inertia.

➲ **DEMO** Spread out a tablecloth and set some dishes and a glass of water on the cloth. Hold the two slack ends of the table cloth and give a quick pull (straight back) to it. It is best to not snap the cloth. If done correctly, the table setting will remain undisturbed.

➲ **DEMO** Place an empty Coke bottle on the table and invert a second Coke bottle on top of it. Slide a dollar bill between the mouths of the two bottles and invite your students to try and remove the dollar bill without disturbing the bottles. To remove the dollar bill, hold the free end of the dollar bill with one hand and give a quick chopping action (vertically) with the forefinger of the other hand. This will pull the bill out without rocking the Coke bottles.

➲ **DEMO** Place three beakers of water next to each other so they form a triangle. Place a flat piece of pie pan on top of the beakers. Now arrange three small cylinders (these can be cut out of PVC tubing and they must be of the same height) on top of the pie pan so that each cylinder is centered over each of the three beakers. Now place three eggs on top of the cylinders so they are seated in a stable position. Make sure that the pie pan is slightly off the edge of the table. Take a broom, place one foot on the bristles of the broom and bend the handle back toward you. Now quickly let go off the handle so it hits the edge of the pie pan. The pan will shoot forward and the eggs will drop into the beakers of water. This never ceases to amaze students.

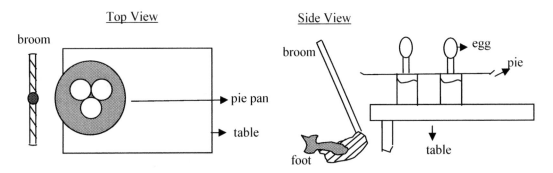

In discussing **Newton's second law**, emphasize the significance of Equation 4-6 as well as 4-8a – 4-8c. Students need to recognize that it is the **net force** that causes the object to have a certain acceleration, and this acceleration is in the direction of the **net force**. The latter set of equations is particularly useful when dealing with **two-** and **three-dimensional motion**.

➲ **DEMO** An Atwood's machine can be purchased from Central Scientific. This machine is a good way to demonstrate accelerations and string tensions. Use slotted masses to alter the tension in the string.

The **third law** can be misleading in its simplicity. Ask students about it and they will readily say that for every **action** there is an equal and opposite **reaction**. However, present them with the situation of a head-on collision between a semi and a Volkswagen Bug. Have them qualitatively describe the **force** exerted by the semi on the Bug and the **force** the Bug exerts on the semi. Don't be surprised if the majority answers that the semi will exert the greater **force**. Use this to point out that a **force** exerted by an object and the effect of this **force** on another object are two different things. Just because the Volkswagen is crushed does not imply that it experiences the greater **force**.

Correctly identifying the **action-reaction** pair of **forces** for different situations will not be as easy for most students either. Cite plenty of examples to show that an **action force** on A by B will produce a **reaction force** on B by A. **Action** and **reaction forces** do not act on the same object.

➲ **DEMO** Blow a balloon up with air. Hold the neck of the balloon and let go. The balloon will shoot forward as the air is released through the neck in the opposite direction.

➲ **DEMO** This one can be built easily. Make two carts out of two pieces of wood and four wheels. Get two volunteers to stand on the carts and hold on to the two ends of a rope. One student should pull on the rope while the other does not. Both will move. Warn the students that a sudden jerk on the rope can throw them off and that can be dangerous.

➲ **DEMO** Set up a cart on an air track that has been leveled. Attach a fan to the cart so it is facing the far end of the cart. Turn on the fan and the cart will move. Now attach the sail in front of the fan, turn it on and have the students observe the results. This is a good demonstration of action and reaction forces. The track, fan cart and sail can all be bought from Pasco Scientific.

➲ **DEMO** Here is another action-reaction demo. Stand on the cart (like the one used in the earlier demo) and hold on to a fairly heavy ball. When you toss the ball to a student, you and the cart will recoil backwards.

Section 4-4

Many students will find the concept of **non-inertial frames** difficult to relate to. The book gives several good examples to explain this and the concept of **fictitious forces**.

Sections 4-5 – 4-6

The use of **free-body diagrams** is most invaluable when solving problems using the **second law.** As I mentioned before, students have a great reluctance to drawing diagrams/sketches of any kind. So it would be a good idea to go through the steps involved in solving problems as outlined in the book. See the section called Problem-Solving Techniques. When working examples in class, follow these steps so students get used to it and recognize the importance of it. Point out that the acceleration vector shown on the diagram is different from the **force vectors**. The importance of working out examples in class cannot be stressed enough.

It is quite common for students to assume that the **normal force** equals the weight of the object for all situations. Take the example of an object on a horizontal surface being pulled by a rope at an angle to the surface or a block on an inclined plane. In these cases the **normal force** does not equal the weight of the object. If students start from $F_{y,net} = ma_y$ they will avoid making this mistake.

Again, it is not unusual for them to assume that F_N and mg are equal and opposite as a direct consequence of the **third law**. Point out why these two **forces** do not constitute an **action-reaction** pair. Also draw their attention to the fact that the **reaction force** of F_N and the **reaction force** of g are not included in the **free-body diagram**. Discuss the idea of identifying and isolating the system, however simple it may be. This is very important if they are to differentiate between **external** and **internal forces** as well. Stress that the **second law** relates to the **net external force** acting on the object in question.

Textbook Resource Information

Transparency Acetates

Fig. 4-9	Spring force and acceleration on a mass
Fig. 4-15	Non-inertial frames and fictitious forces
Fig. 4-19	How to draw a free-body diagram

Physlet Physics Illustrations

4.1	Newton's First Law and Reference Frames
4.2	Free-Body Diagrams
4.3	Newton's Second Law and Force
4.4	Mass on an Incline
4.6	Newton's Third Law and Contact Forces

Physlet Physics Explorations

4.1	Vectors for a box on an incline
4.2 – 4.5	Applying the laws of motion
4.7	Atwood's machine

Physlet Physics Problems

4.1 Block on a horizontal surface
4.4 Force versus time graph
4.8 Elevator problem
4.9 Atwood's machine
4.10 Two boxes suspended from the ceiling
4.12 Two car collision

Ranking Task Exercises in Physics, Student Edition

Page 14 – 16 Carts on a horizontal surface
Page 20 – 22 Falling rocks – net force
Page 34, 35 Forces on objects on smooth surface
Page 38, 39 Elevator moving up/down – scale weight
Page 40 – 42 Force difference on two blocks

End of Chapter Problems with Solutions in the *Student Study Guide*

17, 21, 27, 35, 55, 71

Suggested Readings

Bao, L., Hogg, K., and Zollman, D., "Model Analysis of Fine Structures of Student Models: An Example with Newton's III Law," *Am.J.Phys.* (July 2002), p. 766 – 778.

Cross, R., "Standing, Walking, Running, and Jumping on a Force Plate," *Am.J.Phys.* (April 1999), p. 304 – 309.

Gettrust, E., "An Extraordinary Demonstration of Newton's III Law," *The Physics Teacher* (October 2001), p. 392 – 393.

Haugland, O., "Physics Measurements for Sprots," *The Physics Teacher* (September 2001), p. 350 – 353.

Hewitt, P., "Normal Forces," *The Physics Teacher* (December 2003), p. 514.

Huebner, J.S., Fletcher, A.S., Cato, J.A., and Barrett, J.A., "Micro-Rockets for the Classroom," *Am.J.Phys.* (November 1999), p. 1031 – 1033.

Johns, R., "Acceleration Without Force?," *The Physics Teacher* (March 2003), p. 156 – 157.

Mainardi, R., "Demonstration Experiments with Platform Scales," *The Physics Teacher* (November 2001), p. 488 – 489.

Martin, B.E., and Connors, M., "Testing a Model for Sliding Motion on an Incline," *The Physics Teacher* (December 2003), p. 534 – 536.

Minstrell, J., "Explaining the 'At Rest' Condition of an Object," *The Physics Teacher* (January 1982), p. 10 – 14.

Styer, D.F., "The Word "Force"," *Am.J.Phys.* (June 2001), p. 631 – 132.

Thornton, R.K., and Sokoloff, D.R., "Assessing Student Learning of Newton's Laws: The Force and Motion Conceptual Evaluation," *Am.J.Phys.* (April 1998), p. 338 – 352.

Williams, H.T., "Semantics in Teaching Introductory Physics," *Am.J.Phys.* (August 1999), p. 670 – 680.

Williams, K., "Inexpensive Demonstrator of Newton's First Law," *The Physics Teacher* (February 2000), p. 80.

Notes and Ideas

Preparation time: *Estimated:* _____   *Actual:* _____

Class time spent on material: *Estimated:* _____   *Actual:* _____

Related laboratory activities:

Demonstration materials:

Notes for next time:

Chapter 5: Applications of Newton's Laws

Outline

Summary

While Chapter 4 introduced the **three laws of motion** and its application to solving problems, it ignored the effect of friction. In this chapter we see **friction forces** included when applying **Newton's laws** to various situations. The effect of **drag forces** on falling objects and **terminal speed** are discussed. **Forces** in **circular motion** are considered both for **uniform** and **non-uniform motion**. Finally, a brief introduction is given of the concept of **fundamental forces** and **unification** of forces.

Major Concepts

- Common forces revisited
    - Gravity
    - Weight and mass
    - Tension
    - Normal force
    - Applying Newton's laws with constant forces

- Friction
    - Static friction
    - Kinetic/sliding friction
    - Properties of friction forces
    - Coefficient of friction

- Drag forces
    - Drag coefficient
    - Terminal speed
    - Drag force proportional to v^2
    - A better approximation to drag force

- Forces and circular motion
    - Uniform circular motion
    - Centripetal force
    - Centripetal acceleration
    - Banked and unbanked curves
    - Non-uniform circular motion
    - Tangential force
    - Tangential acceleration

- Circular motion and non-inertial frames
    - Non-inertial frames
    - Centrifugal force

- Fundamental forces
    - Fundamental forces
    - Secondary forces
    - Unifications
    - Universal gravitation
    - Weak force
    - Electromagnetic force
    - Electroweak force
    - Strong force

Teaching Suggestions and Demonstrations

Most of the material in this chapter is an extension of what has been covered in Chapter 4. However, continue to stress the importance of **free-body diagrams** when applying **Newton's laws** to various physical situations. The challenge here is in identifying the **radial force** correctly in the case of **circular motion**.

Section 5-1

The first section once again deals with the different kinds of **forces** that were introduced in the previous chapter, so this serves as a good review for the students. Stress the difference between **weight** and **mass** and the more rigorous definition of these in physics terms.

Some students will feel compelled to include a **normal force** for all problems. They need to remember that the normal force is the force exerted by a surface on an object and that it is always perpendicular to the surface and not the object. So a mass hanging in mid-air from a pulley will not have a **normal force** acting on it.

In the case of **tension** in ropes/strings, we know that the **tension** will be the same in every part of a string. However, depending on the situation or the system under consideration, the force due to this **tension** can be in two different directions for the same string. Take the example of a block on a horizontal table with a string attached to it and going over a pulley. At the end of the string is a second mass hanging vertically down. The **free-body diagram** for the first mass will have the **tension** pointing away from this mass and towards the pulley. On the other hand, the **free-body diagram** for the second (hanging) mass will have the **tension force** in the upward direction. To the students this can be confusing. Remind them that the two diagrams are not dealing with the same system. We isolate each block and treat them as two separate systems.

There are plenty of worked examples in the text that should give students ample practice in once again using **free-body diagrams** and applying **Newton's laws** to solve a variety of problems.

➲ **DEMO** Set up a block and pulley system to show the tension force in a string. Tie a string to one end of a block and pass the string over a pulley. Attach a spring scale to the free end to read the tension in the string. The force pulling the block will be the tension in the string. A large spring scale will make the demonstration visible to the whole class.

Sections 5-2 – 5-3

Friction force and its effect on the motion of an object are not unfamiliar to most students. However, the difference between **static** and **kinetic friction** will have to be introduced. They will in all probability have a little difficulty in accepting that **kinetic friction force** is always slightly less than the maximum **static friction force**. A common misconception is that the **friction force** is affected by the surface area of contact. With suitable demonstrations you can show that the **friction force** depends on the normal force and the kind of surfaces and not on the area of contact.

> ⮑ **DEMO** Attach a spring scale to a wooden block (the block has a hook on one face of it). Pull on the spring scale with a small force so the block does not move. Slowly increase the force on the block until it starts to move. Have the students note the reading on the scale during this process. They will be able to see that the static friction force increases to a maximum and once the block starts moving, the kinetic friction force will be slightly less than this maximum value.

> ⮑ **DEMO** To demonstrate that the friction force is affected by the normal force and the kind of surfaces and not on the area of contact, repeat the above demonstration with the following variation: Turn the block onto the narrow side and repeat the experiment. Place another block on top of the first one to increase the normal force and repeat the process. Glue a piece of sand paper to one face of the block and have this side slide over the table as you take the scale reading.

Drag forces are of particular interest to students as they can relate to parachuting from a plane and to drag racing. Equation 5-30 will help in discussing the effect of the cross-sectional area of the moving object and its shape on the **drag force**. This section can lead to a very lively classroom discussion. Again make use of the many worked examples in the text to familiarize the students with applying **Newton's laws** when **friction forces** are involved.

Section 5-4

Chapter 3 briefly introduced **uniform circular motion** and **radial acceleration** to the students. As a review it might be a good idea to emphasize that the **acceleration** produced here is due to the change in the direction of the velocity. The magnitude of the velocity is constant in the case of **uniform circular motion**. When solving problems, students will think of **centripetal force** as an additional force. But this is not the case. The **radial** or **centripetal force** is a name given to that **force** that is directed toward the center of the circle and hence makes the object to have circular motion.

While the concept of banked curves is treated in the worked example, it will be beneficial to go over the problem in class. It will surprise the students to find out that the velocity is independent of the mass of the car and depends on the banking angle. You can also discuss why a car goes off the curve when it takes the turn at a high speed.

The discussion on **circular motion** and **non-inertial frames** helps to dispel the myth of the **centrifugal force**.

> ⮑ **DEMO** A tennis ball is tied to one end of a sting that is then twirled in a vertical circle. This is a simple way to show the tension in the string is the centripetal force that makes the ball go around.

⊃ **DEMO**   A small mass and a large mass are connected via a string that is passed through a cylinder. Hold the cylinder so that the large mass hangs down and the smaller mass is pulled to the cylinder. Now spin the smaller mass in a circle. Depending on the rotational speed, the tension in the string will change and the larger mass will be lifted up or lowered. This is a simple way to show that the centripetal force is dependent on the angular velocity as well as the radius of the circle and not just the mass.

⊃ **DEMO**   Drill small holes at three points (evenly spaced and forming the vertices of an equilateral triangle) on a piece of wood or sturdy cardboard. Pass three strings through these holes and tie them together at the other end to form a nice swinging platform. Place a glass of water on the platform and hold the strings from the knotted end so the platform (with the glass of water) is suspended below. Now start swinging the platform from side to side and increase the arc slightly with each swing. Once you have it swinging smoothly, twirl it in a vertical circle at a good speed. The water will stay inside the glass and will not spill out. It will take a little practice to start the motion as well as to stop it without spilling the contents of the glass.

Section 5-5

The chapter ends with a very brief discussion of the three **fundamental forces** and the concept of **unification**. It gives the students a taste of some of the topics to be discussed later on in the course.

Textbook Resource Information

Transparency Acetates

Fig. 5-2	Weight of an object using spring scale
Fig. 5-3	Tension force
Fig. 5-5	Examples of normal force
Fig. 5-8	Lifting an object using a system of pulleys
Fig. 5-9a	Atwood's machine – free-body diagram
Fig. 5-12	Static friction force and its dependence on the pushing force
Fig. 5-20	Terminal speed of a parachutist
Fig. 5-24	Tension as the centripetal force
Fig. 5-27	Car on an icy banked road

Physlet Physics Illustrations

5.1	Static and Kinetic Friction
5.5	Air Friction
5.2	Uniform Circular Motion
5.3	The Ferris Wheel

Physlet Physics Explorations

5.1	Circular motion
5.2	Force an object around a circle
5.5	Damping forces
5.6	Air friction

Physlet Physics Problems

5.1   Book against a wall –static friction
5.2   Book against a wall – kinetic friction
5.5   Free-body diagram for a two-mass system
5.7   Block on an inclined plane
5.8   A Ferris wheel problem
5.9   Mass on a turntable
5.11 Coin on a turntable

Ranking Task Exercises in Physics, **Student Edition**

Page 36   Objects on a rough surface – velocity changes
Page 37   Objects on rough surface – speed changes

End of Chapter Problems with Solutions in the *Student Study Guide*

13, 27, 33, 45, 53, 73

Suggested Readings

Andereck, B.S., "Measurement of Air Resistance on an Air Track," *Am.J.Phys.* (June 1999), p. 528 – 533.

Bacon, M.E., Heald, G., and James, M., "A Closer Look at Tumbling Toast," *Am.J.Phys.* (January 2001), p. 38 – 43.

Dietz, E.R., "Centripetal Acceleration: Another Round," *Am.J.Phys.* (October 1999), p. 932.

Gluck, P., "Air Resistance on Falling Balls and Balloons," *The Physics Teacher* (March 2003), p. 178 – 180.

Larabee, D., "Car Collisions, Physics, and State Highway Patrol," *The Physics Teacher* (September 2000), p. 334 – 336.

Leff, H., "Acceleration for Circular Motion," *Am.J.Phys.* (May 2002), p. 490 – 492.

Reichert, J., "How Did Friction Get So Smart?," *The Physics Teacher* (January 2001), p. 29 – 31.

Touger, J., "The Role of Language in Learning Physics Beyond Semantics," *Am.J.Phys.* (April 2000), p. 306 – 307.

Van den Berg, W., "The Best Angle for Dragging a Box," *The Physics Teacher* (November 2000), p. 506 – 508.

Watts, R.G., and Moore, G., "The Drag Force of an American Football," *Am.J.Phys.* (August 2003), p. 791 – 793.

Wick, D.P., and Ramsdell, M.W., "Modeling the Motion of a Toy Car Traveling on an Arbitrarily Shaped Track," *Am.J.Phys.* (July 2002), p. 670 – 679.

Zebrowski, Jr., E., "On the Derivation of the Centripetal Acceleration Formula," *The Physics Teacher* (December 2002), p. 554 – 555.

Notes and Ideas

Preparation time: *Estimated:* _____   *Actual:* _____

Class time spent on material: *Estimated:* _____   *Actual:* _____

Related laboratory activities:

Demonstration materials:

Notes for next time:

Chapter 6: Work and Kinetic Energy

Outline

6-1   Kinetic Energy, Work, and the Work-Energy theorem
6-2   Constant Forces in more Than One Dimension
6-3   Forces that Vary with Position
6-4   Conservative and Nonconservative Forces
6-5   Power
6-6   Kinetic Energy at Very High Speeds

Summary

Chapter 6 introduces the idea of **energy of motion** or **kinetic energy** by looking at the **work** done by a **constant** as well as a **varying force**. The **work-energy theorem** shows that **work** and **energy** are very closely related and how this becomes a powerful and sophisticated tool in solving kinematic problems. The distinction between conservative and **nonconservative forces** is discussed. The time rate of change of doing work (**power**) is introduced. Finally, the **kinetic energy** of an object moving at **relativistic speeds** is considered.

Major Concepts

- Kinetic energy
  - Net work done
  - Work-energy theorem
  - Units of work and energy
  - Work done by an individual force

- Work
  - Work done by constant force in two and three dimensions
  - Scalar or dot product of two vectors
  - Work as dot product of the force and displacement vectors
  - Force perpendicular to the direction of motion
  - Positive, negative and zero work

- Varying forces
  - Position dependent force in one dimension
  - Work done by a varying force
  - Hooke's law
  - Work done by a spring
  - Forces varying in both magnitude and direction
  - Work done in uniform circular motion

- Conservative and nonconservative forces
  - Work done by gravity
  - Work done by friction forces
  - Work done by a spring
  - Path dependence or independence of work
  - Definition of conservative and nonconservative forces

- Power
  - o Definition of power
  - o Units of power
  - o Kilowatthour as unit of energy
  - o Power as dot product of force and velocity

- Relativistic speeds
  - o Kinetic energy at speeds comparable to that of light
  - o Limiting case of $v \ll c$

Teaching Suggestions and Demonstrations

It is very important that students recognize the difference between the technical definition and the everyday usage of the terms **energy, work** and **power**. The law of conservation of energy, which is discussed in the next chapter, is one of the most fundamental of physics principles. So students can appreciate the power of this principle, make sure they understand the concepts of **kinetic energy** and the **work-energy theorem** first.

Sections 6-1 – 6-3

Showing that the **net work** done equals the change in **kinetic energy** is fairly straightforward. However most students will not recognize the implications of this equation. Discuss the fact that when the **net work** done is zero, the change in **kinetic energy** is zero, which in turn implies that the object has constant velocity and hence no acceleration. In reverse, they should be able to make the connection that in the case of an object moving at constant velocity the **net work** done will be zero. To complete the discussion, be sure to point out that the **net work** done will be negative if the change in **kinetic energy** is negative; i.e. the object's velocity is decreasing.

> ⊃ **DEMO** A block and pulley system can be set up fairly easily to show that the work done will depend on the force and the displacement. Tie a string to one end of a block and pass the string over a pulley. Attach a hanger and mass on the free end and allow the block to move across the table. The force pulling the block will be the tension in the string. You can adjust the hanging mass to have the block move with constant velocity or with acceleration. The latter case can be used to discuss the work-energy theorem. Alternately, you can pull the block with a spring scale.

The idea that **work** is done only when there is a displacement in the direction of the force is an important one. Equally important is the fact that while several forces may be acting on an object, the **work** done by each of the forces will depend on the direction of the motion. Then go on to the idea of **net work** done. Show the students that **net work** done can be calculated by either using the net force, or by adding up the **work** done by each of the individual forces.

> ⊃ **DEMO** You can extend the previous demo to discuss the net work done due to multiple forces acting on an object. Instead of pulling the block along the horizontal surface of the table, use an inclined plane. Determine the angle between the gravitational force and the displacement vector and show that the work done will depend on the component of the gravitational force parallel to the plane.

Most students will be familiar with the unit of **work Joule**. However, they will not always recognize that the **N.m** and the **Joule** are equivalent. It is also a good idea to stress that **kinetic energy** will have the same units as **work**.

The **scalar dot product** is another method by which to calculate the **work** done. Students are apt to forget that **work** is a scalar quantity, so this would be a good time to stress that once again. Also point out that the **work** done by a force depends on the angle between the force and displacement vectors. Discuss the fact that the **work** done can go from negative maximum to zero to positive maximum since $\cos\theta$ can have values between -1 and $+1$.

The **work** done by a **varying force** is given by the area under the curve of a force vs. position graph. This comes from integrating the force (which is position dependent) over the interval x_o and x_f. Again use different kinds of curves to show students examples of the **work** done being negative.

The negative sign in **Hooke's law** often confuses students. It might be a good idea to explain the concept of **restoring force**. Use Fig. 6-13 to show that the stretch or compression of the spring (which is x) is opposite to the force direction. Another common mistake that students make is in assuming that twice as much **work** will be done when the spring is stretched/compressed twice as much. Emphasize that the **work** done by a spring is proportional to the square of the stretch or compression.

> ↪ DEMO A spring is suspended from a rod and masses are added to the free end of the spring. The extension for the addition of each mass can be measured using a scale mounted behind the spring. This is a straightforward and simple way to demonstrate Hooke's law.

Students were introduced to **circular motion** in an earlier chapter and should be familiar with the concept of **radial forces** and **tangential velocity**. But a brief review might be needed before discussing why no **work** is done in **uniform circular motion**

Section 6-4

Take the example of lifting an object of mass m through a height h (a) by lifting it vertically, (b) by taking it up an incline and (c) by taking it up a flight of steps. For each case, calculate the **work** done by the gravitational force and show that it depends only on the vertical height through which the object is lifted and not how it got there. This is a good way to introduce the concept of **conservative force** and path independence. From this you can show why the **work** done by a **conservative force** in moving along a closed path is zero.

Section 6-5

In discussing **power**, be sure to point out that the **instantaneous power** is the **scalar product** of the force and velocity vectors. Students will relate easily to the concept of **horsepower** but will also assume that it is part of the SI system of units. The other common misconception students have is that the **kilowatt hour** is a **unit** of **work**. Point out that it is an **energy unit**. They will find it interesting to learn that their power company bills them for the amount of energy they have consumed and not for **power**.

Section 6-6

While the detailed derivation of the **relativistic equation** is to be found much later in the book, it might pique the interest of students to get a taste of it here. Show them how the equation reduces to the simple and familiar $\frac{1}{2}mv^2$ when the velocity of an object is small compared to that of light.

Textbook Resource Information

Transparency Acetates

Fig. 6-8   Dependence of work done on the angle between the force and position vectors
Fig. 6-11   Work done by a varying force
Fig. 6-13   Force exerted by a spring and the work done by a spring
Fig. 6-15   Forces that vary in magnitude and in direction
Fig. 6-21   Work done by friction force – path dependence

Physlet Physics Illustrations

6.1   Dot Product
6.2   Constant Force
6.3   Force and Displacement
6.4   Springs
7.2   Energy Representation

Physlet Physics Explorations

6.2   Kinetic energy in case of two-block push
6.4   Varying force – change in direction
6.6   Forces, path integrals and work

Physlet Physics Problems

6.2   Work and average force
6.3   Pushing a block on a horizontal surface
6.9   Block sliding down an incline
6.11   Work done by various forces

Ranking Task Exercises in Physics, Student Edition

Page 63   Work done in change of velocity
Page 65   Bouncing cart – work done by barrier
Page 66   Bouncing cart – work done on the barrier
Page 67   Model rockets – kinetic energy
Page 68   Sliding masses on incline – kinetic energy
Page 71   Ball motion diagram – kinetic energy
Page 73   Pushing Box with friction – change in kinetic energy

End of Chapter Problems with Solutions in the *Student Study Guide*

11, 37, 45, 53, 69, 85

Suggested Readings

Arons, A.B., "Development of Energy Concepts in Introductory Physics Courses," *Am.J.Phys.* (December 1999), p. 1063 – 1067.

Hilborn, R., "Let's Ban Work from Physics," *The Physics Teacher* (October 2000), p. 447.

Ingham, W., "A Consistent Sign Convention for Work," *The Physics Teacher* (March 2000), p. 160.

Jordan, R.G., "Work Revisited," *The Physics Teacher* (December 2002), p. 526 – 527. (Also see letters to the editor in the May 2003 issue).

Malone, J., and Holzwarth, D., "A Real Look at Speeds and Stopping Distances," *The Physics Teacher* (February 1998), p. 95 – 96.

Mendelson, K.S., "Physical and Colloquial Meanings of the Term 'Work'," *Am.J.Phys.* (March 2003), p. 279 – 281.

Piatek, S., and Gautreau, R., "Constant Acceleration and Kinetic Friction," *The Physics Teacher* (May 1998), p. 316.

Van Heuvelen, A., and Zou, X., "Multiple Representations of Work-Energy Processes," *Am.J.Phys.* (February 2001), p. 184 – 194.

Velazquez-Aviles, A.L., "Using the Work-Energy Theorem with Car and Driver Website Data," *The Physics Teacher* (April 2002), p. 235 – 237.

Waring, G., "Energy and the Automobile," *The Physics Teacher* (October 1980), p. 494 – 503.

Notes and Ideas

Preparation time: *Estimated:* _____   *Actual:* _____

Class time spent on material: *Estimated:* _____   *Actual:* _____

Related laboratory activities:

Demonstration materials:

Notes for next time:

Chapter 7: Potential Energy and Conservation of Energy

Outline

Summary

In Chapter 6 we learned about energy of motion (**kinetic energy**) and the work-energy theorem. This chapter looks at another aspect of energy – **potential energy** which is a function of position. Conservative and nonconservative forces and the work done by these forces are also discussed. The **law of conservation of energy** which is one of the fundamental principles of physics and its application to problem solving are explained.

Major Concepts

- Potential energy and conservative forces
  - Work done by a conservative force
  - Definition of potential energy
  - Conservation of energy
  - Total mechanical energy

- Applications of the conservation of energy
  - Gravity
  - Spring force
  - Energy of systems

- Energy Conservation and allowed motion
  - Energy diagram
  - Equilibrium points
  - Stable, unstable and neutral equilibrium

- Motion In two or three Dimensions
  - Potential energy function
  - Potential energy for projectile motion
  - Central forces

- Energy conservation as a general principle
  - Work done by nonconservative forces
  - Thermal energy
  - Energy conservation as a fundamental principle

Teaching Suggestions and Demonstrations

The topics in this chapter are a natural sequence to those we saw in Chapter 6. Students will learn to appreciate the importance of the **conservation of energy** principle in solving two- and three-dimensional kinematic situations. The more complicated problems from earlier chapters will now be easier to solve. To illustrate this, be sure to work the same projectile motion and other kinematic problems using the **energy conservation** approach. With this in mind, I have suggested some of the ranking task questions from Chapter 3 once again in this chapter.

Sections 7-1 – 7-3

The concept of **potential energy** is straightforward. The definition of conservative and nonconservative forces from Chapter 6 should still be fresh in the students' minds. Still, it would be a good idea to review why gravitational force is a **conservative force**. Equations 7-4 and 7-5 are important in that they show the relationship between the force function and the **potential energy** function. This will be of greater significance when dealing with two and three dimensional situations. In calculating the **potential energy**, the "zero point" of the **potential energy** is chosen depending on the particular situation and this will determine the **potential energy** of the object with respect to the zero level chosen. For example, find the **potential energy** of the text book that is lying on the table. If the floor is chosen to be at zero **potential energy**, then on the table the book will have a positive **potential energy**. The same book will have no **potential energy** with respect to the table and a negative **potential energy** with respect to the ceiling.

> ⟳ **DEMO** A pile driver is a very simple but effective way to show the work done by the gravitational force. Place an empty soda can at the bottom. Raise the pile driver to a small height and let go. The soda can will be slightly crushed. Now raise the mass to a greater height and allow it to fall. (Be sure to use a second soda can now.) The can will be crushed, showing that the driver has a greater potential to do work in the second case.

In the context of the **law of conservation of energy**, the word "*conserve*" has a different meaning from everyday usage of "conserving energy". A couple of minutes spent on discussing this will help the students to understand this section better.

Worked Examples 7-4 and 7-5 are two typical problems that appear complicated but are easy to solve using the **energy conservation principle**. Point out that this involves no free-body diagrams or vector calculations. It is also important to work through a problem where a numerical value is not assigned to the mass of an object. Since the mass is a factor in every term of the equation, it can be factored out and cancelled. However, since students are very partial to using numerical values from the very first step in solving a problem, they will conclude that sufficient information is not available to solve the problem.

> ⟳ **DEMO** Central Scientific has a nice demo to show conservation of energy. The apparatus has four tracks of the same height but with different profiles. Allow four identical spheres to start from the top of the tracks. Since the balls have fallen through the same height, they will have lost the same amount of potential energy. Thus the balls will have the same final velocity at the bottom of the tracks. If you have access to photogates, the final velocities can be measured quantitatively. To show the effect of friction, use the plastic cup provided with the apparatus. Allow the ball to come down the track and fall into the cup. The ball will be pushed back onto the track. The distance the ball is pushed back will be the same for each of the tracks as long as the balls are released from the same height.

The **energy diagram** is a simple but useful tool to visualize the change from **kinetic** to **potential energy** as well as to qualitatively discuss **stable**, **unstable** and **neutral equilibrium**. In Example 7-6 we have a fairly complicated **potential energy function**. The expression by itself tells us nothing about the motion, but the **energy diagram** gives us a great deal of information about the motion of an object in such a **potential**.

Section 7-3 extends the **potential energy function** to include all three of the variables x, y and z. Again, choose problems on projectile motion and show how much easier it is to solve them using the **law of conservation of energy**.

➲ **DEMO** Here is another simple set-up to show conservation of energy. Suspend a bowling ball by a long thin wire from the ceiling. The length must be adjusted so that the ball will be up to your nose when pulled to one side. Pull the ball so it is very close to your nose and release it without giving it a push. The ball will swing back to the same height from which it was released. You need to stand very still through the whole process. It is best if you can stand with your back against the wall so you don't flinch backwards.
Be sure to stand very straight. You should not lean forward as you release the ball. If you give the ball an initial velocity by pushing on it, it will hit your face.

➲ **DEMO** A loop-the-loop apparatus can be built without too much difficulty using metal tracks that can be bought from a hardware store. Release the ball from different heights to see when it will go round the loop without falling off the track. You can have the students do the calculations before you show them the demo. They will find that the minimum height needed to complete the loop is much higher than the calculated value. This fact can be used to discuss energy losses due to friction.

➲ **DEMO** If you are unable to build the loop-the-loop, you could purchase a simpler version from Central Scientific. This is a track that is bent to form a shallow U. Release a ball from one side of the U and the ball will rise to almost the same height on the other arm of the U.

Section 7-4

The introductory paragraph in this section is important if only to introduce the idea of **energy conservation** as one of the most **fundamental principles of physics**. Discuss the difference between **total energy** of a system and **total mechanical energy** of the system (as used in sections 7-1 – 7-3). Since friction is an integral part of everyday situations, it is important to discuss its contribution to the work-energy theorem. Students will know by now how to calculate the work done by friction force. However, quite often they will not make the connection between this and the term W_{nc} in Equation 7-18.

Textbook Resource Information

Transparency Acetates

Fig. 7-8a – 7-8d   Energy diagram
Fig. 7-9   Total energy and turning points
Fig. 7-10   Stable, unstable and neutral equilibrium

Physlet Physics Illustrations

7.1   Choice of System
7.3   Potential Energy Diagrams
7.5   Block on an Incline

Physlet Physics Explorations

7.2   Choice of zero for potential energy
7.6   Different interactions
7.7   Potential energy functions

Physlet Physics Problems

7.1   Mass in a bowl
7.3   Block on an incline
7.5   Block and pulley system
7.6   Two-mass system
7.7   Projectile motion
7.10 Spring and mass system

Ranking Task Exercises in Physics, Student Edition

Page 49, 50   Maximum heights
Page 51   Horizontal speed at top of projectile
Page 65   Change in potential energy – masses on incline
Page 71   Pendulum – maximum speed of the bob

End of Chapter Problems with Solutions in the Student Study Guide

11, 13, 27, 37, 47, 49

Suggested Readings

Edge, R., "String and Sticky Tape Experiments: The Bouncy Paper Clip – Potential and Kinetic Energy," *The Physics Teacher* (November 2000), p. 470.

Hecht, E., "An Historico-Critical Account of Potential Energy: Is PE Really Real?," *The Physics Teacher* (November 2003), p. 486 – 493.

Jolly, P., Zollman, D., Rebello, N.S., and Dimitrova, A., "Visualizing Motion in Potential Wells," *Am.J.Phys.* (January 1998), p. 57 – 63.

Keeports, D., "How Does the Potential Energy of a Rising Helium Balloon Change?," *The Physics Teacher* (March 2002), p. 164 – 165.

LoPresto, M.C., "Another Look at Atwood's Machine," *The Physics Teacher* (February 1999), p. 82 – 83.

Mancuso, R., "Work and Potential Energy – Letters to the Editor," *The Physics Teacher* (May 2003), p. 260.

Newburgh, R., "Hewitt's Oscillating Block - Letters to the Editor," *The Physics Teacher* (March 2003), p. 132.

Tanner, R.R., "Roller-Coaster Design Project," *The Physics Teacher* (March 1997), p. 148 – 149.

Taylor, J.R., Carpenter, A.W., and Bunton, P.H., "Conservation of Energy with a Rubber Stamp," *The Physics Teacher* (March 1997), p. 146 – 147.

Website devoted to amusement-park physics: http://www.learner.org/exhibits/parkphysics

Notes and Ideas

Preparation time: *Estimated:* _____   *Actual:* _____

Class time spent on material: *Estimated:* _____   *Actual:* _____

Related laboratory activities:

Demonstration materials:

Notes for next time:

Chapter 8: Linear Momentum, Collisions, and the Center of Mass

Outline

Summary

The study of **collisions** is important since colliding objects are all around us. **Conservation of momentum** is another fundamental principle of physics that helps us to understand how colliding objects behave. This chapter discusses collisions of different kinds and the **conservation laws** that can be applied to each of them. **Center of mass** and the motion of extended objects in terms of the motion of the **center of mass** of the object are also included.

Major Concepts

- Momentum and its conservation
    - Linear momentum
    - Momentum and the second law
    - Momentum in terms of kinetic energy
    - Conservation of momentum
    - Conservation for a system of many objects

- Collisions and impulse
    - Impulsive forces
    - Impulse
    - Classification of collisions
    - Energy considerations in collisions
    - Elastic collision
    - Inelastic collision

- Perfectly inelastic collisions
    - Perfectly inelastic collisions
    - Energy loss
    - Explosions

- Elastic two-body collisions
    - Elastic collisions in one dimension
    - Relative velocity of colliding objects
    - Elastic collisions in two and three dimensions

- Center of mass
    - Center of mass – definition
    - Position vector of center of mass
    - Cartesian components of center of mass
    - Center of mass motion in the absence of external forces
    - Center of mass in the presence of external forces
    - Equations for linear motion of the center of mass
    - Conservation of momentum in different inertial frames
    - Center of mass frame
    - Center of mass of a continuous mass distribution
    - Continuous objects in two and three dimensions

- Rocket motion
    - Exhaust speed
    - Rate of change of mass
    - Thrust
    - Fundamental equation in rocket propulsion
    - Rocket motion in the presence of gravity

Teaching Suggestions and Demonstrations

There are many kinds of **collisions** that are common occurrences in our lives. To understand how these objects behave before, during and after the process, we need to have a clear concept of **momentum, impulse** and the **law of conservation of momentum**. The **law of conservation of momentum** is as important as the law of conservation of energy. Together they form two of the most fundamental laws of physics. Much of kinematics can be understood starting from these two principles. Students in the introductory physics classes quite often fail to grasp the importance of these two laws. Work out as many different **collision** problems as possible and make use of the demos listed in here.

Section 8-1

Begin by defining **momentum**. Discuss the fact that an object can have a large **momentum** because of a large mass or high speed. Equations 8-3 and 8-4 are very important. Equation 8-3 connects **momentum** (or rather rate of change of **momentum**) to Newton's second law, while Equation 8-4 expresses kinetic energy in terms of **momentum**. It is common for students to use $p = mv^2$ instead of $p = mv$ as they are now used to finding $K = \frac{1}{2} mv^2$, having just finished Chapter 7.

As was mentioned in the summary, **conservation of momentum** is a very important law. Through the rest of the chapter, this law is used repeatedly for different kinds of collisions. Since **momentum** is a vector, the direction is important when using Equation 8.9 or 8.12. Take the example of a ball bouncing off the floor with the same speed as it hit the floor. The change in **momentum** will be $\Delta p = p_f - p_i = m(v - (-v)) = 2mv$ and not $\Delta p = m(v - v) = 0$ as many students are apt to think.

Sections 8-2 – 8-5

Another way of looking at momentum or the change in **momentum** is in terms of the quantity called **impulse**. The relationship $\Delta p = F_{ave} \Delta t$ helps us to understand how to maximize the change in **momentum** for a given average force or how to minimize the impact force for a given change in **momentum**. Contrary to what students will expect, in both cases the time of contact will have to be large. There are many examples one can use to illustrate this. For instance, talk about the "follow through" of a bat /racket in baseball, tennis or golf (or for that matter any sport involving bat and ball). By increasing the time of contact Δt (during the follow through), the batter is able to give a large Δp to the ball thus ensuring that the ball travels a much further distance than it otherwise would. In the case of a tightrope walker in a circus, a safety net increases the time of contact Δt thus minimizing the force of impact F_{ave}.

The greatest misconception is that students will often take the magnitude of the impact force and the effect of this impact force to be the same. Go back to the semi and the Volkswagen example discussed in Chapter 4 and stress the difference between them.

➲ **DEMO** Egg in sheet - All you need for this demo is a large bedsheet and a raw egg. Get two students to hold the sheet up by its four corners in such a way that the sheet forms a pocket at the bottom edge; i.e. make a 'J' with the sheet. A third student is then asked to hurl the egg at the bedsheet with as much force as he/she can muster. If you have a baseball player in class, have him or her pitch the egg. Make sure the students are aware of the fact that the egg is a raw one. The egg will drop into the pocket without breaking. You can then talk about the large time of contact minimizing the impact force in the equation $F = \Delta p / \Delta t$

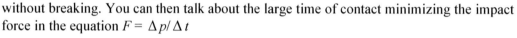

➲ **DEMO** Impulse pendulum - Set a block of wood upright on the table. Make a pendulum out of a super bounce ball and a second one from a nonbouncing ball. Pull the pendulum bob to one side and let go. As it swings down it should collide with the block. The block will topple when hit with the super bounce ball, while it will stay in place when hit with the other pendulum.

➲ **DEMO** Here is a different version of the same demo. Place the block of wood close to a track as shown. Allow the bounce and no-bounce balls to roll down the track and collide with the block of wood. The no-bounce ball will not be able to topple the block of wood. This apparatus can be obtained from Central Scientific.

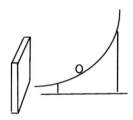

Collisions are classified based on the behavior of the masses after **collision** as well as the kinetic energy before and after the process. All of these **collisions** are important, and the text goes through each of them very methodically. Students need to learn to identify if a **collision** is **elastic**, **inelastic** or **perfectly inelastic** and if the law of conservation of energy is applicable or not. In solving word problems, this is where they experience a lot of indecisiveness. Also, since they have been drilled on this law in Chapter 7, they will have the tendency to automatically apply this law to every **collision**.

The word **collision** brings to mind two objects hitting each other head on. In physics, an **explosion** (breaking up of a single object into two or more parts) is also considered a **collision**. The textbook has plenty of worked examples dealing with the different kinds of **collisions**. Students will benefit immensely if you go through some of these examples in class.

➲ **DEMO** Edmund Scientific has a set of collision balls, otherwise known as Newton's balls. Displace one ball first and observe the effect. Repeat by displacing two, then three and so on, up to five balls at once. You can use this demo to discuss collisions and conservation of energy.

➲ **DEMO** Bouncing eggs: You will need a basketball and a second ball slightly smaller in size than the basketball and two eggs. First drop one egg and let is splash on the floor. Next, hold the second egg on top of the basketball and let them bounce to the floor. The egg will shoot up to a great height. This is a very good demo to illustrate the concept of momentum transfer. If you want to dramatize the effect, you can hold the second egg on top of smaller ball which is on top of the basketball (as shown in the figure). When you let this set-up bounce on the floor, the height to which the egg rebounds will be much higher than in the first case.

If you don't want to deal with the mess, you could use boiled eggs. However, this will not be half as much fun.

Sections 8-4 and 8-5 are an extension of the **conservation of momentum** principle to two and three dimensional **collisions**. While the physics is the same, the algebra is not as straightforward. Don't be surprised if many students have forgotten how to solve a system of equations with more than one unknown.

Section 8-6

This section is useful in understanding the behavior of extended objects (objects that are not mere point objects). The concept of **center of mass** is not a difficult one. However, it will not be easy to visualize the motion of an extended non-uniform object (however symmetric or odd shaped it might be) in terms of the **center of mass**. Once they get a grasp of this, they will appreciate the usefulness of this technique. The section on 'A Few Tips for Finding the **Center of Mass**' should be very helpful.

➲ **DEMO** Make a cardboard cutout of the state in which you live. Make holes at three or four places along the edge of the shape. Suspend the piece from one of the holes and allow a plumb line to hang in front of it. Trace the vertical line of the plumb line. Repeat by suspending the piece from the other holes. The center of mass will be at the intersection of the plumb lines. Discuss the fact that this only gives the location of the center of mass of the piece of cardboard and not the actual state, since it does not take into account population density, mountains, rivers, valleys etc.

Section 8-7

Most curricula suggest this as optional and often we omit **rocket motion** for lack of time. However, students will enjoy this section very much as they can relate to it well. For that reason I try to make time for this in my classes. Go through the derivation of Equation 8-69 and point out that mass is not a constant in the **conservation of momentum** equation.

➲ **DEMO** Water rocket - This is a toy rocket that is available in stores like Wal-Mart or K-Mart. Do the demo first without water. Insert the pump into the rocket and pump about 20 times. Release the rocket by sliding off the catch. The rocket will not go very far. Next, fill the rocket with a cap full of water and repeat the process. The rocket will go much farther now.

Textbook Resource Information

Transparency Acetates

Fig. 8-1	Contact forces in collisions
Fig. 8-4	Impulsive force vs. time graph
Fig. 8-7	Two cart collision
Fig. 8-9	Perfectly inelastic collision
Fig. 8-15	Elastic collision in one dimension
Fig. 8-18	Elastic collision in one and two dimensions
Fig. 8-21	Center of mass of two and three masses
Fig. 8-25	Internal forces in a three-object system
Fig. 8-32	Center of mass of object with a hole
Fig. 8-34	Rocket propulsion

Physlet Physics Illustrations

8.1	Force and Impulse
8.2	Difference between Impulse and Work
8.4	Relative Velocity in Collision
8.7	Center of Mass and Gravity
8.8	Moving Objects and Center of Mass

Physlet Physics Explorations

8.2	An elastic collision
8.4	Elastic and inelastic collisions and Δp
8.5	Two and three ball collisions
8.6	An explosive collision
8.7	A bouncing ball

Physlet Physics Problems

8.3	Two cart collision
8.4	Find the mass of the cart
8.8	Spring and two mass system
8.9	Elastic or inelastic collision?
8.11	Inelastic collision
8.12	Two-dimensional collision

Ranking Task Exercises in Physics, Student Edition

Page 74	Cars and barriers – stopping time with the same force
Page 75	Exploding shells – final location of center of mass
Page 76 – 78	Bouncing cart – change in momentum
Page 81	Impulse during a change of velocity
Page 82	Change in momentum during a change of velocity

End of Chapter Problems with Solutions in the *Student Study Guide*

5, 17, 33, 37, 61, 75

Suggested Readings

Bouffard, K., "Physics Olympics - The Inertia Ball," *The Physics Teacher* (January 2001), p. 46 – 47.

Cross, R., "The Coefficient of Restitution for Collisions of Happy Balls, Unhappy Balls and Tennis Balls," *Am.J.Phys.* (November 2000), p. 1025 – 1031.

Fakhruddin, H., "Maximizing Imparted Speed in Elastic Collision," *The Physics Teacher* (September 2003), p. 338 – 339.

Finney, G.A., "Analysis of a Water-Propelled Rocket: A Problem in Honors Physics," *Am.J.Phys.* (March 2000), p. 223 – 227.

Huebner, J.S., Fletcher, A.S., Cato, J.A., and Barrett, J.A., "Micro-Rockets for the Classroom," *Am.J.Phys.* (November 1999), p. 1031 – 1033.

Itza-Ortiz, S.F., Rebello, N.S., Zollman, D.A., and Rodriguez-Achach, M., "The Vocabulary of Introductory Physics and Its Implications for Learning Physics," *The Physics Teacher* (September 2003), p. 330 – 336.

Larabee, D., "Car Collisions, Physics, and the State Highway Patrol," *The Physics Teacher* (September 2000), p. 334 – 336.

Loveland, K.T., "Simple Equations for Linear Partially Elastic Collisions," *The Physics Teacher* (September 2000), p. 380 – 381.

Lyublinskaya, I.E., "Central Collisions – The General Case," *The Physics Teacher* (January 1998), p. 18 – 19.

Millet, L.E., "The One-Dimensional Elastic Collision Equation: $v_f = 2v_c - v_i$," *The Physics Teacher* (March 1998), p. 186.

Nicoll, M., "Apparatus for Teaching Physics: The Surgical-Hose Rocket," *The Physics Teacher* (March 1998), p. 181 – 182.

Roeder, J.L., "Analyzing Collisions in Terms of Newton's Laws," *The Physics Teacher* (February 2003), p. 97 – 99.

Widmark, S.A., "Rocket Physics," *The Physics Teacher* (March 1998), p. 148 – 153.

Notes and Ideas

Preparation time: *Estimated:* _____   *Actual:* _____

Class time spent on material: *Estimated:* _____   *Actual:* _____

Related laboratory activities:

Demonstration materials:

Notes for next time:

Chapter 9: Rotation of Rigid Bodies

Outline

9-1   Simple Rotations of a Rigid Body
9-2   Rotational Kinetic Energy
9-3   Evaluation of Rotational Inertia
9-4   Torque
9-5   Angular Momentum and Its Conservation
9-6   Rolling

Summary

Thus far in the book, the laws of physics governing translational motion of point particles have been considered. In this chapter, for the first time, students will learn about the behavior of rigid objects when they undergo rotational motion. The connection between the variables in **rotational motion** and their counterparts in linear motion are discussed. Students will learn about yet another conservation law, the **conservation of angular momentum**.

Major Concepts

- Simple rotation of a rigid body
    - Angular displacement
    - Angle of circular motion
    - Radian
    - Angular velocity, average and instantaneous
    - Right-hand rule for angular velocity direction
    - Angular acceleration, average and instantaneous
    - Constant angular acceleration
    - Acceleration of a point in a rotating rigid body
    - Radial acceleration
    - Tangential acceleration

- Rotational kinetic energy
    - Rotational kinetic energy
    - Definition of rotational inertia or moment of inertia
    - Axis of rotation
    - Mass density for one-, two-, and three-dimensional objects

- Evaluation of rotational inertia
    - Dumbbell
    - Thin cylinder
    - Solid cylinder
    - Rod
    - Parallel-axis theorem

- Torque
    - Definition of torque
    - Lever arm or moment arm

- o   Dynamical equation for rotational motion
- o   Vector equation of motion for torque
- o   Direction of torque
- o   Free-body diagram
- o   Gravity and extended objects

- • Angular momentum and its conservation
    - o   Definition of angular momentum
    - o   Torque in terms of rate of change of angular momentum
    - o   Relation between kinetic energy and angular momentum
    - o   Parallels between rotational and linear motion

- • Rolling
    - o   Rolling – combination of rotational and translational motion
    - o   Energy in rolling
    - o   Dynamics of rolling

Teaching Suggestions and Demonstrations

Even though circular motion has been touched upon in a couple of the earlier chapters, students are for the first time introduced to the mathematical representation of the variables involved in **angular motion**. Because of the two- and three-dimensional nature of **angular motion**, they will have difficulty visualizing and understanding the concepts discussed in this chapter. Visual aids such as demos and diagrams will be particularly helpful.

Section 9-1

To get a solid understanding of the variables involved in **rotational inertia**, it is important to go through the definitions of displacement, velocity (average and instantaneous), and acceleration (average and instantaneous) for angular motion. While students might be familiar with the word **radian**, they would not have had as much experience in actually using this unit. Point out the parallel in the definition of these quantities to the corresponding variables in linear motion as well as to the kinematic equations studied in Chapter 2. The difference between tangential and angular quantities should be discussed, as they will now have to contend with **radial**, **tangential** and **angular acceleration**.

⊃ **DEMO**   Draw a big circle on the board. Use the vector sticks described in chapter 1 of this manual to indicate the position vector of a particle at a point p on the circle. Use a second vector stick to show the position of the same particle after a small interval of time to indicate the angular displacement.

⊃ **DEMO**   Use a large clock that has a well-defined hour, minute and second hands. Use this to discuss the angular velocity of the three hands. Don't be surprised if quite a few students use 24 hrs as the time taken for the hour hand to complete a circle. This is a good opportunity to make the students use different units to calculate angular velocity and then convert the value to radian/sec.

Sections 9-2 – 9-3

Rotational inertia is to **rotational motion** what mass is to linear motion. Discuss this parallel and use the demos suggested here to illustrate this. Be sure to point out that the **rotational inertia** depends not just on the mass of the object, but on how this mass is distributed. Students will also forget that the **rotational inertia** is dependent on the **axis of rotation**. Go through Table 9-1 to show them how to evaluate the **rotational inertia** of some standard solid objects with **axes of symmetry**. You can also use the same table to compare the **rotational inertia** of a rod, a cylinder, a sphere and a disk of equal mass and equal radius.

⟳ **DEMO** Attach a weight to one end of a dowel. It will be easier to vertically balance the dowel (because it does not rotate easily due to the greater rotational inertia) when the weight is further from the hand than when the weight is closer to the hand. This is a simple and effective way to introduce the concept of rotational inertia. Alternately, you can use a broom or a baseball.

⟳ **DEMO** Tape a book well so it does not open up. Now spin the book about its three principle axes. The book will be stable when spinning about the axis with the maximum and minimum moments. The book will not be stable spinning about the axis with the intermediate moment. Discuss relation between stability and rotational inertia. Alternately, you can use a good-sized board instead of the book.

The **parallel-axis theorem** is very useful in computing the **moment of inertia** of an object about an axis other than through the center of mass. This is often confusing to students, so it might be helpful to work out some examples.

Rotational kinetic energy has a formula very similar to kinetic energy of linear motion. However, it is important for students to realize that this equation is valid only if the **angular velocity** is in radians/sec. Remind them that if linear velocity is given, they can find the angular velocity using $\omega = v/r$. Students often forget this fact and claim that sufficient information is not available to solve the problem.

Section 9-4

Torque is not an unfamiliar concept to students. However, they will have difficulty in determining the **lever arm** for different situations. Quite often they will also not recognize that the **torque** is zero when the line of action of a force passes through the **axis of rotation**.

⟳ **DEMO** Partially open the door to the classroom. Tell the students that you are now going to attempt to shut the door by applying about the same force each time. Then push on the door at a point close to the doorknob with your finger. Repeat the process by pushing on the door at points closer to the hinge each time. It will be obvious that the door swings through smaller and smaller angle each time. Finally, push on the hinge to shut the door. The door will not rotate. It will also not rotate when you apply a force at the outside edge of the door but parallel to the face of the door. This is a good demo to start off a discussion about the dependence of the torque on the length of the lever arm as well as the line of action of the force.

⟳ **DEMO** All you need for this demo is a long meter stick, a mass hanger and slotted weights. You can either do this as a demo in front of the class or have students try it out. Hold the meter stick at one end and move it up and down in a vertical motion. You will have no problem doing this. Next hang a small weight close to your hand and repeat the process. Progressively move the weight away from your hand and repeat. As the distance between your hand and the hanging weight increases, the torque that you will need to exert (to produce the same angular rotation) will also increase. Now hang the smallest weight at the far end of the meter stick. Repeat the process by increasing the weight and you will find that the torque needed to rotate the meter stick through the same angle will increase proportionately with the increase in the hanging weight.

⟳ **DEMO** Walking the spool – This is a very effective demo to show the relationship between the force direction and the torque. Construct a large spool with paper towel holder and two cardboard circles. Wrap a string around it. Depending on the angle between the string and table, the spool will roll in a certain direction when you pull on the string. Have students predict the direction before you pull on the string.

⟳ **DEMO** Rolling uphill – A wooden disk is weighted on one side. Place the disk on an inclined plane so that the weighted part is uphill from the disk's geometric center. The center of mass is now on the uphill side. Contrary to expectations, the disk will roll uphill.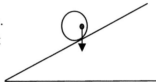

Equations 9-29 and 9-30 are the equivalent of Newton's second law in **rotational motion**. When the **net torque** is zero, the object will have no **angular acceleration**, or it will have constant **angular velocity**.

In solving problems in **rotational dynamics**, stress the importance of free-body diagrams. Point out that in a multi-body system, one object can have translational motion while a second one can have **rotational motion**. Take the example shown in Fig. 9-30 and discuss the fact that both linear and **rotational equations of motion** will have to be used. This is a good exercise for using equations like $v = r\omega$ and $a = r\alpha$. Remind the students that **angular quantities** have to be in **radian** values.

Sections 9-5 – 9-6

While Equation 9-37 looks simple, students will not recognize several key points here. **Angular momentum** depends on the **axis of rotation** just as **torque** does. This comes from the fact that the **rotational inertia** is dependent on the **axis of rotation**. Secondly, an object moving in a straight line can have an **angular momentum** about a certain axis. This is discussed in detail in Chapter 10. Point out the parallel between Equation 9-38 and its counterpart in linear motion. Also, Equation 9-39 is similar to the linear motion equation $K = p^2/2m$.

We are now introduced to the third conservation law, the **conservation of angular momentum**, which is a direct consequence of Equation 9-38. Just as linear momentum is conserved when the sum of the external forces acting on a body is zero, when the **net external torque** is zero, we have **conservation of angular momentum** for a system. The system can be a single object or more than one object. The world of sports has numerous examples that can be used to explain this law. Ice skaters, swimmers, and gymnasts all control their angular velocities by changing the **moment of inertia**.

⟳ **DEMO** Sit on a rotating stool and hold small equal weights (dumbbells will work) in each of your hands. Get yourself spinning and slowly bring your arms outwards and then toward your chest. Your angular velocity will increase when you have your arms closer to your chest and you will spin slower when you hold your arms out. (See Fig. 10-23 in Chapter 10).

Section 9-6 discusses the kinematics of **rolling**. This is where students will be asked to use most of what they have learned about translational as well as **rotational motion**. In considering conservation of energy, they will have to take into account both **kinetic energy of rotation** and kinetic energy of translation. In applying the law of conservation of energy, they will have to use both $K_{rot} = \frac{1}{2}I\omega^2$ and $K_{trans} = \frac{1}{2}mv^2$. Quite often the mass will not be given and one of the two quantities, linear velocity or **angular velocity** will not be given either. Point out that **rotational inertia** I can be written in terms of mass, and linear velocity can be written in terms of **angular velocity** or vice versa. This will result in the mass getting factored out, and the equation will have just one single unknown for which it can be solved.

Discuss the difference between sliding motion and rolling without slipping.

➲ **DEMO** You can purchase disks and hoops of equal masses and radii. Set up an inclined plane and release the disk and hoop from the top of the incline at the same time. Before you do this, have the students predict which one will reach the bottom first. Point out that reaching the bottom first is different from which one will have the greater final velocity at the bottom of the incline. See Fig. 9-37.

➲ **DEMO** Instead of using disks and hoops, you can use 14-oz cans of different products such as clear broth, soup with chunky food particles and a can of refried beans. Set up an inclined plane and release the cans from the top of the incline. Measure the time taken for each can to reach the bottom. Again, before you do this, get the students to predict which one will reach the bottom first.

Textbook Resource Information

Transparency Acetates

Physlet Physics Illustrations

Physlet Physics Explorations

Physlet Physics Problems

Ranking Task Exercises in Physics, Student Edition

End of Chapter Problems with Solutions in the *Student Study Guide*

11, 37, 45, 53, 69, 85

Suggested Readings

Altshuler, K., and Pollock, P., "Apparatus for Teaching Physics: Inexpensive Rotating-Arm Device for Angular-Motion Labs," *The Physics Teacher* (October 1998), p. 424 – 425.

Bacon, M.E., Heald, G., and James, M., "A Closer Look at Tumbling Toast," *Am.J.Phys.* (January 2001), p. 38 – 43.

Bird, W., "Pictorial Representation of Torque and Rotational Inertia," *The Physics Teacher* (November 1998), p. 492.

Buchanan, M., Graham, M., and Hunter, T., "A Nostalgic Demonstration of the Radian," *The Physics Teacher* (April 1999), p. 253.

Carr, R., Cohen, H., and Ragsdale, T., "Apparatus for Teaching Physics: Demonstrating Angular Momentum Conservation," *The Physics Teacher* (March 1999), p. 169 – 171.

Denardo, B., "Demonstration of the Parallel-Axis Theoerm," *The Physics Teacher* (January 1998), p. 56 – 57.

Etkina, E., "Physics on Rollerblades," *The Physics Teacher* (January 1998), p. 32 – 35.

Henderson, C., "Apparatus for Teaching Physics: Measuring the Force Required for Circular Motion," *The Physics Teacher* (February 1998), p. 118 – 121.

Johns, R.H., "Apparatus for Teaching Physics: Physics on a Rotating Frame," *The Physics Teacher* (March 1998), p. 178 – 180.

Makous, J.L., "Variations of a Circular Motion Lab," *The Physics Teacher* (September 2000), p. 354 – 355.

McDonald, K.T., "Physics in the Laundromat," *Am.J.Phys.* (March 1998), p. 209 – 211.

Penny, D.N., "A Non-Uniform Circular Motion Experiment," *The Physics Teacher* (November 2000), p. 483 – 486.

Webb, J., "Don't the Texts Have It Wrong?," *The Physics Teacher* (March 1998), p. 184. (Also see letters to the editor, May 1998).

Notes and Ideas

Preparation time: Estimated: _____   *Actual:* _____

Class time spent on material: Estimated: _____   *Actual:* _____

Related laboratory activities:

Demonstration materials:

Notes for next time:

Chapter 10: More on Angular Momentum and Torque

Outline

Summary

This chapter is an extension of the study of **angular momentum** and **torque** to systems of particles that are not rigid bodies. **Torque** and **angular momentum** are expressed as **cross products** and the **angular momentum** of an object in linear motion is studied. **Central forces**, **Kepler's second law**, and **precession** are also discussed.

Major Concepts

- Generalization of angular momentum
    - Angular momentum of a point particle
    - Angular momentum of large system of point particles
    - Instantaneous value of angular momentum
    - Vector or cross product of two vectors
    - Angular momentum as a vector product
    - Right-hand rule for vector cross product

- Generalization of torque
    - Torque as cross product of force and lever arm
    - Dynamical equation for rotation
    - Torque in unit vector notation

- The dynamics of rotation
    - Torque and angular momentum for a system of discrete particles
    - Internal forces and effect on torque
    - The role of the reference point
    - Equations for angular momentum and torque about any reference point
    - Usefulness of reference point
    - Angular impulse

- Conservation of angular momentum
    - Central forces – definition
    - Angular momentum and central forces
    - Sun and planetary motion
    - Kepler's second law
    - Non-rigid objects and angular momentum conservation

- Work and energy in angular motion
  - Rate of change of energy or instantaneous power
  - Work energy theorem for rotation
  - Energy of an extended object in motion
  - Kinetic energy of center of mass
  - Rotational kinetic energy

- Parallels between linear and rotational motion

- Quantization
  - Quantization of angular momentum
  - Quantization of energy
  - Allowed states
  - Energy level

- Precession
  - Symmetry axis
  - Nutation
  - Torque on a spinning top
  - Angular frequency of precession

Teaching Suggestions and Demonstrations

Most of the topics covered in this chapter were dealt with in Chapter 9. However, now the vector nature of these quantities is discussed in detail. It is very tempting for students to merely look at the end result of the derivations in this chapter (which are very similar to those they have studied in Chapter 9), and ignore the physics behind the derivations. This will not serve them well in understanding the **rotation of a system** of particles that do not comprise a rigid body.

Sections 10-1 – 10-3

A particle moving in a straight line with constant linear momentum has an **angular momentum** about a chosen **reference point**. This will be a difficult concept to understand for first year physics students. Section 10-1 explains this well and derives the equation for the **angular momentum** of a point particle with respect to a **reference point**. Make sure students realize that Equation 10-2 is the **angular momentum** for a free particle at all times. However, the same equation gives the **instantaneous angular momentum** at a particular time for a particle moving along a curve (it has torque acting on it).

> ⊃ **DEMO** This demo shows both conservation of angular momentum and the fact that an object in linear motion can have angular momentum about an axis. Sit on a rotating chair. Have a student throw a bag of rice that you have to catch by extending your arm to your side. You will begin to rotate. The system is you on the chair and the bag of rice. Initially you and the chair are at rest and hence have no angular momentum. After you catch the bag, you, the chair, and the bag are all in rotational motion and hence have an angular momentum. Conservation of angular momentum shows that the bag of rice had some angular momentum about the axis of rotation when the student threw the bag toward you.

Students were introduced to the scalar or dot product in Chapter 6. Now they learn the **vector cross product**. There are three points to be remembered: unlike the dot product, the **cross product** of two vectors is also a vector. Secondly, the order in which the **cross product** is carried out will make a difference. The third point to remember is, when using the **right-hand rule**, move the tail of **B** to the head of **A** before curling the fingers. (See Fig. 10-8 for example).

Sections 10-2 and 10-3 deal with **torque** and **angular momentum** extended to systems and expressed as a **cross product**. Make sure the students understand the importance of the choice of **reference point** when dealing with **torque**, **angular momentum**, and **rotational inertia**. Example 10-6 is a standard problem that can be used to stress this point.

Sections 10-4 – 10-6

Central forces and **angular momentum** of objects subjected to such forces are important to the study of **planetary motion**. **Angular momentum** is conserved for **central forces** and from this conservation law **Kepler's second law** is derived.

Angular momentum is also conserved for non-rigid objects. As pointed out in Chapter 9 of this manual, the world of sports provides numerous examples to illustrate this. Ice skaters, swimmers (divers), and gymnasts, all control their angular velocity by changing the **rotational inertia**.

➲ **DEMO** A bicycle wheel is very useful in demonstrating various phenomenon of rotational motion. Sit on a rotating stool. Hold the wheel and give it some rotation. Hold it so the axis of rotation is vertical. Now tip the spinning wheel 180° and hand the wheel to a student. The student now turns it once more through 180° and hands it back to you. As this process is repeated, you will spin faster and faster. You can control the speed of rotation by "adding" or "subtracting" from your angular momentum. This will depend on the direction in which the wheel is flipped as you hand it over to the student or vice versa. (See Fig. 10-25).

Section 10-5 derives the **work-energy theorem** for rotating objects. In the case of extended objects, it is important to recognize that the total kinetic energy of a rigid body has contributions from the linear velocity of the center of mass as well as from the rotation of the object. Equation 10-38 includes both of these terms. Point out that an object can rotate without translational motion (in this case $V_{CM} = 0$). Objects can also roll without slipping or slide without rolling.

Table 10-1 in section 10-6 shows the **parallel** between **linear** and **rotational motion**. Complete the table by including the kinematic equations for **linear** and **rotational motion** as well. It will also be helpful to write the connecting relationship between **linear** and **angular quantities** for displacement, velocity, and acceleration. I usually write this in a middle column.

Sections 10-7 – 10-8

Quantization and **precession** are optional to most curricula. However, Section 10-7 gives a brief introduction to **quantization** so students can get a taste for what is to come in future chapters. **Precession** is not as difficult as may appear at first glance. Go through the worked Example 10-13. Then point out that the **angular momentum** changes in direction and not in magnitude due to a **torque** and that is what causes the top to spin. The actual derivation of Equation 10-43 could be optional depending on the time available.

Textbook Resource Information

Transparency Acetates

Physlet Physics Illustrations

Physlet Physics Explorations

Physlet Physics Problems

Ranking Task Exercises in Physics, Student Edition

End of Chapter Problems with Solutions in the *Student Study Guide*

7, 17, 21, 33, 37, 49

Suggested Readings

Arjmandi, S., Brinkman, J.G., and Toepker, T.P., "Physical Push-ups," *The Physics Teacher* (September 2003), p. 323 – 324. (Also see letters to the editor, November 2003).

Bracikowski, C., "Feeling Forces that Produce Torques," *The Physics Teacher* (January 1998), p. 15.

Bryant, A., "Apparatus for Teaching Physics: Rotating Stool Mounted on a Low-Friction Hub," *The Physics Teacher* (November 2000), p. 476 – 477.

Ho, A., Contardi, L.H., Dion, P.W., and Griffioen, E., "Rotating Wheels as Seen on Television," *The Physics Teacher* (September 1998), p. 367 – 369.

Pechan, M.J., O'Brien, A., and Burgei, W.A., "Conservation of Angular Momentum Apparatus Using Magnetic Bearings," *The Physics Teacher* (January 2001), p. 26 – 28.

Pritchett, T., Nelson, R.C., Creamer, T.J., and Oldaker, B.G., "Does an Ideal Wheel Really Rotate About Its Instantaneous Point of Contact?," *The Physics Teacher* (March 1998), p. 167 – 170.

Notes and Ideas

Preparation time: *Estimated:* _____   *Actual:* _____

Class time spent on material: *Estimated:* _____   *Actual:* _____

Related laboratory activities:

Demonstration materials:

Notes for next time:

Chapter 11: Statics

Outline

Summary

Chapters 9 and 10 discussed the different motions extended objects can have. This chapter looks at the conditions necessary for a rigid object to be in **equilibrium**. How solids deform under forces is discussed, and the concepts of **Young's, bulk** and **shear** moduli are introduced.

Major Concepts

- Static conditions for rigid bodies
    o Conditions for translational equilibrium
    o Conditions for rotational equilibrium
    o Reference point for rotational equilibrium

- Gravity and rigid bodies
    o Center of Mass
    o Center of Gravity

- Applications of statics
    o Problem-solving techniques
    o Undetermined systems

- Solids and how they respond to forces
    o Lattice structure
    o Simple cubic lattice
    o Lattice imperfections or defects
    o Longitudinal stress and compressional strain
    o Poisson's ratio
    o Volume stress and strain
    o Shear stress and strain
    o Young's modulus or elastic modulus
    o Bulk modulus
    o Shear modulus
    o Tensile strength

Teaching Suggestions and Demonstrations

There are only two basic concepts and two basic equations to deal with in this chapter. These are the conditions for **translational** and **rotational equilibrium**. Though students by now are familiar with one-, two- and three-dimensional problems, there are enough variations in the situations they will come across to cause them some confusion. Go through as many of the worked examples in class as possible.

Sections 11-1 – 11-2

The behavior of objects in **translational motion**, **rotational motion** or simultaneous **translational** and **rotational motion** have been considered thus far. **Statics** is the study of **equilibrium conditions** for rigid objects. It is important to remember that static **equilibrium** cannot be achieved unless both **translational** and **rotational equilibrium** is achieved at the same time.

⮮ **DEMO** Balance a ruler on a knife-edge. Hang a known mass at a point 5 cm from the edge. Pull at the other end (5 cm from the edge) with a spring scale so the upward force equals the downward force at the first end. Point out that the net external force is zero and so the center of mass of the system has no acceleration or velocity. The system is in translational equilibrium. However, the meter ruler will rotate because the two torques are clockwise – the system is not in rotational equilibrium.

Finding the **lever arm**, recognizing when the **lever arm** is zero for a particular force and choosing a convenient **reference point** – these are the common stumbling blocks for many students. Go through the definition of **lever arm**, and for the same force choose two or three **reference points** and show how to calculate the **torque** with respect to each of these points. Discuss the concept of line of action of the force.

⮮ **DEMO** Balance a meter ruler on a knife-edge. It is obvious that the ruler is in static equilibrium. However, students will not recognize that there are forces acting on the ruler. Use this to start a discussion on the forces acting on the ruler and why the ruler is in static equilibrium.

You have already discussed **center of mass** in Chapter 8. It is important to talk about it here since it plays an important role when considering the **equilibrium** of extended objects.

⮮ **DEMO** Repeat the demo from Chapter 8 on how to find the center of mass of your home state. (See Fig. 11-8.)

⮮ **DEMO** Have a student touch his/her toe without bending the knee. Most students can do this without much difficulty if they are in a fairly reasonable state of physical fitness. Now have him/her attempt to do the same when standing against the wall with legs flush against the wall. The student will tend to fall forward since the center of mass will protrude beyond the base of support. (Figure inspired by Fig. 7-23 in *Conceptual Physics* – 8th ed. by Paul Hewitt).

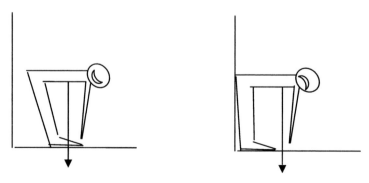

⮕ **DEMO** The center of gravity of men in general is higher than in women. This is because women tend to be proportionately lighter in the upper body and heavier in the pelvic region. A good way to illustrate this fact is to get a woman to kneel on the floor with her lower body touching her heels. She now places her elbows on her knees and with palms touching, places them on the floor in front of her. Place a piece of chalk just in front of her palms. Now with her hands behind her back, (and without lifting up her lower body from her heels) get her to touch the piece of chalk with her nose. Repeat the procedure with a man. The woman will be able to do so while the man will tend to topple forward. However, some men who are very broad shouldered can touch the chalk if they are very lithesome. This will not work well with teenagers, very slim men or very slim women, since the difference in their body structures will not be well pronounced. A word of caution: some students can be sensitive regarding their physique. So use your judgment when calling on them.

Section 11-3

This section is devoted to applying the **conditions of equilibrium** to various situations. Go through the steps discussed under problem-solving techniques. There are plenty of worked out examples in this section that you can use to take your students through the six steps needed to solve such problems.

Section 11-4

The material in this section is simple and straightforward. It introduces the students to the behavior of solids when subjected to **deforming forces**. It is important to go through the definitions and point out the difference between **deformation** in **length**, **area** and **volume**. Tables 11-1 and 11-2 will help the students get a feel for how different solids behave when deformed. Example 11-9 and the discussion of tensile **strength** will help students see the practical application of this concept.

Textbook Resource Information

Transparency Acetates

Fig. 11-2	Forces and choice of origin
Fig. 11-15	Force diagram for an undetermined system
Fig. 11-16	Lattice structure – schematic diagram
Fig. 11-17	Sketch of a simple cubic lattice
Fig. 11-20	Lattice distortions – schematic diagram
Fig. 11-22	Shear stress
Table 11-1	Young's modulus for various solids
Table 11-2	Tensile strength for various solids

Physlet Physics Illustrations

13.1   Equilibrium of Block on a Ramp
13.2   Finding X_{CM}
13.3   Equilibrium of a Rigid of Rod
13.4   Diving Board Problem

Physlet Physics Explorations

13.1   Balance of a mobile
13.3   Distributed load
13.4   Stacking of bricks

Physlet Physics Problems

13.1   Box on a ramp
13.3   Equilibrium of a truck on a level road
13.7   Two rods hinged to a wall
13.8   Seesaw
13.13 Box on a horizontal board

Ranking Task Exercises in Physics, Student Edition

Page 94, 95   Meter stick in horizontal equilibrium

End of Chapter Problems with Solutions in the *Student Study Guide*

3, 19, 35, 47, 55, 65

Suggested Readings

Binder, P.M., Sinisterra, P., and Esguerra, F., **"The Five-Legged Table,"** *The Physics Teacher* (September 1999), p. 360 – 363.

Ficken Jr., G.W., "Balancing a Tilting Canal Bridge," *The Physics Teacher* (November 1988), p. 510.

Gallant, J., "The Shape of the Eiffel Tower," *Am. J. Phys.* (February 2002), p. 160 – 162.

Meyer, J., "Ladder Physics," *The Physics Teacher* (November 1988), p. 532 – 535.

Niculescu, A., and Shumaker, R., "Apparatus for Measuring Young's Modulus," *The Physics Teacher* (September 2003), p. 364 – 367.

Notes and Ideas

Preparation time: *Estimated:* _____   *Actual:* _____

Class time spent on material: *Estimated:* _____   *Actual:* _____

Related laboratory activities:

Demonstration materials:

Notes for next time:

Chapter 12: Gravitation

Outline

Summary

Gravitational force is one of the fundamental forces that govern the motion of all objects here on Earth as well as those of the Sun, planets and galaxies. Starting with a brief historic review of **planetary motion**, Chapter 12 discusses **Kepler's laws, Newton's law of universal gravitation** and **orbits of planets** in detail. Interesting topics like **dark matter**, **tidal forces** and **Einstein's theory of gravitation** are also studied.

Major Concepts

- Early observation of planetary motion
  - The Copernican picture
  - Kepler's laws

- Newton's inverse-square law
  - Inverse-square force law
  - The law of universal gravitation
  - The gravitational constant
  - The potential energy associated with Newton's gravitational force
  - The superposition principle

- Planets and satellites
  - The escape speed
  - Types of orbits
  - Properties of non-circular orbits

- Gravitation and extended objects
  - The gravitational force due to a spherically symmetric object
  - Dark matter
  - How g varies with altitude
  - Tidal forces

- A Closer look at gravitation
  - Effects of other objects (perturbation)
  - Equality of inertial and gravitational masses

- Einstein's theory of gravitation
  - Equivalence principle

- o Gravitational lenses
- o Black holes
- o Precession of planetary orbits

Teaching Suggestions and Demonstrations

Gravitation is a topic that does not lend itself very easily to simple classroom demonstrations. While topics in this chapter are not difficult to comprehend and have a universal appeal, you will find that students have several misconceptions about gravitation.

Sections 12-1 – 12-3

Begin by giving a brief historical review of the motion of planets in a **geocentric** and **heliocentric** frame. Astronomy buffs in your class will find it interesting to learn about the cultural climate of the times in which **Ptolemy**, **Copernicus** and **Tyco Brahe** lived.

Kepler's three laws are very important to the understanding of **planetary motion**. Remind students that **Kepler's second law** discussed in Chapter 10 follows from the law of conservation of angular momentum. It also emphasizes the point that **gravitational force** is a central force. The **second law** was also the starting point for **Newton's inverse-square law**. Equations 12-1 and 12-3 are basically one and the same equation. However, it is easy for students to overlook the fact that the constant k in Equation 12-3 is proportional to the mass of the planet. If this were not so, then the constant C will not be independent of the mass of the planet.

The force between any two objects in the universe as expressed by Equation 12-4 (also known as **Newton's law of universal gravitation**) is one of the most fundamental forces. This is an attractive force that is inversely dependent on the square of the distance between the masses. Stress that the distance is measured between the centers of the two masses.

Students will be able to accept that such a force exists between the Moon and Earth or between the planets and the Sun. However, it is difficult for them to recognize that this law holds true for all objects in the universe. As an in-class exercise, have them estimate the distance between them and their nearest neighbor. Then ask them to calculate the force between them and their neighbor. Because of the small value of the constant G, they will find that this force is indeed so small that its effect is not obvious to us.

Two applications of the **universal law of gravitation** are shown in Examples 12-2 and 12-3. Example 12-2 shows how to calculate the mass of the Sun (or a planet for that matter) using **Newton's gravitational law** and **Kepler's third law**. Example 12-3 deals with the concept of a geosynchronous satellite. This can lead to interesting discussions about weather satellites.

In Chapter 7 we saw that a conservative force can be derived from the **potential energy function**. The **gravitational force** is also a conservative force, and Equation 12-8 gives the potential energy associated with this force. Discuss the significance of the negative sign (because U is defined to be zero at an infinite distance) and the $1/r$ dependence. Again, the distance is measured from the center of the mass. Also note that the potential energy is a scalar quantity while the **gravitational force** is a vector.

⟳ **DEMO** It is easy to make a simple model of a potential well. Cut off the end of a balloon and stretch it over the mouth of an empty coffee can. When you place a heavy object in the middle of the stretched balloon, it will create a well in the center. A small sphere placed at the rim of the can will roll toward the middle.

Section 12-3 discusses **escape velocity** and the different types of **orbits** for **planets** and **satellites**. Starting from the sum of the kinetic and potential energies it gives a simple and direct explanation of the possibility of a **hyperbolic/parabolic/elliptical trajectory**. Go through worked Examples 12-6, 12-7 and 12-8 in class, as they illustrate the concepts discussed in these three sections.

Sections 12-4 – 12-6

This section deals with the **gravitational force** due to Earth (or any spherically symmetric object). Note that Equation 12-17 comes from combining Newton's second law and the **law of universal gravitation**. Point out that while g is directly proportional to the mass of Earth, it is not dependent on the mass of an object that is on or near Earth. In other words, all objects on Earth are subjected to the same acceleration due to gravity.

⊃ **DEMO** Look at the penny and feather demo listed in Chapter 2 of this manual.

The last two sections of this chapter take a brief look at several interesting topics that can make for some lively classroom discussion and pique the interest of the students. If you find yourself running out of time, urge your students to read them.

Textbook Resource Information

Transparency Acetates

Fig. 12-1	Ptolemaic system of planetary motion
Fig. 12-3a,b	Kepler's laws – first and second
Fig. 12-4	Types of orbits
Fig. 12-5a	Measuring the gravitational constant
Fig. 12-10	Elliptical orbits of Pluto and Halley's comet
Fig. 12-13	Set of possible orbits
Fig. 12-15	View of Earth's internal structure
Fig. 12-16	Gravitational force inside a spherical shell
Fig. 12-17	Gravitational force of mass inside Earth
Fig. 12-21 & 12-22	Tidal forces due to the moon
Fig. 12-25	Accelerating elevator and bending of light
Fig. 12-27	Gravitational lens

Physlet Physics Illustrations

12.2 Orbits and Planetary Mass
12.3 Circular and Noncircular Motion
12.5 Kepler's Second Law
12.6 Heliocentric vs. Geocentric

Physlet Physics Explorations

12.1 Different x_o and v_o for planetary orbits
12.3 Properties of elliptical orbits
12.4 Angular momentum and energy

Physlet Physics Problems

12.2 Finding the mass of a star
12.3 Net force on a star due to two other stars
12.6 Kepler's laws
12.7 Orbit of a satellite
12.10 Gravitational force inside the earth

End of Chapter Problems with Solutions in the *Student Study Guide*

5, 9, 25, 35, 47, 57

Suggested Readings

Bucher, M., "Kepler's Third Law: Equal Volumes in Equal Time," *The Physics Teacher* (April 1998), p. 212 – 214.

Cohen, H., "Testing Kepler's Laws of Planetary Motion," *The Physics Teacher* (January 1998), p. 40 – 41.

Doherty, R., Rembert, J., Boice, N., and Laws, P., "Star Wars and Gravitational Constants," *The Physics Teacher* (May 1998), p. 270 – 273.

Metz, J., "Finding Kepler's Third Law with a Graphing Calculator," *The Physics Teacher* (April 2000), p. 242.

Ruby, L., "Gravitational Force Due to a Sphere: A Non-calculus Calculation," *The Physics Teacher* (October 2003), p. 416 – 418.

Sawicki, M., "Myths About Gravity and Tides," *The Physics Teacher* (October 1999), p. 438 – 441.

Vogt, E., "Elementary Derivation of Kepler's Laws," *Am. J. Phys.* (April 1996), p. 392 – 396.

Notes and Ideas

Preparation time: *Estimated:* _____   *Actual:* _____

Class time spent on material: *Estimated:* _____   *Actual:* _____

Related laboratory activities:

Demonstration materials:

Notes for next time:

Chapter 13: Oscillatory Motion

Outline

Summary

Any kind of repetitive rhythmic motion is a **periodic motion,** and when a **periodic motion** is subject to a **restoring force** we have **oscillatory motion**. This chapter looks at a basic form of **oscillatory motion** – **simple harmonic motion**. The **periodic motion** of a mass at the end of a **spring** and a **pendulum** are discussed in detail. The effect of **driving forces** and **dissipative forces** on **oscillatory motion** is also considered.

Major Concepts

- Kinematics of simple harmonic motion
    - Simple harmonic or oscillatory motion
    - Angular frequency, amplitude and phase
    - Properties of simple harmonic motion
    - Relations among position, velocity and acceleration in simple harmonic motion

- A connection to circular motion

- Springs and simple harmonic motion
    - Hooke's law
    - Angular frequency for mass on a spring
    - Period and frequency for mass on a spring
    - Additional constant forces

- Energy and simple harmonic motion
    - Potential energy for mass on a spring
    - Total energy for mass on a spring
    - Objects other than springs that are in simple harmonic motion

- Simple pendulum
    - Period and frequency for a simple pendulum
    - Energy of the simple pendulum

- More about pendulums
    - The physical pendulum

- Damped harmonic motion

- Driven harmonic motion
    - Equations of motion for driven harmonic motion
    - Properties of resonance
    - Resonance and uncertainty

Teaching Suggestions and Demonstrations

Periodic motion can be observed all around us as we go about our daily chores. To understand the physics of such **oscillatory motion**, students will have to be comfortable with graphs of sine and cosine functions as well as in using radians as the preferred unit. A quick review of these graphs might make the material in this chapter easier to understand.

Sections 13-1 – 13-2

A good way to start this topic would be to have students make a list of some examples of **periodic motion**. Set up a **spring** and **mass system** and a **simple pendulum**. Use these to define **displacement**, **amplitude**, **period** and **frequency** of any **simple harmonic motion**. Take a little time to define one complete oscillation. Stress that a complete oscillation is when the mass is back to the starting point and is in the same displacement mode as in the beginning of the cycle.

While students will have no problem understanding **period** and **frequency**, they will have a harder time interpreting the physical significance of Equations 13-1, 13-7 and 13-8. They will also not understand the concept of phase and how to apply the initial conditions. The following demo will be helpful.

> ↪ **DEMO** Use the spring and mass system and a motion sensor to plot the position vs. time graph. Repeat the procedure by changing the starting time (zero time) to when the mass is at the (a) lowest, (b) equilibrium and (c) highest positions. Point out that the starting conditions will determine whether to use the sine or cosine function.

Use Fig. 13-3 to explain the relation between position, velocity and acceleration for a **simple harmonic motion**, given a certain initial condition.

The idea of the **projection** of a circular motion will not be a familiar one to most students. Take time to draw several positions of the object around the circle. For each position draw the **projection** (preferably with a different colored chalk or pen). Show that the foot of the projection is executing **simple harmonic motion**.

Sections 13-3 – 13-4

Hooke's law was discussed in Chapter 6. Now derive the expression for **angular frequency**, **period** and **frequency** starting from **Hooke's law**. Remind the students about the significance of the negative sign in **Hooke's law**.

> ↪ **DEMO** Set up different springs with different spring constants. Find the time for ten oscillations and determine the period for each of the springs. Repeat by varying the mass attached to the springs. Show that the period is not affected by the amplitude (for small amplitudes) but that it depends on the mass and the spring constant.

Quite often the effect of gravity is ignored when we demonstrate an oscillating mass and spring in class. The addition of a **constant force** (in this case it is gravity) is discussed clearly in the text, and Fig.13-9 shows the free-body diagram for this situation. This paragraph is useful in that it shows the students that gravity does not affect the motion of the spring to any significant degree.

Fig. 13-8 shows a snapshot of the mass as it goes through one cycle of oscillation. This is a very clear illustration that will help students see the relation between position, velocity and acceleration for a **mass-spring system**. It also shows how the energy changes from potential to kinetic while the total energy remains the same. Use this along with Fig 13-10 to discuss the behavior of the system in terms of its energy.

Sections 13-5 – 13-6

⮑ **DEMO** As in the case of the spring and mass system, set up several pendulum of varying lengths and with different masses. Determine the period for each, and discuss the dependence of the period on the mass and on the length for small amplitudes.

Go through the derivation for **period** starting from Equation 13-29 which is the **restoring force** for a **pendulum**. Fig 13-14 will help the students to understand why Equation 13-29 is the correct expression for the **restoring force**. Stress that Equation 13-36 is valid for small **amplitudes** only.

The **physical pendulum** takes the derivations one step further. Many introductory textbooks do not include this topic, but your students will relate to it better than expected.

Sections 13.7 – 13.8

Damped and **driven harmonic motions** deal with more realistic situations than the **simple harmonic motions** discussed thus far. The derivation is for a varying force that is proportional to the velocity. Point out **damping forces** with more complicated dependence on the velocity is possible in nature. Discuss the significance of the exponential function in Equation 13-46 and use Fig 13-20 to illustrate this point.

To introduce the concept of **driven harmonic motion**, discuss the situation of a child on a swing and what "pumping" would do to the motion of the swing. Another example would be the rattling of windows in nearby buildings when a train goes by or soldiers breaking step as they march across a bridge.

⮑ **DEMO** The collapse of the Tacoma Narrows Bridge is an excellent example of resonance and its effect on an oscillation. The ten-minute video is very powerful and impressive. The disc is available from the American Association of Physics Teachers (see www.aapt.org/catalog).

Textbook Resource Information

Transparency Acetates

Fig. 13-3	Plots of position, velocity and acceleration vs. time
Fig. 13-7	Comparing circular motion to simple harmonic motion
Fig. 13-8	Velocity and acceleration of a mass on a spring
Fig. 13-9	Free-body diagram – vertical spring-mass system
Fig. 13-10	Kinetic and potential energy plots – simple harmonic motion
Fig. 13-17	A physical pendulum

Physlet Physics Illustrations

Physlet Physics Explorations

Physlet Physics Problems

Ranking Task Exercises in Physics, Student Edition

End of Chapter Problems with Solutions in the *Student Study Guide*

5, 13, 29, 45, 57, 79

Suggested Readings

Akridge, R., "Period and Amplitude," *The Physics Teacher* (November 1998), p. 507 – 508.

Bensky, T., "Measuring g with a Joystick Pendulum," *The Physics Teacher* (February 2001), p. 88 – 89.

Erlichson, H., "Galileo's Pendulum," *The Physics Teacher* (November 1999), p. 478 – 479.

Esparza-Barrera, C., "Energy Considerations in a Vertical Spring," *The Physics Teacher* (April 1999), p. 250.

Froehle, P., "Reminder about Hooke's Law and Metal Springs," *The Physics Teacher* (September 1999), p. 368.

Feliciano, J., "Apparatus for Teaching Physics: The Variable Gravity Pendulum," *The Physics Teacher* (January 1998), p. 51 – 52.

Kanamori, H., and Brodsky, E., "The Physics of Earthquakes," *Physics Today* (June 2001), p. 34 – 40.

Pecori, B., and Torzo, G., "Physics of the Seesaw," *The Physics Teacher* (November 2001), p. 491 – 495.

Slogoff, H., and Berner, B., "A Simulation of the Tacoma Narrows Bridge Oscillations," *The Physics Teacher* (October 2000), p. 442 – 443.

Szapiro, B., "Simple Pendulum Lab with a Twist," *The Physics Teacher* (March 2002), p. 158 – 163.

Notes and Ideas

Preparation time: *Estimated:* _____   *Actual:* _____

Class time spent on material: *Estimated:* _____   *Actual:* _____

Related laboratory activities:

Demonstration materials:

Notes for next time:

Chapter 14: Waves

Outline

Summary

Staring with types of **waves** this chapter discusses **periodic**, **traveling** and **standing waves**. It looks at the energy and power transported by these **waves**. **Sound waves**, **Doppler effect** and **shock waves** are also discussed.

Major Concepts

- Types of waves
    - Transverse waves
    - Longitudinal waves
    - Standing waves

- The wave equation

- Periodic waves

- Traveling waves
    - Transverse waves
    - Longitudinal waves
    - How the wave speed depends on the medium
    - The speed of sound in air
    - Shear waves in solids
    - Propagation of arbitrary wave forms

- Energy and power in waves
    - Power delivered by waves
    - Energy transport

- Standing waves
    - The frequency of standing waves
    - Harmonics
    - Energy and standing waves

- More about sound
  - Nature of sound waves
  - Standing sound waves
  - The excitation of standing sound waves
  - Hearing sounds

- The Doppler effect
  - A moving source
  - A moving observer
  - A moving source and a moving observer
  - A moving medium
  - Uses of the Doppler shift

- Shock waves
  - Mach number
  - Cherenkov radiation

Teaching Suggestions and Demonstrations

Chapter 13 should have given students the basics of oscillatory motion, so the study of **wave motion** in this chapter will be easier. There are plenty of examples in our daily lives (especially in the area of music) that you can draw from to explain the concepts in this chapter.

Sections 14-1 – 14-5

Begin with the definition of **transverse** and **longitudinal wave**. Some simple demos will help to stress the difference between the vibration of the individual particles and the propagation of the disturbance.

➲ **DEMO** This is a simple but very effective demonstration of transverse waves. Start at one end of the class and have the students do the human wave like they have seen in a football stadium.

➲ **DEMO** To demonstrate longitudinal waves, get eight to ten students come up to the front and face the class. They should stand with their feet firmly planted on the ground and with shoulders touching. Give a slight push to the student at the beginning of the row. This push will make each successive student lean into the next one. When the "disturbance" reaches the other end, have the last student push back. This back and forth pushing will simulate a longitudinal wave.

➲ **DEMO** Transverse and longitudinal waves can also be shown using a slinky. Stretch the slinky on the table and have two students hold one end each. One of the students should then move the end of the slinky back and forth perpendicular to the length of the slinky. Watch the transverse wave traveling along the length of the slinky.
For a longitudinal wave, the student should push the end of the slinky back and forth parallel to the length of the slinky.

Depending on the availability of time, you may decide against the derivation of the **wave equation**. However, be sure to discuss the significance of Equation 14-9 and 14-10.

In Section 14-3 we once again come across the concept and definition of **frequency**, **wavelength** and **amplitude**, but **wave number** is a term that is introduced for the first time here. Equation 14-21 is significant in that it gives the relation between **wavelength**, **frequency** and **wave velocity**. Discuss the dependence of each on the other two factors in this equation.

Compare the equation for the speed of **longitudinal waves** to the equation for the speed of **transverse waves** in strings. Point out the similarity in the equations. Emphasize that **sound waves** are **longitudinal waves** and need a medium to propagate the waves.

> ⟳ **DEMO**   A bell is placed inside an inverted jar. The bell is
> connected to a battery (the battery is on the outside of the
> jar). The sound of the bell can be heard very clearly. Now
> switch on the vacuum pump. As the air inside the
> jar is pumped out, the sound of the ringing bell
> will fade out.

When discussing **shear waves** be sure to go through the section Think About This… How do We Know What's Inside Earth.

Sections 14-6 -14-7

Standing waves in strings and **air columns** have many practical applications, especially in the area of music and musical instruments. I usually ask students to bring their guitars and wind instruments and demonstrate their skills. We then discuss the concept of **fundamental mode** of vibration and **harmonics**, as well as the dependence of **frequency** on the **tension** and **linear density** of the string (see Equation 14-44c).

Sections 14-8 – 14-9

Doppler effect is caused by the relative motion of a **source** and **observer**. To facilitate understanding of this concept, go through the explanation case by case as discussed in the textbook. Use Figs. 14-31, 14-32 and 14-33 to illustrate this phenomenon. Students will invariably get confused as to the sign of the velocity of the moving source or observer in Equations 14-48, 14-55 and 14-57. Point out that when the relative distance between source and observer decreases, we will hear a higher **frequency**, and when the distance increases we hear a lower **frequency**.

There are many practical applications of **Doppler effect** in medicine, astronomy and police work. Be sure to mention these, and discuss them in class if time permits. Encourage students to read the section on **shock waves** – they are sure to find that very interesting, especially the idea of **mach numbers** and breaking the sound barrier.

> ⟳ **DEMO**   This can be built without too much difficulty. Install a buzzer and a battery in a tennis
> ball and tie a long string to the tennis ball. As you whirl the buzzer in a horizontal circle over
> your head, students will hear the frequency change as the ball approaches them and then
> recedes from them. Be sure to point out the difference in sound when the buzzer is stationary
> and when it is moving.

Textbook Resource Information

Transparency Acetates

Fig. 14-1   Propagation of transverse disturbance
Fig. 14-3   Propagation of longitudinal disturbance
Fig. 14-5   Transverse waves in a slinky
Fig. 14-8   Cork floating on an ocean wave
Fig. 14-9   Wave pulse on a string
Fig. 14-10   Periodic wave on a rope
Fig. 14-12   Plot of a harmonic traveling wave
Fig. 14-15   Elongation of a rod due to a stress force
Fig. 14-17   Traveling wave pulse
Fig. 14-21   Some modes of standing waves on a string
Fig. 14-24   Wave propagation in air
Fig. 14-25   Standing waves in a closed pipe
Fig. 14-26   Standing waves in a pipe open at one end
Fig. 14-27   Standing waves in an open pipe
Fig. 14-29   Waves in a three-dimensional medium
Fig. 14-30   Intensity levels as a function of frequency
Fig. 14-31   Doppler effect in a ripple tank
Fig. 14-32   Doppler effect due to a moving receiver
Fig. 14-34   Shock wave front

Physlet Physics Illustrations

17.1   Wave Types
17.2   Wave Functions
17.5   Resonant Behavior on a String
18.4   Doppler Effect
18.5   Location of a Supersonic Airplane

Physlet Physics Explorations

17.3   Measure the properties of a wave
17.5   Superposition of waves
17.6   Make a standing wave
18.2   Creating sounds by adding harmonics
18.4   Doppler effect and the velocity of the source
18.5   An ambulance drives by with its sirens on

Physlet Physics Problems

17.2   Velocity of wave
17.6   Superposition of two waves
17.8   Standing waves on a string – finding mass
17.15 Standing waves – finding properties
18.5   Standing waves on a string – doubling the tension
18.7   Doppler effect

18.8   Doppler effect
18.12 Standing waves in an open pipe
18.14 Standing waves in a half open pipe

Ranking Task Exercises in Physics, Student Edition

End of Chapter Problems with Solutions in the *Student Study Guide*

17, 29, 41, 49, 59, 79

Suggested Readings

Barrett, R.P., "Kundt's Tube and an Air Track Blower," *The Physics Teacher* (December 2001), p. 552.

Baxter, G.W., and Hagenbuch, K.M., "A Student Project on Wind Chimes. Tuning in to Standing Waves," *The Physics Teacher* (April 1998), p. 204 – 208.

Crane, R.H., "How Things Work: Folded-Path Doppler and the Measurement of Blood Flow," *The Physics Teacher* (September 1999), p. 362 – 363.

Dibble, W., "A Pedagogical Note on the Doppler-Effect Formulas," *The Physics Teacher* (September 2000), p. 362 – 363.

Gibson, G., and Johnston, I., "New Themes and Audiences for the Physics of Music," *Physics Today* (January 2002), p. 42 – 48.

Gibbs, R.E., "Standing Waves on a Hanging Rope," *The Physics Teacher* (February 1998), p. 108 – 110.

Graham, M., "Melde's Experiment with an Aquarium Aerator; Rich Dynamics with Inexpensive Apparatus," *The Physics Teacher* (May 1998), p. 276 – 279.

Greenslade, Jr., T.B., "Models of Traveling Waves," *The Physics Teacher* (November 2001), p. 466.

Greenslade, Jr., T.B., "Waves in the Movies," *The Physics Teacher* (February 2000), p. 78.

Greenslade, Jr., T.B., "Marloye's Harp and Thumb Piano," *The Physics Teacher* (May 2001), p. 310 – 312.

Haws, L., "Resonating Blow-Pipe Drum," *The Physics Teacher* (March 2001), p. 176.

Hoyt, D., "A Different Viewpoint on Doppler-Effect Calculations," *The Physics Teacher* (January 2002), p. 14 – 16.

Huebner, J.S., and Sundaralingam, N., "Simple Sound Demonstrations," *The Physics Teacher* (January 1998), p. 16.

Hults, M.G., "Sound Waves," *The Physics Teacher* (September 2001), p. 377.

Notes and Ideas

Preparation time: *Estimated:* _____   *Actual:* _____

Class time spent on material: *Estimated:* _____   *Actual:* _____

Related laboratory activities:

Demonstration materials:

Notes for next time:

Chapter 15: Superposition and Interference of Waves

Outline

Summary

In the last chapter we looked at standing waves in strings and air columns. This chapter considers how waves **superpose** and the various ways in which they can combine to form waves. You will also learn what conditions will result in the formation of **standing waves** and waves of other shapes. The phenomena of **beats** and **Fourier decomposition** of waves are also discussed.

Major Concepts

- The superposition principle
    - Interference
    - Coherence

- Standing waves through interference
    - Interference of incident and reflected waves

- Beats
    - Calculation of the beat frequency

- Spatial interference phenomenon
    - Locations of maxima and minima
-
    Pulses
    - Collision between pulses
    - Reflection
    - Transmission
    - Amplitude of reflected and transmitted pulses
    - Consequences of the conservation of energy
    - Change in velocity with a change in medium

- Fourier decomposition of waves
    - Fourier decomposition of a triangular wave
    - Fourier analysis and the ear

- Pulses and uncertainty principle
    - The Fourier decomposition of pulses
    - Uncertainty relations

Teaching Suggestions and Demonstrations

This chapter looks at the theory behind the formation of **standing waves** and **beats**. The math, or rather trigonometry, is fairly straightforward and will give students a better understanding of the **superposition principle** and its consequences. Even if you normally prefer to skip derivations, you will find it worthwhile to go through the derivations in this chapter.

Sections 15-1 – 15-2

Begin by defining the **superposition principle** and the concept of linearity. Point out that for **constructive** and **destructive interference** to take place, the source must be a **coherent** one. Use Fig. 15-1 to show the **interference effects** between two waves when they differ slightly in phase or **amplitude** or **frequency**. Before you start with the derivation in Section 15-2, review the concept of **wavelength**, **frequency**, **phase** and **amplitude** and the relationship between these quantities (see Section 14.1). Point out that Equation 15-6 is similar to that of 14-39, except for a **phase difference**. The additional factor of 2 can be folded into the **amplitude**.

Section 15-3

The phenomenon of **beats** has practical applications in the field of music. Discuss how a piano tuner tunes a piano by listening for **beats** as he works on the piano.

> ⮂ **DEMO** Ask two of your students to bring their guitars. Tune them to slightly different frequencies and show how the beats vanish when they are completely in tune.

> ⮂ **DEMO** Two tuning forks of the same frequency are mounted on a wooden box. Attach a small piece of putty on a prong of one of the tuning forks. When the forks are set in vibration you will hear the maximum and minimum as beats occur. Use two forks whose frequencies are very different. You will not hear the beats now.

> ⮂ **DEMO** Use the set-up described in Fig. 15-4 to illustrate the concept of beats.

Equations 15-15 and 15-6 give the **beat wavelength** and the **beat frequency**. Note that the **beat frequency** is given by $f_1 - f_2$. However, if $f_2 > f_1$ the **beat frequency** will be $f_2 - f_1$. In other words, the **beat frequency** is the absolute value of the difference in frequency of the two waves.

Sections 15-4 – 15-5

The sketch shown below helps to define **constructive** and **destructive interference**.

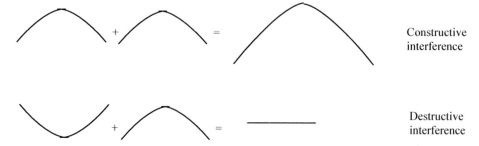

Constructive interference

Destructive interference

To relate this to a familiar occurrence, talk about the dead space in a room where the music cannot be heard because of **destructive interference** from the two speakers. Equations 15-17 and 15-8 are important. They give the conditions for **constructive** and **destructive interference**. Equations 15-20 and 15-21 are the same as 15-7 and 15-8 but expressed in terms of the angular locations of the maxima and minima. Point out that the same quations hold true for interference of all waves, whether they are sound waves or electromagnetic waves. The students will be seeing the same equation when they come to optics. Note that in a given space **constructive** or **destructive interference** can happen at different locations as long as the conditions stated in Equations 15-7 and 15-8 are met.

Section 15-5 looks at the behavior of a **single pulse**. The **reflection** and **transmission** of **pulses** are discussed. Figs. 15-17 through 15-21 look at the behavior of a **pulse** at different kinds of boundaries. Go through worked Example 15-7 to show that energy is conserved as the **pulse** is **transmitted** and or **reflected**. The following demonstrations illustrate the effect of the boundary on the incident pulse.

> ⮕ **DEMO** Attach one end of a long rope to the wall or a doorknob or a metal stand. Hold the other end taut and give it an upward motion with a quick flip of the wrist. A pulse will travel toward the wall. When the pulse reaches the wall, it will be reflected back toward you. Point out that the reflected wave will be inverted if the end of the rope is fixed. On the other hand, if the end of the rope is not fixed but allowed to slide up, then the reflected wave will be upright. (See Fig. 15-19)

> ⮕ **DEMO** To show transmission of a pulse, attach a lightweight rope to the end of the heavier rope and repeat the demo. If you flick the free end of the lighter rope, the pulse will be transmitted across the boundary to the heavier rope. However, if the incident pulse is produced on the heavier rope, you will get both a reflected and transmitted pulse. (See Fig. 15-21). Point out the difference in amplitudes of the two waves.

Sections 15-6 – 15-7

Fourier analysis of waves is optional and as such omitted from most curricula. However, it helps to understand the physics of music, so consider discussing it if time allows it.

Textbook Resource Information

Transparency Acetates

Fig. 15-1	Superposition of two waves
Fig. 15-2	Time sequence of two traveling waves
Fig. 15-5	Beat formation of two waves of equal amplitudes
Fig. 15-6	An enlarged view of beat formation
Fig. 15-9	Path difference of two interfering waves
Fig. 15-10	Waves generated by two coherent sources
Fig. 15-11	Condition for maxima and minima
Fig. 15-17	Superposition of two pulses moving toward each other
Fig. 15-18	An incident pulse reflecting from the end of a string
Fig. 15-19	Reflection of a pulse from the free end of a string
Fig. 15-21	Reflection and/or transmission of a pulse
Fig. 15-24	Examples of non-harmonic periodic waves
Fig. 15-26	Fourier analysis of triangular waveform

Physlet Physics Illustrations

17.3   Superposition of Pulses
17.4   Superposition of Traveling Waves
18.3   Interference in Time and Beats

Physlet Physics Explorations

17.1   Superposition of two pulses
17.3   Traveling pulses and barriers
17.5   Superposition of two waves
18.3   A microphone between two loudspeakers

Physlet Physics Problems

17.6   Superposition of two waves
18.6   Superposition of two waves on a string

Ranking Task Exercises in Physics, Student Edition

Page 201   Pairs of transverse waves – superposition

End of Chapter Problems with Solutions in the *Student Study Guide*

5, 11, 15, 21, 25, 53

Suggested Readings

Boucher, D.E., "A Visual and Acoustic Demonstration of Beats and Interference," *The Physics Teacher* (March 1999), p. 177 – 178.

Dindorf, W., "String of Pearls Resonance," *The Physics Teacher* (April 2001), p. 251.

Easton, D., The Buzzing of Flies' Wings," *The Physics Teacher* (February 1999), p. 72.

Gaffney, C.A., and Kagan, D., "Beats in an Oscillator Near Resonance," *The Physics Teacher* (October 2002), p. 405 – 407.

Greenslade, Jr., T.B., "Foot Beats," *The Physics Teacher* (December 2002), p. 534.

Greenslade, Jr., T.B., "Apparatus for Teaching: A Modification of Young's Harmonic Sliders," *The Physics Teacher* (April 2001), p. 234.

Larson, J.H., "Beats on a Vibrating String," *The Physics Teacher* (September 1999), p. 373.

Potter, D., "Phase Change in Reflected Sound Waves," *The Physics Teacher* (January 2003), p. 12 – 13.

Notes and Ideas

Preparation time: *Estimated:* _____   *Actual:* _____

Class time spent on material: *Estimated:* _____   *Actual:* _____

Related laboratory activities:

Demonstration materials:

Notes for next time:

Chapter 16: Properties of Fluids

Outline

Summary

Starting with a brief look at the different **states of matter**, Chapter 16 discusses in detail the properties of **fluids** at rest as well as in motion. Important topics such as **buoyant forces**, **Archimedes' principle** and **Bernoulli's Equations** are treated. The concept of **viscosity** is also discussed.

Major Concepts

- States of matter

- Density and pressure
    o Density
    o Pressure

- Pressure in a fluid at rest

- Buoyancy and Archimedes' principle
    o Buoyant force
    o Archimedes' principle

- Fluids in motion

- Equation of continuity

- Bernoulli's equation
    o Bernoulli's equation
    o Problem-solving techniques

- Applications of Bernoulli's equation
    o Hydrostatic relation between pressure and height
    o The Bernoulli's effect
    o Fluid motion with constant speed
    o Flow from a tank
    o Lift

- Real fluids
  - o Viscosity
  - o Turbulence

Teaching Suggestions

Most students would have had at least one year of chemistry and so will be familiar with the concept of **density**. However, the rest of the topics in this chapter will be new to them. They will have intuitive ideas about **buoyancy,** some of which will be incorrect. Several demonstrations are listed in this manual, which will be helpful when teaching this topic.

Sections 16-1 – 16-2

Define the terms *solids, liquids* and *gases* in terms of their molecular separation and force between the molecules.

Section 16-2 lays the groundwork for the rest of the chapter. Even though students will be familiar with the concept of **density**, it will be useful to go through the definition. Students will easily replace *heavy* for *dense*. Use as many examples as you can think of to help them differentiate between the two words. The following demonstrations will be useful.

➲ **DEMO** You can either have students do this in groups or you can perform this as a demo in front of the class. Measure 50 g of lead or aluminum pellets and pour them into a graduated beaker. Find its mass. Now repeat the experiment with 25g of lead pellets. In both cases, find the density. This will show the relationship between mass and volume for an incompressible solid. Also point out that 50 g of lead pellets is heavier than the 25 g, but they both have the same density.

➲ **DEMO** Take some cotton balls and loosely fill a graduated beaker. Measure the mass of these cotton balls. Repeat the experiment, but now squeeze in as many cotton balls as you can into the same beaker and find its mass. Find the density in both cases and show that the density of a compressible solid is not constant.

Remind students to look at Table 16-1 to get an idea of the **densities** of different materials.
Stress the difference between **density** and **specific gravity** and why water has a value of 1 for **specific gravity**. Students who have had chemistry will be familiar with the value of 1g/cc for the density of water. Point out the fact that in the SI system the **density** of water is 1000 kg/m^3.

The definition of **pressure** as the force per unit area is applicable to **solids**, **liquids** and **gases**. Point out that this **pressure** is measured in terms of the force acting perpendicular to the area. Students will be familiar with the units of psi (pounds per square inch) but not with the SI unit of Pascal.

➲ **DEMO** You will need a large garbage bag, 25 straws and a light wooden board. Take the garbage bag, tape it shut and insert 25 straws around it at the seam. Place the garbage bag on the table and place the wooden board on top of the garbage bag. Get a person (weighing up to 250 lbs) to sit on the board. Get 25 non-smokers to come up and blow on the straws. The garbage bag will fill up with air and lift the person (sitting on the board) up.

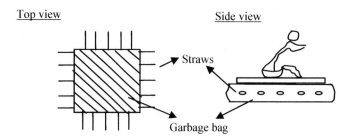

Top view Side view

Straws

Garbage bag

➲ **DEMO** This can be done as a project outside of class time or as an in class demonstration. Take a sheet of paper and place it in front of one of the tires of your car. Drive the car forward so the tire is on top of the piece of paper. Trace the outline of the area of contact on the piece of paper. Remove the paper after carefully reversing the car a little. Draw grids of one-inch square on the paper and find the area of contact by counting the grids. You will have to approximate partial grids. Measure the air pressure on the tire. From these two values (the air pressure and the area of contact) calculate the weight of the car. Compare this with the value from the car's specifications. This is a good exercise to discuss possible sources of error.
Note: Since you used the surface area of just one tire, you will have to multiply the value you get by a factor of 4 to get the weight of the car.
Caution: The car should be on level ground and care should be taken when driving the tire on to the paper.

➲ **DEMO** This is a very effective demonstration to show the relationship between pressure and area of contact. Have some of your female students bring in their high-heeled shoes and a pair of flat-soled shoes. With the flat-soled shoes on, trace the outline of one foot on to a piece of paper. Make sure the student is standing with both feet side by side and with equal pressure on both feet. Calculate the area of contact and knowing the weight of the student, calculate the pressure exerted on each foot. Repeat with the high-heeled shoes.
The pressure exerted on a foot by the high-heeled shoes will be greater by a factor of 4 to 10 (depending on the extent of the spike on the shoes). This difference is remarkable and will be an eye opener for many students. Use this to discuss the long-term negative effects of wearing high-heeled shoes.
Note: In the case of the high-heeled shoes, only the heel area should be taken into account because all of the pressure is felt there and not on the toe area.

➲ **DEMO** Bed of nails: This set-up can be built with a little bit of planning.
You will need: A ½ -inch thick plywood board about 6 ft by 3 ft in dimension and roofing nails 1.5 inches long. (The number of nails you will need will depend on the number of grids you draw on the board. You could get by with a board that is about 5 ft by 2.5 ft in dimension. This will reduce the number of nails you will have to use). Draw lines 1 inch apart along the length and width of the board to form equally spaced grids. Drive in the roofing nails at the corners of the square grids. This will ensure that the nails are evenly spaced. When you turn the board over, the nail tips will be at the same horizontal level. To illustrate that pressure exerted is inversely proportional to the area of contact, with your back to the board, place each foot on either side of the board. Support yourself with your hands on either side of the board and gently lower yourself on to the board. Once your upper body and head are flat on the board, bring your legs in so you are stretched straight out on the board. If you place a book under your head it will be more comfortable! To get off the board, have two students help raise you as you support yourself on your feet, so you are not sitting on the nails, because this will not be very pleasant. Ask the students what would happen if the nails

were few and far apart. Be sure to wear clothes that will not snag on the nails, or wear a lab coat.

Sections 16-3 – 16-4

To understand the significance of Equation 16-6 (**pressure** in a **fluid** at rest), it is best to go through the derivation. Remind students that this equation is valid for all **fluids**, which includes **gases**. However, atmospheric pressure will be studied in detail in Chapter 19.

Equation 16-6 shows that the **pressure** in a **fluid** depends only on the depth and not on the horizontal position. One consequence of this is that liquids will find their own level.

➲ DEMO   Glass tubes of varying shapes are interconnected at the bottom. Pour liquid into one of the tubes and the liquid will distribute itself to the same height in every tube, all of which are open to the atmosphere. (See Fig. 16-8.)

The second consequence of Equation 16-6 is **Pascal's principle**, which states that **pressure** applied at one point in a **fluid** will be transmitted equally to all points in the **fluid**. Go through worked Example 16-3 to illustrate this principle. Also point out that this principle is applied not just in the hydraulic lift used in automotive garages, but also in the chairs used in a dentist's office and in a hair salon, to name a few.

Ask students why a brick sinks in water while a piece of cork floats, and most of them will answer that the brick is heavier while the cork is lighter. This is a very common misconception. It is very important to stress the difference between heavy and dense.

Use Figs. 16-12 and 16-13 to explain the conditions for an object to sink, float or be totally submerged. Point out that the **buoyant force** (given by Equation 16-10) determines whether the object will sink, float or be submerged. Show them how this can be looked at in terms of the **density** of the object and the **density** of the **fluid**. Take the example of a steel ship and a block of steel. Point out that the volume of **displaced fluid** in both cases is very different, which is why the **buoyant force** is also different. This is what causes the ship to float while the block will sink, even though both are equally "heavy."

➲ DEMO   Cut out two square sheets of aluminum foil of equal dimension. Crumple one piece into a ball and make a floating boat out of the other. Take about six nails, place them inside the boat and float the boat in a fish tank. (You can use any transparent container instead of a fish tank, to make it visible to the whole class). Next take the balled-up piece of aluminum foil, stick the same number of nails into it and place it in the water. This will now sink to the bottom. This demo is analogous to the steel ship and the block of steel.

➲ DEMO   Take several different kinds of sodas and place them in the fish tank. See which ones sink and which ones will float. Use this to compare the densities of regular and diet sodas.

➲ DEMO   Take a beaker of water and an egg. When the egg is placed in water, it will sink. Add salt to the water and stir and continue to do so until the egg floats in the water. This shows that the density of freshwater is less than that of salt water.

Fig. 16-13 shows that the ratio of the volume of object under the **fluid** to the total volume of the object is equal to the ratio of the **density** of the object to the **density** of the **fluid**. In other words, if half of an object is underwater, one can make the conclusion that the **density** of the object is half that of water. This is an important connection that most students will fail to make.

Archimedes' principle relates the **buoyant force** to the weight of the **displaced liquid**. Students will invariably think of the weight of the **displaced fluid** and the volume of the **displaced fluid** to be the same. Go through Examples 16-7 and 16-8 to show how **Archimedes' principle** can be used to determine the **density** of an object in the lab.

> ⮑ **DEMO** Take an object (a metal ball or a block of some material that will normally sink in the water) and suspended it from a spring scale that can easily be read by the whole class. Now place the mass half submerged in a beaker of water and take the scale reading. Next, let the mass be completely submerged in the water and take the scale reading. In each case the scale reading will give the difference between the force of gravity (on the mass) and the buoyant force. (See Fig. 16-15.)

Sections 16-5 – 16-9

The rest of this chapter has to do with **fluids** in motion. The **equation of continuity** and **Bernoulli's equation** are the major ideas discussed and have many practical applications.

Here are two practical consequences of **Bernoulli's effect**: as soon as the shower is turned on, the shower curtain will be sucked into the shower cubicle. When a heavy truck passes your car in the opposite direction, you feel your car being sucked toward the truck.

> ⮑ **DEMO** Turn on a hair dryer and hold it so the air is blown vertically up. Place a ping-pong ball in the air stream a little above the nozzle of the hair dryer. The ball will dance around in the air stream without falling out.

> ⮑ **DEMO** Hold a strip of paper in front of your mouth and blow air across the top of the paper. The paper will be lifted. (See Fig. 16-22.)

A practical application of **Bernoulli's effect** is the Venturi flowmeter. To illustrate this, use Fig. 16-23 and go through the concept discussed under Think About This…How is Fluid Speed in a Closed Pipe Measured'.

> ⮑ **DEMO** Here is a simple but effective demo to show how the flow of water from a tank is related to the pressure (and hence to the fluid depth). Take a Styrofoam cup and make three holes at different heights directly one below the other. Fill the cup with water and watch the water flow out of the holes. The water from the bottom hole will come out at a greater speed and will hence have a greater range. (See Fig. 16-25.)

Viscosity and **turbulence** are discussed qualitatively and very briefly. The following demo will give students a feel for the concept of **viscosity**.

> ⮑ **DEMO** Take two tall beakers. Fill the first one with water and the second with oil. Drop a small metal sphere into each beaker and see the rate at which the sphere falls through the water and the oil.

Textbook Resource Information

Transparency Acetates

Fig. 16-3	Lattice structure of solids
Fig. 16-5	Schematic of a manometer
Fig. 16-6	Pressure in a fluid
Fig. 16-12	Net force on a block submerged in a fluid
Fig. 16-13	Buoyant force on a floating/sinking/submerged solid
Fig. 16-19	Streamline flow in a fluid
Fig. 16-21	A stream tube at different heights
Fig. 16-23b	The Venturi flowmeter
Fig. 16-25a	Flow of fluid through a hole in a tank
Fig. 16-28	Velocity profile for laminar flow in a pipe
Fig. 16-29	Fluid flow between two glass plates

Physlet Physics Illustrations

14.1 Pressure in a Fluid
14.2 Pascal's Principle
14.3 Buoyant Force
15.1 The Continuity Equation
15.2 Bernoulli's Principle at Work
15.3 Ideal and Viscous Fluid Flow
15.4 Airplane Lift

Physlet Physics Explorations

14.1 Floating and density
14.3 Buoyancy and oil on water
15.1 Blood flow and continuity
15.3 Application of Bernoulli's equation

Physlet Physics Problems

14.1 Hydraulic lift
14.3 Density of an object
14.9 Melting ice cube
15.1 Blood flow in an artery
15.7 Ideal fluid flow

End of Chapter Problems with Solutions in the *Student Study Guide*

7, 19, 25, 43, 53, 63

Suggested Readings

Barrett, B., "Physics in a Soap Dispenser—Dancing Dolphins," *The Physics Teacher* (November 2000), p. 480.

Bierman, J., and Kincanon, E., "Reconsidering Archimedes' Principle," *The Physics Teacher* (September 2003), p. 340 – 344

Cohen, H., and Horvath, D., "Two Large-Scale Devices for Demonstrating a Bernoulli Effect," *The Physics Teacher* (January 2003), p. 9 – 11.

Eastlake, C.N., "An Aerodynamicist's View of Lift, Bernoulli, and Newton," *The Physics Teacher* (March 2002), p. 166 – 173.

Edge, R., "Sundogs, Ice Crystals, and Bernoulli," *The Physics Teacher* (December 2002), p. 522.

Fakhruddin, H., "An Archimedes' Principle Activity," *The Physics Teacher* (September 2002), p. 376.

Gaffney, C., "The Hydrostatics of Trapped Bubbles in Fluids," *The Physics Teacher* (November 2000), p. 458 – 460.

Gallagher III, F.W., and Fredrickson, S.E., "Meteorological Pressure-Sensor Inaccuracies" *The Physics Teacher* (November 2000), p. 466 – 469.

Gardner, M., "Archimedes' Pump," *The Physics Teacher* (January 1999), p. 41.

Greene, N.R., "Tossing a Garden Hose," *The Physics Teacher* (January 1999), p. 46 – 47.

Greene, N.R., and Dworsak, M.R., "Bernouli at the Gas Pump," *The Physics Teacher* (September 2001), p. 346 – 348.

Güémez, J., Fiolhais, C., and Fiolhais, M., "A Demonstration Apparatus for the Cartesian Diver," *The Physics Teacher* (November 2003), p. 495 – 496.

Noll, E.D., "Confronting the Buoyant Force," *The Physics Teacher* (January 2002), p. 8 – 10.

Peckham, G.D., and Sutherland, L., "Pressure Measurements: A Diagrammatic Comparison," *The Physics Teacher* (February 1999), p. 100 – 101.

Wardle, D.A., "Measurement of Aeroplane Takeoff Speed and Cabin Pressure," *The Physics Teacher* (October 1999), p. 410 – 411.

Notes and Ideas

Preparation time: *Estimated:* _____   *Actual:* _____

Class time spent on material: *Estimated:* _____   *Actual:* _____

Related laboratory activities:

Demonstration materials:

Notes for next time:

Chapter 17: Temperature and Ideal Gases

Outline

Summary

The study of **temperature** is important because it affects the properties of the physical world. This chapter is a study of the different **temperature** scales, the **ideal gas**, and the **equation of state of gases.** Finally, **blackbody radiation** and the background **radiation** of the universe are discussed.

Major Concepts

- Temperature and thermal equilibrium
    - o   Thermal systems
    - o   Thermometers

- Ideal gases and absolute temperature
    - o   Ideal gases and Kelvin scale
    - o   Other temperature scales

- Thermal expansion
    - o   Linear and volume expansion

- The equation of state of gases
    - o   Boyle's Law
    - o   Ideal gas law
    - o   Changing the thermodynamic variables of a gas
    - o   How close do real gases come to being ideal?
    - o   The van der Waals equation of state

- Blackbody radiation
    - o   Planck formula
    - o   Background radiation of the universe

Teaching Suggestions and Demonstrations

The ideas presented in this chapter give the necessary background for the understanding of the **laws** of **thermodynamics** as well as **statistical mechanics**. **Temperature** relates directly to the **energy** of the system. The chemistry background of your students will decide how detailed your discussion of these topics will have to be.

Sections 17-1 – 17-3

Begin by defining **thermal equilibrium** and the **zeroth law of thermodynamics**.
Briefly discuss the different kinds of **thermometers** possible based on the properties of matter that are **temperature** dependent. Table 17-1 lists some of these properties.

Most students will be familiar with the **Kelvin scale** of **temperature** and the **ideal gas law**. To give a feel for **temperature**, look at Table 17-2, which lists the **temperature** of certain materials.
When converting from **Celsius** to **Fahrenheit** scale and vice versa, the most common mistake made is in adding or subtracting 32 (which is the ice point of water in the Fahrenheit scale). Figure 17-7 and Fig. 17-8 compare the three scales of **temperature**.

Thermal expansion and **volume expansion** are relatively easy concepts for students. There are several examples and demos that can be used to illustrate these properties.
Expansion joints in bridges, road surfaces and railroad tracks as well as the sagging of power lines can be used to discuss the concept of thermal expansion.

➲ **DEMO** The ball and ring apparatus can be used to show that the linear dimensions of a material expand proportionate to the temperature increase. The metal ball (when cold) will easily slip into and out of the metal ring. Both the ball and ring have handles that are well insulated. Slip the ball through the ring and then heat it. After a few minutes of heating, try to pull the ball out of the ring. Because of the expansion of the ball, its diameter will now be larger than the opening in the ring.

➲ **DEMO** A bimetallic strip is a thin strip of two different metals, one on either face of the strip. Heat the strip, and it will bend very noticeably due to the different coefficient of thermal expansion of the two metals. This is used to break contact in electrical circuits.

➲ **DEMO** Holding the metal lid under a tap of hot water can loosen a metal lid on a glass jar that is hard to open. Since the metal lid will expand more than the glass jar, this will loosen the metal lid.

➲ **DEMO** Attach a strip of nickel wire to a variac (can be purchased from Central Scientific) with leads. As you turn up the variac the wire will heat up and expand, thus causing it to sag. Note: The wire can become very hot and even break. If it starts to glow, it is an indication that it is going to break.

Sections 17-4 – 17-5

Boyle's law and the **ideal gas law** will be familiar to most students. Remind them that the dimensions of RT and kT in Equations 17-10 and 17-12 have the dimensions of energy because pV/n and pV/N have the dimensions of force times length.

➲ **DEMO** Constant temperature: Place a partially blown up balloon inside a sealed bell jar. The bell jar is attached to a vacuum pump through a lead at the bottom. Turn on the vacuum pump. The balloon will "blow" up.

⮌ **DEMO** This is similar to the demo above. Instead of a balloon, use a small amount of gel shaving cream placed inside a tall beaker. As the air is pumped out of the bell jar, the shaving cream will rise up fast. Don't let the shaving cream flow out of the beaker.

⮌ **DEMO** Constant volume: A sealed sphere (filled with air) is attached to a pressure gauge that will measure the pressure in psi. Measure the pressure when the sphere is placed in boiling water and compare it to the pressure when it is placed in ice water. Remember that atmospheric pressure is 14.7 lbs/in^2. (This setup can be purchased from Central Scientific).

⮌ **DEMO** Constant pressure: Fill a balloon with air and place it in a dish. As you pour liquid nitrogen over the balloon it will shrink. When you take the balloon out, it will return to its original volume.

Students will find the discussion in Think About This…How Do We Get the Fizz into Dispensed Drinks interesting. Figure 17-14 will prove useful in this discussion. For the same reason, be sure to discuss conceptual Example 17-10.

The discussion of **blackbody radiation** and **Plank's formula** are important as they led to the Discovery and measurement of the background **radiation** of the universe. Let the time available to you dictate the depth to which you want to discuss these topics in class. In any case, encourage your students to read some of the suggested references given at the end of the chapter in this manual.

Textbook Resource Information

Transparency Acetates

Table 17-1	Some thermometers
Table 17-2	Temperatures occurring in nature
Table 17-3	Coefficients of thermal and volume expansion
Fig. 17-12	Phase diagram of water
Fig. 17-16	Intensity vs. frequency plot for an electromagnetic radiation

Physlet Physics Explorations

19.2 Expansion of materials
20.3 Ideal gas law

Physlet Physics Problems

19.3 Linear expansion of a rod
19.4 Linear expansion – square
19.5 Linear expansion - circle
20.5 Ideal gas
20.7 Volume expansion

Ranking Task Exercises in Physics, Student Edition

End of Chapter Problems with Solutions in the *Student Study Guide*

11, 23, 45, 49, 75, 87

Suggested Readings

Crane, R.H., "Popping Bimetal Can Keep You Warm or Cool," *The Physics Teacher* (May 1998), p. 302 – 303.

Crane, R.H., "A Thermometer Whose Memory is a One-Sided Magnet," *The Physics Teacher* (March 1999), p. 148 – 149.

Gash, P., "So You Thought a Glass Thermometer Measured Temperature," *The Physics Teacher* (February 2002), p. 74 – 76.

Heavers, R.M., and Bayly, T.E., "A Demonstration Seasonal 'Thermocline'," *The Physics Teacher* (October 2003), p. 425 – 429

Houser, J., Johnson, D., and Siegel, P., "Getting Pumped Up on the Ideal Gas Law," *The Physics Teacher* (October 2002), p. 396 – 397.

Ivanov, D.T., "Experimental Determination of Absolute Zero Temperature," *The Physics Teacher* (March 2003), p.172 – 175.

Reif, F., "Thermal Physics in the Introductory Physics Course: Why and How To Teach It from a Unified Atomic Perspective," *Am.J.Phys.* (December 1999), p. 1051 – 1062.

Wenning, C.J., "A Variation on Temperature Conversion," *The Physics Teacher* (October 2001), p. 434.

Notes and Ideas

Preparation time: *Estimated:* _____   *Actual:* _____

Class time spent on material: *Estimated:* _____   *Actual:* _____

Related laboratory activities:

Demonstration materials:

Notes for next time:

Demonstration materials:

Chapter 18: Heat Flow and the First Law of Thermodynamics

Outline

Summary

The **first law of thermodynamics** is the major topic discussed in this chapter. **Heat capacity, phase changes, calorimetry, thermal conductivity** and **mechanical equivalent of heat** are described as an introduction to the **first law of thermodynamics**. The work done in various transformations (at constant **volume, constant pressure** and **constant temperature**) and the **internal energy** of an **ideal gas** are discussed. Under applications of **ideal gases**, the **isothermal** and **adiabatic transformations** and the variation of **atmospheric temperature** with height are considered.

Major Concepts

- Changes in thermal systems
    - Reversible and irreversible processes

- Heat flow
    - Heat capacity
    - Path dependence of heat flow
    - Calorimetry
    - Phase changes and heat flow

- Heat flow in materials
    - Thermal conductivity
    - Thermal resistance
    - Thermal resistances in series and in parallel

- Mechanical equivalent of heat
    - Joule's experiment

- Work done by thermal systems
    - Work done by a gas
    - Cyclic transformations
    - Isobaric transformation
    - Isochoric transformation
    - Adiabatic transformation
    - Internal energy

- First law of thermodynamics
    - o The first law in closed cycles
    - o Energy changes in constant volume transformations
    - o Energy changes in constant pressure transformations

- Internal energy of ideal gases
    - o Relation between C_p and C_v for ideal gases

- More applications for ideal gases
    - o Isothermal transformations of an ideal gas
    - o Adiabatic transformations of an ideal gas
    - o Derivation of the adiabatic transformation on a *p-V* diagram
    - o Variation of atmospheric temperature with height

Teaching Suggestions and Demonstrations

Many curricula prefer to omit **first** and **second law** of **thermodynamics** based on the premise that these topics are covered in a chemistry class. However, keep in mind that the **first law of thermodynamics** is another way of looking at the **conservation of energy** as applied to **thermal systems**.

Sections 18-1 – 18-4

Begin by asking students to give as many examples of **reversible** and **irreversible** processes. Use Figs. 18-1 and 18-2 to define these two processes from a physics point of view. When discussing **heat flow**, stress that **heat flow** is related to the work done on or by a system. Students often fail to make the distinction between work done on a system and work done by a system. Point out that the **calorie** is defined in terms of the **heat flow** into 1 g of water rather than 1 kg of water. Students are by now trained to use the SI system so this can cause some confusion.

Make the distinction between **heat capacity**, **specific heat capacity** and **molar heat capacity**. Water has a very high **specific heat** (look at Table 18-1 to compare the **specific heats** of various materials). To discuss the significance of **heat capacity**, ask your students the following questions:
1. Why does the filling inside an apple pie retain heat longer than the crust or why is the skin of a baked potato much cooler than the inside?
2. Why is sand much hotter than the water on a summer day?
3. Why is water preferred as a coolant more than other material?

    ⟳ DEMO This demonstration illustrates the high heat capacity of water. A balloon filled with air will pop when it is held over a flame. On the other hand, a balloon filled with water will not pop when held to the flame.

Figure 18-7 explains the different steps water has to go through to change from ice to vapor. It is important to understand that there is no temperature change during a **phase change**. Table 18-2 gives the **latent heat of fusion** and **vaporization** for some materials. Discuss the section Think About This…Why are **Latent Heats** of **Vaporization** Significantly Larger Than **Latent Heats of Fusion**? to show the difference in the **phase-change** process between solid/liquid and liquid/gas.

Section 18-3 looks at the **heat flow** in materials and **thermal conductivity**. **Thermal resistance** (R values) is of particular importance in the construction industry. Look at Table 18-3 to compare the **thermal conductivity** of different materials. Point out that a high R value (and hence a small thermal conductivity) refers to a good insulator. Double-paned windows are a good example of effective insulation. Discuss why having air between the two panes is not a good idea.

⮌ **DEMO** Conductivity of different metals: This demo from Central Scientific has four different metals radiating out from a central hub. Coat the ends of each arm with wax and heat the central hub using a burner. Alternately, you could heat it using boiling water underneath it. Have the students rank the metals in order of conductivity before you do the demonstration.

Ask your students to compare a wool sweater and a cotton sweater in terms of its insulation property. Wool fiber has air molecules trapped inside, and since air is a bad **conductor** of heat, the body heat will not escape as easily as it would with a cotton sweater. Example 18-8 is of practical importance. It shows how quickly the R value can be affected (adversely) when a small hole in a wall is patched with plywood.

⮌ **DEMO** Convection: The apparatus is a simple square glass tubing with an opening at the top. Place a few drops of food coloring in the opening of the tube. When the tube is heated on one side, the water will rise on the warm side. The food coloring shows up the motion of the heated molecules. The water should not be filled to the top because it will expand on heating and spill out.

⮌ **DEMO** Mechanical equivalent of heat: To show the relation between heat and work, here is a quick and simple demonstration. Fill a bag with lead shots and tie the opening. Measure the initial temperature of the lead shots by sticking a temperature probe into the bag. Now drop the bag from about a height of 2 m 10-20 times. Measure the temperature of the lead shots again. There should be an increase of $2 - 3^{\circ}$ in the temperature of the lead shots.

⮌ **DEMO** Take a Styrofoam cup and half fill it with water. Measure its temperature with a thermometer. Insert a heating coil into the water and allow current to flow through it until the temperature increases by 10°. Note the time taken for this temperature change. Knowing the mass of water and the temperature change, the quantity of heat flowing into the water can be calculated. From the voltage and the current flowing through the coil and time of flow of current, the work done on the system can be determined. Compare the two.

Section 18-5

When using Equation 18-16 two points have to be kept in mind. First, the path must be specified in order for the integral to be valid. Secondly, the work done is nothing but the area under the *p-V* **curve**. This translates to the area enclosed by the *p-V* **curve** in the case of a closed cycle. (See Figs. 18-15 and 18-16.) In discussing the work done in various transformations, emphasize the difference between **isobaric**, **isochoric** and **isothermal transformations,** as well as **adiabatic transformations**.

⮌ **DEMO** This is a simple but effective way to demonstrate an adiabatic process. The apparatus consists of a thick-walled test tube that is closed by a rubber stopper through which passes a clear plastic tube. A small wisp of cotton fiber is placed at the bottom of the tube. When the piston is pushed down very quickly, the cotton will ignite.

Sections 18-6 – 18-7

The **first law of thermodynamics** deals with the conservation of energy principle extended to include **thermal energy** of systems. To understand the working of **thermal systems** like engines and power plants we must first understand the **first law of thermodynamics**. Point out the differences in Equations 18-27 and 18-28. In both of these equations, the **heat capacities** C_v and C_p cannot be treated as a constant because they could be temperature dependent.

The last part of this chapter discusses the variation of **atmospheric temperature** with height. Students will find this interesting, so it is well worth the time to go through the derivation. Point out the approximations made and the possible sources of error as listed in the last paragraph.

Textbook Resource Information

Transparency Acetates

Fig. 18-1	Constant temperature reversible transformation of a gas
Fig. 18-2	Irreversible transformation of a gas
Fig. 18-7	Phase changes for water
Fig. 18-10	R values for two materials in series
Fig. 18-11	R values for two materials in parallel
Fig. 18-13	Schematic diagram of Joule's experiment apparatus
Fig. 18-14	Work done by a gas on its surroundings
Fig. 18-15	Area under the p-V curve – work done by a gas
Fig. 18-16	Work done by a gas in a closed cycle
Fig. 18-20	Schematic diagram of Joule's experiment

Physlet Physics Illustrations

19.1   Specific Heat
19.2   Heat Transfer - Conduction

Physlet Physics Explorations

19.1 Mechanical equivalent of heat
19.3 Calorimetery
19.4 Heat balance – conductivity
20.5 *PV* diagrams and work
20.6 Specific heat at constant pressure and constant volume

Physlet Physics Problems

19.1 Heat capacity
19.6 Specific heat capacity and latent heat of fusion
19.8 Specific heat capacity
19.9 Thermal conductivity
19.10 Thermal conductivity – double-paned windows
19.11 Thermal conductivity

20.8 *PV* diagram and work
20.12 Ratio of C_p and C_v

Ranking Task Exercises in Physics, **Student Edition**

Page 109   Work done by a gas

End of Chapter Problems with Solutions in the *Student Study Guide*

7, 19, 33, 43, 51, 57

Suggested Readings

Bartlett, A.A., "Thermal Patterns in the Snow: Structure of a Roof," *The Physics Teacher* (February 1999), p. 120 – 121.

Bohan, R.J., and Vandegrift, G., "Temperature-Driven Convection," *The Physics Teacher* (February 2003), p. 76 – 77.

Greenslade, Jr., T.B., "Nineteenth-Century Measurements of the Mechanical Equivalent of Heat," *The Physics Teacher* (April 2002), p. 243 – 248.

Güémez, J., Fiolhais, C., and Fiolhais, M., "Revisiting Black's Experiments on the Latent Heats of Water," *The Physics Teacher* (January 2002), p. 26 – 31.

Ivanov, D.T., "Experimental Determination of Absolute Zero Temperature," *The Physics Teacher* (March 2003), p. 172 – 175.

Jadrich, J., and Haan, S.L., "Class Simulation of Thermal Energy and Heat," *The Physics Teacher* (February 1999), p. 98 – 99.

Mattos, C.R., and Gaspar, A., "Introducing Specific Heat through Cooling Curves," *The Physics Teacher* (October 2002), p. 415 – 416.

McIntosh, G., and Sharratt, B.S., "Thermal Properties of Soil," *The Physics Teacher* (November 2001), p. 458 – 460.

Mungan, C.E., "Irreversible Adiabatic Compression of an Ideal Gas," *The Physics Teacher* (November 2003), p. 450 – 453.

O'Connell, J., "Heating Water: Rate Correction Due to Newtonian Cooling," *The Physics Teacher* (December 1999), p.551 – 552.

Yeo, S., and Zadnik, M., "Introductory Thermal Concept Evaluation: Assessing Students' Understanding," *The Physics Teacher* (November 2001), p. 496 – 504.

Notes and Ideas

Preparation time: *Estimated:* _____   *Actual:* _____

Class time spent on material: *Estimated:* _____   *Actual:* _____

Related laboratory activities:

Demonstration materials:

Notes for next time:

Chapter 19: The Molecular Basis of Thermal Physics

Outline

Summary

This chapter focuses on the behavior of **gases** from a **molecular** aspect. Using **statistical physics**, the **kinetic theory** of gases is studied. The **statistical distribution** of the **velocity** of molecules and the **transport phenomenon** are discussed.

Major Concepts

- A Microscopic view of gases

- Pressure and molecular motion
    - o   Some average values in a gas
    - o   The origin of pressure

- The meaning of temperature
    - o   Temperature as energy
    - o   Interpretation of the van der Waals gas

- Probability distribution
    - o   The distribution of a set of test grades
    - o   Continuous distributions

- The velocity distribution of gases
    - o   Ideal gas velocity distribution
    - o   The average of the velocity squared

- The Maxwell-Boltzmann distribution
    - o   Maxwell-Boltzman distribution
    - o   The energy distribution for diatomic molecules
    - o   Equipartition

- Collisions and transport phenomena
    - o   Collisions and molecular movement in a gas
    - o   The random walk and diffusion

Teaching Suggestions and Demonstrations

This chapter makes use of **probability** and **statistical distribution** to look at the behavior of **molecules** of **gas**. Even if your students have not had a course in statistics, the extent of statistical theory used in this chapter is elementary and should not present too much of a problem.

Sections 19-1 – 19-3

The first section is a brief overview of the reasons for studying **gases** by looking at their **molecular** behavior. Begin by defining the **root-mean-square** (rms) value of the speed of a molecule. Students will have a tendency to assume that the square root of the square of the velocity is nothing but the velocity of the molecule. Point out that the quantity inside the square root is the average of the square of the velocities of all the molecules and this is not the same as just squaring the velocity and taking its square root.

When going through the derivation of Equation 19-6, remind students that momentum is a vector and why the net change in momentum is $-2mv_x$.

Equation 19-11 gives the **pressure** exerted by the gas **molecules** in terms of the **energy** of the molecules. This has great significance because it shows the relation between the macroscopic variables of a gas (p, V and energy) using the microscopic properties of the **gas**. Go through worked Example 19-1 in class to illustrate the application of this equation.

Section 19-3 discusses the dependence of the **average kinetic energy** of the **gas molecules** to the **temperature** of the gas. Emphasize that the **temperature** of the gas is not dependent on the amount of gas present, as is obvious from this equation. Use Fig. 19-3 to show that the motion of the **molecules** is very closely dependent on the **kinetic energy**. This figure also shows that the work done by the system is related to the change in the energy.

Encourage students to read the brief discussion on Think About This…What Does **Absolute Zero** Mean at the Molecular Level.

Sections 19-4 – 19-6

The next three sections look at **probability distributions of velocity** and **energy** of the **molecules** in a gas. To better understand the **distribution properties** of the gas **molecules**, Section 19-4 gives an introduction to the **distribution theory** by looking at a set of test grades. It is best not to skip this section, because it will help in the understanding of what is to follow. For the same reason, go through the steps leading to the derivation of Equations 19-28, 19-33 and 19-35. Go through the section Think About This…Why is There So Little Hydrogen In Earth's Atmosphere?, and point out that there is more to this than just statistical theory.

The discussion of the **energy distribution** of **diatomic molecules** and the **equipartition theorem** introduces the idea of **degrees of freedom**. This concept can be a little difficult to grasp for some students. Figure 19-9 illustrates the different kinds of motion a **diatomic molecule** can have. Point out that while the **molecule** can have translational motion in the three mutually perpendicular directions, it can have rotational inertia about only two of the axes (see Fig. 19-8). Two more **degrees of freedom** are added if the **diatomic molecules** are not rigidly attached but behave like a spring. Discuss how a **monatomic molecule** will be different in terms of the **degrees of freedom** it can have. To complete this discussion, Equation 19-42 shows the dependence of the heat **capacity** on the **degrees of freedom**.

Section 19-7

This last section looks at the **transport phenomenon** by considering the movement of **molecules** as **random collisions**. This is known as **diffusion.**

⟳ **DEMO**   Take a beaker of water. With a pipette inject a little dye into the bottom of the beaker. The dye will spread out slowly due to diffusion, and given enough time the contents of the beaker will be uniformly colored. This is a simple illustration of the diffusion process. (See Fig. 19-13.)

The definition of the **collision cross section**, **mean collision time** and the **mean free path** are essential to the understanding of this section.

Textbook Resource Information

Transparency Acetates

Fig. 19-1	Particle in a box
Fig. 19-2	Molecules with an x component of velocity
Fig. 19-3	Macroscopic and microscopic views of the work done by an insulated gas
Fig. 19-4	Bar graphs of quiz grades
Fig. 19-7	Two schematic representations of molecular shapes
Fig. 19-8	Rotational inertia of a dumbbell-shaped molecule
Fig. 19-9	Schematic diagram of the motion of a diatomic molecule
Fig. 19-11	Plot of C'_v/R vs. temperature
Fig. 19-12	Zigzag path of a molecule due to multiple collisions
Fig. 19-14	Collision cross section
Fig. 19-15	Random walk

Physlet Physics Illustrations

20.1   Maxwell-Boltzmann Distribution
20.2   Kinetic Theory, Temperature and Pressure
20.3   Thermodynamic Processes

Physlet Physics Explorations

20.1   Kinetic theory, microscopic and macroscopic connections
20.4   Equipartition theorem

Physlet Physics Problems

20.4   Kinetic energy of monatomic and diatomic molecules
20.12 Equipartition theorem

End of Chapter Problems with Solutions in the *Student Study Guide*

7, 17, 21, 35, 49, 67

Suggested Readings

Akridge, R., "Particle-Model Derivation of pV^{γ}" *The Physics Teacher* (February 1999), p. 110 – 111.

Bauman, R.P., and Harrison, J.G., "Note on a van der Waals Gas," *The Physics Teacher* (April 1996), p. 248 – 249.

Graham, M.T., "Investigating Gases' Masses in Impecunious Classes," *The Physics Teacher* (March 2002), p. 144 – 147.

Ringlein, J., "Interactive Instruction on Ideal and "Real" Gases," *The Physics Teacher* (February 2004), p. 92 – 97.

Thompson, D., "Derivation of the Ideal Gas Law from Kinetic Theory," *The Physics Teacher* (April 1997), p. 238 – 239.

Notes and Ideas

Preparation time: *Estimated:* _____   *Actual:* _____

Class time spent on material: *Estimated:* _____   *Actual:* _____

Related laboratory activities:

Demonstration materials:

Notes for next time:

Chapter 20: The Second Law of Thermodynamics

Outline

Summary

Chapter 19 discussed the behavior of gases from a molecular aspect and the statistical distribution of the velocity of molecules. The present chapter looks at the spontaneous transfer of energy as established by the **second law of thermodynamics**. The concept of **entropy** and the **degree of order** in thermal systems are considered. The **Carnot cycle**, other types of **engines** and their **efficiencies** are also discussed.

Major Concepts

- Beyond energy conservation
    - Engines and refrigerators
    - Spontaneous processes

- The second law of thermodynamics
    - The Kelvin form
    - The Clausius form

- The Carnot cycle
    - How to find the efficiency of the ideal gas Carnot engine
    - The importance of the Carnot engine

- Other types of engines
    - The Stirling engine
    - How to get the efficiency of the Stirling engine
    - Other engines and their efficiencies
    - Heat pumps and refrigerators

- Entropy and the second law
    - Entropy as a thermodynamic variable
    - How entropy changes for irreversible or spontaneous processes
    - The entropy of an isolated system never decreases

- Entropy and ideal gases

- The Meaning of entropy
    - Engines and entropy
    - Order, entropy, probability, and the arrow of time

Teaching Suggestions and Demonstrations

The majority of students will find the **second law of thermodynamics** and the concept of **entropy** to be two of the most difficult topics to understand. Using simple examples with practical applications will make it less abstract. **Heat engines** and **refrigerators** on the other hand will be easier to teach as students can relate to them more readily.

Sections 20-1 –20-2

There are two main points that lead into the **second law of thermodynamics**. The first of these is the fact that the amount of **thermal energy** available to do work is less than the total **thermal energy** of a system. The second point deals with the direction of flow of **thermal energy** in a **spontaneous process**. Start the discussion of the **second law** by introducing these two main ideas and then discuss the key features of a useful **engine** as stated in the textbook. The concept of **thermal reservoirs** (especially a high-temperature reservoir and a low-temperature reservoir) will seem strange to students. Use Fig. 20-1 to introduce the idea of **thermal reservoirs** and point out that you will be coming back to this in greater detail several times before you are finished with this chapter.

Define the term *efficiency* as it relates to **engines** and stress the fact that the **efficiency** of an **engine** can never be 100%. Fig. 20-3 is a clear illustration of how one could determine the **efficiency** by considering the work done. Remind students that in Chapter 18 they had found the net work done to be the area enclosed in a *p-V* diagram.

To better understand the basis of the **second law**, discuss the concept of a **spontaneous process** using as many examples as you can. The book uses several examples like ice cubes in a cup of hot tea or the expansion of gas molecules through a small opening into an evacuated chamber.

> **⟳ DEMO** The example of the ice cubes and hot tea can actually be used as a demo. Take a cup of hot tea and put a few ice cubes into it. Ask the students what will happen to the ice cubes and what would be the direction of heat flow (thermal energy) in this case. Use this to lead on to a discussion of irreversibility and directional flow of thermal energy.

Sections 20-3 – 20-4

To understand the working of **engines** it is important that the **Carnot cycle** be understood. Go through the *p-V* **diagram** (see Fig. 20-5) for each step of the **cycle**. Make sure the students are able to identify the **adiabatic** and **isothermal** operations. It is also important to explain why the work done during a complete **Carnot cycle** is positive. If you decide that you don't have the time to go through the derivation of Equation 20-5, point out that it essentially is the same as Equation 20-4. This equation also shows that the **efficiency** will always be less than one. Work through Example 20-2 to solidify this idea.

Section 20-4 discusses other types of **engines** and how they differ from the **Carnot engine**. Students will find it interesting to learn about the **diesel engine** as well as how **heat pumps** and **refrigerators** work. Use Fig. 20-9 to show the main features of the **diesel engine**. Point out that **heat pumps** and **refrigerators** are merely **engines** run in reverse, where **thermal energy** is transferred from a low-temperature reservoir to a high-temperature reservoir. At first glance, students might think of this as a violation of the **second law of thermodynamics**. Be sure to discuss the difference between work done by the system and work done on the system.

Sections 20-5 – 20-7

The rest of the chapter discusses the concept of **entropy**, changes in **entropy** for a **spontaneous process**, how it relates to an **ideal gas** and the study of **entropy** in terms of **probability** and **order**. These are some of the most abstract topics and students generally think of **entropy** in terms of these 'buzz' words.

Entropy can be demystified a little (one hopes) by going through the derivation of Equation 20-18. Work through Example 20-7 to show that one can indeed calculate the **entropy change** of an **ideal gas** that undergoes a thermal transformation. Conceptual Example 20-9 shows how the different processes that make up a **Carnot cycle** can be represented on an *S-T* **plane** by looking at the **entropy change** for each step of the cycle. Point out that the area of the *S-T* **curve** is the work done during one cycle.

Section 20-7 relates **entropy** to the order or disorder of a system. By using concrete examples (like the broken plate and demolition of a building as cited in the textbook) you can make this idea more understandable.

Textbook Resource Information

Transparency Acetates

Fig. 20-1	Abstract representation of an engine
Fig. 20-2	Work done during an isothermal process
Fig. 20-3	Determining efficiency η
Fig. 20-4	Relative probability for a configuration of ten molecules
Fig. 20-5a	The Carnot cycle – schematic
Fig. 20-5b	The Carnot cycle – *PV* graph
Fig. 20-6	Efficiency of two Carnot engines connected together
Fig. 20-8	The ideal Stirling cycle
Fig. 20-9a	The diesel cycle
Fig. 20-9b	The Otto cycle
Fig. 20-9c	The Brayton cycle
Fig. 20-10	Diagram of how a refrigerator operates
Fig. 20-11	Diagram of a room air conditioner
Fig. 20-17	Entropy of mixing

Physlet Physics Illustrations

21.1 Carnot Engine
21.2 Entropy and Reversible/Irreversible Processes
21.4 Engines and Entropy

Physlet Physics Explorations

21.1 Engine efficiency
21.4 Entropy of expanding ideal gas

Physlet Physics Problems

21.2 Otto engine cycle
21.6 Temperature-entropy graph matching
21.7 Change in entropy of an ideal monatomic gas
21.8 Refrigerator and entropy calculation

End of Chapter Problems with Solutions in the *Student Study Guide*

11, 29, 41, 51, 59, 75

Suggested Readings

Alonso, M., and Finn, E.J., "An Integrated Approach to Thermodynamics in the Introductory Physics Course," *The Physics Teacher* (May 1995), p. 296 – 310.

Chen, M., "An Electrical Model of a Carnot Cycle," *The Physics Teacher* (April 1989), p. 272 – 2 73.

Henriksen, P.N., "Entropy of Mixing," *The Physics Teacher* (October 1979), p. 475.

Hobson, A., "Energy Flow Diagrams for Teaching Physics Concepts," *The Physics Teacher* (February 2004), p. 113 – 117.

Leff, H., "What If Entropy Were Dimensionless?," *Am.J.Phys.* (December 1999), p. 1114 – 1122.

Lieb, E., and Yngvason, J., "A Fresh Look at Entropy and the Second Law of Thermodynamics," *Physics Today* (April 2000), p. 32 – 37.

LoPresto, M.C., "Some Simple Black Hole Thermodynamics," *The Physics Teacher* (May 2003), p. 299 – 301.

Nicastro, A.J., "A Dynamical Model of a Carnot Cycle," *The Physics Teacher* (October 1983), p. 463 – 464.

Nolan, M.J., "Thermodynamic Cycles—One More Time," *The Physics Teacher* (December 1995), p. 573 – 575.

Schoepf, D., "A Statistical Development of Entropy for the Introductory Physics Course," *Am.J.Phys.* (February 2002), p. 128 – 136.

Styer, D., "Insight into Entropy," *Am.J.Phys.* (December 200), p. 1090 – 1096.

Notes and Ideas

Preparation time:　　　　　　*Estimated:* _____　　*Actual:* _____

Class time spent on material:　　*Estimated:* _____　　*Actual:* _____

Related laboratory activities:

Demonstration materials:

Notes for next time:

Chapter 21: Electric Charge

Outline

Summary

The atomic nature of all matter can be explained by studying the **electromagnetic forces**. This chapter introduces the concept of **charge** and its properties, the **electric force of interaction** between two **charges** as stated by **Coulomb's law**. It also discusses briefly the history of the study of **electricity** and **magnetism**.

Major Concepts

- Charge – A property of matter
  - A brief history of the study of electricity and magnetism
  - The significance of electric forces
  - Matter and electric charge
  - Evidence that charges are of two types
  - Units of charge
  - The electroscope

- Charge is conserved and quantized
  - Evidence of charge conservation

- Coulomb's law

- Forces involving multiple charges
  - Continuous distributions of charges
  - The force due to a spherically symmetric charge distribution

Teaching Suggestions and Demonstrations

The concept of **positive** and **negative charges** and the basic interaction between them (**like charges** repel and **unlike charges** attract) will be familiar to most students. However, students will struggle when it comes to the calculation of the net force on a **charge** due to a particular **charge distribution** or recognizing **symmetry** in a **charge distribution**. Work as many examples as possible to show how **Coulomb's law** is applied for different **charge distributions**, **discrete** or **continuous**.

Sections 21-1 – 21-2

Many students will have heard of Benjamin Franklin and his kite. Start the chapter by giving a brief account of the history of the study of **electricity** and **magnetism**. Students should find this interesting.

Since they will have had one semester of introductory physics course, they will be very familiar with the gravitational force between two objects. This force is significant when considering problems on an astronomical case. Point out that, except for the gravitational force of Earth, the **electric force** between objects is far more significant when dealing with interactions in our everyday life.

The first section may be treated as a read-ahead assignment with a little time devoted to a brief summary of the content. The following demos will be of great interest to students when talking about **charging by induction** and **charging by conduction**.

⮑ **DEMO** You will need PVC or clear plastic rods, small pieces of silk, fur, and chamois cloth, and two small pith balls suspended by light strings from a stand. Rub the PVC rod with the fur cloth and bring the rod close to the pith balls. The pith balls will get the same kind of charge and deflect each other. (See Fig. 21-3.)

⮑ **DEMO** This demo is a slight variation of the previous one. You will need one more PVC rod. Rub the PVC rod on both ends with the fur cloth and balance it on a pivot. Now rub one end of a second PVC rod with fur and bring this charged end close to the rod that is on the pivot. The first rod will swing to one side due to the repulsive force between the ends of the two rods.

⮑ **DEMO** The presence of static charge can also be illustrated using an electroscope. Touch the metal ball at the top of the electroscope with a charged rod. (Rub the rod with fur first.) The excess charge from the rod will be transferred to the two gold foils that will then be repelled. This is an example of charging by conduction.

⮑ **DEMO** To show charging by induction, repeat the above process, but now bring the charged rod close to the electroscope and do not make contact with the metal ball of the electroscope. The leaves of the electroscope will again deflect. See Fig. 21-7.

⮑ **DEMO** If you don't have easy access to an electroscope or pith balls, you can do the same demo with an empty soda can. Place the soda can on the table so the open end faces the students. Rub a PVC rod with fur and bring it close to the soda can. The opposite kind of charge will be induced on the soda can and it will be attracted toward the rod. You can actually 'pull' the soda can by slowly moving the rod away from the can.

⮑ **DEMO** If you have access to a Van de Graaff generator, you can demonstrate that like charges repel. Place a Styrofoam container full of Styrofoam peanuts on the generator. Turn on the generator. As the charge builds up, the peanuts will get the same kind of charge and will be repelled. Actually you will see the peanuts fly off the container.

Alternately, you can stack a bunch of aluminum pie plates on the generator and watch them fly off one at a time.

Note: When using the Van de Graaff generator, be sure to follow all of the recommended precautions.

All of the above demonstrations will work well in the winter. You will not be able to use these demos if you are teaching in the summer or fall semester.

There are several everyday examples that can be used to discuss the phenomenon of **charging by conduction**. Ask students what happens when a person walks across a carpeted floor with socked feet in the winter. Or, talk about why clothes stick together in the drier.

While **conservation of charge** will be discussed in greater detail later in the semester, it is important to introduce the concept here.

Sections 21-3 – 21-4

Coulomb's law is very important because it helps to understand the **interaction** between two or more **charges**. Compare Equation 21-4 to the gravitational force. Point out that both are governed by the **inverse square law**. However, this is where the similarity ends, so discuss the differences between the two forces. While gravitational force is an attractive one, **electric force** can be either **attractive** or **repulsive**. Masses cannot be negative, but **charges** are either **positive** or **negative**.

Be sure to draw attention to Equations 21-4 and 21-8. The first equation gives just the magnitude of the force between two **charges** while the second one includes the direction of this force as well. As mentioned earlier in the chapter in this manual, students will have the greatest difficulty in determining the direction of the force. Here is a simple way to minimize this confusion. When using **Coulomb's law**, it is best to use just the magnitude of the **charges** when substituting in the equation. To find the direction of the force on **charge** 2 due to **charge** 1 ask the students to assume that **charge** 1 is fixed and ask how **charge** 2 will move because of **charge** 1. This, then, will be the direction of the force. If this system is maintained throughout the chapter, students will begin to see the light at the end of the tunnel, so to speak. This will be particularly useful when dealing with **multiple charges** exerting a force on a single **charge**.

When dealing with **multiple charges**, remind students that they will have to use vector addition. Go through problem-solving techniques as outlined in the text and work Example 21-8. Discuss cases where **symmetry of distribution** could make solving of the problem easier than it might appear at first glance. Students will typically fail to recognize the impact of the **charge symmetry**.

This section ends with a discussion of **continuous charge distribution** and the use of **charge density** and integration. As tempting as it might be to skip this part, it is important that students understand the difference between **linear**, **surface** and **volume charge densities**. They will also need plenty of practice in deciding how to judicially choose a small **element of charge** and what the limits of integration might be for that particular situation. Once again stress the importance of recognizing any symmetry properties.

The case of a **spherical charge distribution** is of particular importance. It is important that students recognize the significance of a **spherical charge distribution**. For points outside of such a distribution, for all practical purposes the **charge distribution** acts like a **point charge** at the center of the distribution. However, when considering points inside the **charge distribution**, students will have to determine the **charge density** and then the **charge** on the sphere in question. This can be confusing to many in your class. Be sure to work out some standard examples so students get the procedure clear in their minds.

Textbook Resource Information

Transparency Acetates

Fig. 21-3   Evidence that charges are of two types
Fig. 21-6   Charging by induction

Fig. 21-7b,c   An electroscope
Fig. 21-15   Coulomb's law in the case of continuous charge distribution
Fig. 21-16   One-dimensional charge distribution
Fig. 21-17   Two-dimensional charge distribution
Fig. 21-21   A spherically symmetric charge distribution

Physlet Physics Illustrations

22.1   Charge and Coulomb's law
22.3   Monopole, Dipole and Quadrapole
22.4   Charging Objects and Static Cling

Physlet Physics Explorations

22.2   Effect of multiple charges
22.4   Dipole symmetry
22.6   Coulomb's law

Physlet Physics Problems

22.4   Force due to unknown charge
22.6   Force due to two charges
22.7   Determining sign of unknown charge

Ranking Task Exercises in Physics, Student Edition

Page 122   Electric force due to two charges
Page 125   Electric force due to three charges
Page 126   Electric force due to two nonlinear charges
Page 135   Attractive and repulsive forces due to pairs of charges

End of Chapter Problems with Solutions in the *Student Study Guide*

9, 23, 37, 41, 47, 65

Suggested Readings

Cheyne, S.A., "Getting a Charge from Coffee," *The Physics Teacher* (January 2000), p. 49.

Cortel, A., "Demonstrations of Coulomb's Law with an Electrostatic Balance," *The Physics Teacher* (October 1999), p. 447 – 448.

Dindorf, T., and Dindorf, W., "Trick of the Trade: A Useful Multipurpose Instrument," *The Physics Teacher* (October 2002), p. 440.

Gelbart, W., Bruinsma, R., Pincus, P., and Parsegian, V., "DNA-Inspired Electrostatics," *Physics Today* (September 2000), p. 38 – 44.

Gore, G.R., "The Mysterious Rolling Pop Can," *The Physics Teacher* (December 2003), p. 548.

Harrington, R., "Getting a Charge out of Transparent Tape," *The Physics Teacher* (January 2000), p. 23 – 35.

Jackson, J.D., "A Curious and Useful Theorem in Two-Dimensional Electrostatics," *Am.J.Phys.* (February 1999), p. 107 – 115.

Jonoska, M., Tuntev, A., and Zajkov, O., "Hands-on Experiments with a Voltage Tester," *The Physics Teacher* (January 2003), p .14 – 15.

Van Domelen, D., "A Pocket Electrostatics Demonstration," *The Physics Teacher* (May 2003), p. 306.

Notes and Ideas

Preparation time: *Estimated:* _____   *Actual:* _____

Class time spent on material: *Estimated:* _____   *Actual:* _____

Related laboratory activities:

Demonstration materials:

Notes for next time:

Chapter 22: Electric Field

Outline

Summary

The previous chapter considered the interaction between two charges in terms of Coulomb's law. Here, in Chapter 22 the concept of a **field** due to a **static charge** is considered. **Electric fields** due to **point charges** as well as fields due to **continuous charge distribution** are studied. The behavior of a **moving charge** in an **external field** and the effect of an **external field** on a **dipole** are also discussed.

Major Concepts

- Electric field
    - Definition of electric field
    - The electric field of a point charge
    - The usefulness of the field concept
    - Superposition
    - Electric dipoles and their electric fields

- Electric field lines
    - Properties of electric field lines
    - Drawing electric field lines
    - Some examples of field lines

- The field of a continuous distribution
    - Electric field as an integral
    - Constant charge densities
    - The electric field between two uniformly charged planes with opposite charge

- Motion of a charge in a field
    - Deflection of moving charged particles

- The Electric dipole in an external electric field
    - Torque on an electric dipole
    - The energy of a dipole in an external electric field

Teaching Suggestions and Demonstrations

Electric field and **field lines** are useful in understanding various **electromagnetic** phenomena. The concept of a **field** exerting a force on a **charge** will be a difficult one for most students to understand, especially since they are now somewhat comfortable with the use of Coulomb's law. The text has many examples that can be used to help students grasp this abstract idea.

Sections 22-1 – 22-2

Start by introducing the concept of a **field** as a region where the effect of a **charge** can be felt by another **charge**. Remind students of Earth's gravitational field and how the effect of this field can be experienced by any other mass in this field. Point out that in the case of an **electric field**, only another **charged particle** can feel the effect of this **field**.

The role played by the **test charge** is important. Stress that the **test charge**, by convention, is always a **positive charge** and discuss why the **test charge** has to be very small in magnitude. (See Fig. 22-1.) Equation 22-5 gives the **field** at a point distance r from a **point charge**. It is best to use this equation to determine the magnitude of the **electric field** E (in other words use just the value of q and not substitute the sign of the **charge** into the equation). The direction of motion of the **test charge** will give the direction of this **electric field**.

Draw attention to the fact that the **electric field** is a vector quantity and, as such, the **superposition principle** is applicable. To find the **field** at a point due to more than one **point charge**, the **electric fields** must be added using the rules of vector addition. Once again remind students to look for any symmetry properties that may cancel out some of the **fields**.

Equation 22-7 is a direct consequence of the definition of an **electric field**. Three points have to be remembered with regard to this. The **field** in question can be produced by a single **point charge**, by several **point charges** or by any kind of **continuous charge distribution**. Secondly, the force is experienced by a **charge** that is not the one producing the **field**. The word *external* is important here, and this is a point that is quite often missed by students. Finally, this equation is identical to Equation 22-2, except that we use the idea of a **test charge** to define the **electric field**.

Students very often fail to see the importance of the concept of **fields**. Use the section Think About This… How Does the **Field** Concept Help? to help students see why it is important.

The **field** due to an **electric dipole** is a special case that has important applications. Define the **electric dipole moment** and go through worked Example 22-4. Point out that the **field** is inversely proportional to the cube of the distance (Equation 22-15) and directly proportional to the **dipole moment**. Discuss the fact that a water molecule is a **permanent dipole**. (See Fig. 22-8.) This explains why we don't have a buildup of **static charges** when there is a lot of moisture in the atmosphere as opposed to dry wintry days.

Section 22-2 develops the concept of **electric field lines** for various **charge distributions**. Go through the properties of **field lines** listed in the text and make sure students get familiar with the **field** patterns for different **charge distributions**. Since most of the examples deal with two equal **like charges** or two equal **unlike charges**, it would be a good idea to go through Example 22-6 which has to do with two **unequal charges**.

 ⮑ **DEMO** You will need PVC or clear plastic rods, small pieces of silk, fur, and chamois cloth, and
            two small pith balls suspended by light strings from a stand. Rub the PVC rod with the fur
            cloth and bring the rod close to the pith balls. The pith balls will get the same kind of charge
            and deflect each other. (See Fig. 22-3.)

Sections 22-3 – 22-4

The **electric field** produced by a **continuous charge distribution** involves use of some basic integrals. Equation 22-20 gives the generic equation for any kind of **continuous charge distribution**. The

elemental charge dq will vary depending on whether it is a one-, two-, or three-dimensional distribution. Go through worked Examples 22-7 and 22-8 and discuss how symmetry properties will simplify the process of solving the problem.

Example 22-8 leads into a discussion of the **field** between two uniformly (but oppositely) charged planes. This is the prototype of a capacitor and as such is very important. Fig. 22-19 shows the **fields** due to the two charged planes superposed and resulting in a **uniform field** in the space between the plates.

Section 22-4 looks at the motion of a **charged particle** in an **electric field**. Note that the force on a **charged particle** as given by Equation 22-7 can also be written in terms of the acceleration as given by Newton's second law. Quite often students will forget to make this connection and conclude that sufficient information is not available to solve the problem. Example 22-11 shows how the speed and time of transit can be determined given the **charge density** of the plates.

A particularly interesting example is the deflection of an electron as it moves in the space between the **charged plates**. This is the principle behind the television tubes.

Section 22-5

This section comes back to the **electric dipole** and now considers its behavior in an **external magnetic field**. Remind students that the **dipole** has a net zero **charge**, but has a **dipole moment** that is a vector quantity. Though the net **charge** of a **dipole** is zero, it can still experience a torque in the external field. Use Fig. 22-22 to discuss how the force experienced by the individual **charges** will make the **dipole** rotate in this field. The torque can be shown to be the cross product of the **dipole moment** and the **electric field** vector. Table 22-2 shows the direction and magnitude of this torque for different angles between the **dipole moment** vector and the **electric field** vector. Make sure that your students understand the different situations shown in Table 22-2.

The last part of this section derives the work done by the **field** on the **dipole**. When the potential energy is a minimum, the **dipole** has stable equilibrium, and when the potential energy is a maximum, it experiences unstable equilibrium. These two situations correspond to the **dipole moment** being parallel to the electric field vector or antiparallel, respectively.

Textbook Resource Information

Transparency Acetates

Physlet Physics Illustrations

23.2   Electric Fields from Point Charges
23.3   Field-Line Representation of Vector Fields
23.4   Practical Uses of Charges and Electric Fields

Physlet Physics Explorations

23.1   Fields and test charges
23.2   Field lines and trajectories
23.3   Adding fields

Physlet Physics Problems

23.1   Determining unknown charge
23.2   Determining charge distribution from electric field lines
23.5   Motion of an electron in an external field
23.8   Unknown charge needed to make the field zero
23.9   Field due to four charges at corners of a square

Ranking Task Exercises in Physics, Student Edition

Page 127   Electric field at the center of charged conducting sphere
Page 129   Electric field due to charged conducting sphere
Page 132   Point charges outside conducting spheres – electric field within
Page 136   Force on a charge suspended in an electric field
Page 141   Two electric charges – electric field along line
Page 146   Nonuniform electric field – electric field strength

End of Chapter Problems with Solutions in the *Student Study Guide*

3, 13, 31, 45, 53, 57

Suggested Readings

Alonso, M., "Motion of an Electric Charge in the Field of an Electric Dipole," *Am.J.Phys.* (January 2004), p. 10.

Bracikowski, C., "Graphical Analysis of Electric Fields of Dipoles and Bipoles," *The Physics Teacher* (January 2000), p. 20 – 21.

Jefimenko, O.D., "Dynamic Electric Field Maps of Point Charge Moving with Constant Velocity," *The Physics Teacher* (March 2000), p. 154 – 157.

Lan, B.L., and Lim, J.B.S., "Michael Faraday: Prince of Lecturers in Victorian England," *The Physics Teacher* (January 2001), p. 32 – 36.

Murgatroyd, P.N., and Jones, M.A., "Easy Fields Too," *Am.J.Phys.* (February 1999), p. 156 – 157.

Stahlhofen, A.A., and Druxes, H., "On Scattering by a Coulomb Field in Two-Dimensions," *Am.J.Phys.* (February 1999), p. 156.

Weinstock, R., "Electric Field of a Two-Charge Dipole: A Graphical Approach Extended," *The Physics Teacher* (October 2000), p. 430 – 431.

Weinstock, R., "Two-Charge Dipole Revisited," *The Physics Teacher* (April 2001), p. 218 – 219.

Worner, C.H., "On the Teaching of the Electric Dipole," *The Physics Teacher* (November 2001), p. 462 – 463.

Notes and Ideas

Preparation time: *Estimated:* _____   *Actual:* _____

Class time spent on material: *Estimated:* _____   *Actual:* _____

Related laboratory activities:

Demonstration materials:

Notes for next time:

Chapter 23: Gauss' Law

Outline

Summary

Gauss' law is one of the fundamental laws of **electromagnetism**. This chapter looks at this fundamental law and how the law can be used to determine **electric fields** and study the behavior of conductors. The connection between **Gauss' law** and Coulomb's law is also considered.

Major Concepts

- What does Gauss' law do?
    o Electric flux

- Gauss' law
    o Definition of Gauss' law
    o Coulomb's law and Gauss' law

- Using Gauss' law to determine electric fields

- Conductors and electric fields
    o Electrostatic fields near conductors

- Are Gauss' and Coulomb's laws correct
    o Testing Gauss' law with a null experiment
    o Coulomb's law holds over small and large distances

Teaching Suggestions and Demonstrations

As mentioned in the summary, **Gauss' law** is one of the most fundamental laws in electromagnetism. The study of **fields** due to **charge distributions** are made simpler when **Gauss' law** is used. As simple as the law is, students will find the concept of **Gaussian surfaces** difficult to comprehend. Choose several different **charge distributions** (the text has many worked out examples) and show how to apply the law to solve problems.

Sections 23-1 – 23-3

Gauss' law is based on the concept of **electric field lines** passing through a chosen **Gaussian surface**. Start with this idea and use Fig. 23-1 to show how the **net charge enclosed** inside a surface is determined by considering the number of **field lines** going out of or into the surface. Students might have some trouble visualizing the three-dimensional aspect of the situation from the two-dimensional representation in Fig. 23-1.

Not all surfaces considered will be closed surfaces. Consider Fig. 23-2 next and talk about the **field lines** going through a flat surface of area A. In deriving Equation 23-1, several points have to be emphasized. Students will invariably use the angle between the **electric field** vector and the surface under consideration. Definition of the normal vector is very important. Stress that the angle to be used is between the normal to the area and the **electric field**. The demo below will help students visualize the situation better.

⟳ **DEMO** Make up two stacks of books using two books about a foot apart. Place six to eight long skewers (you can get some inexpensive disposable ones from the grocery store) parallel to each other and with their ends resting on the two stacks of books. The skewers now represent electric field lines in the space between the two stacks of books. Take a sheet of stock card and cut out a rectangle from the center so you have a window. The stock card is now a loop of area A. Hold the loop perpendicular to the field lines (skewers). Now ask the students to count the number of lines that go through the area. Point out that the angle between the normal to the area and the field lines is zero. Next hold the loop so its surface is parallel to the skewers and go through the same exercise. Finally hold the loop at an angle to the skewers so some of the skewers do not go through the loop and repeat the process.

Make sure students see the difference between Equations 23-1 and 23-3. Equation 23-1 gives the **flux** through a small elemental area and this can be extended to any surface of any shape as given by Equation 23-3. Point out that this is valid for closed surfaces alone. Finally, use Fig. 23-3 to show that you will get an obtuse angle when the charge inside the enclosed surface is negative. This comes from the definition of the normal (unit) vector and the fact that the **electric field lines** are now going into the surface. Students often do not recognize this subtle difference.

State **Gauss' law** and explain the relation between the charge and the electric flux through a closed surface. Figure 23-6 shows different ways of choosing **Gaussian surfaces** for an electric dipole. This is an excellent example showing how the electric flux depends only on the net charges enclosed by the surfaces under consideration.

Equation 23-5 along with Equation 23-3 offers us a powerful tool to solve problems involving complex **charge distributions**. The most important point to remember is that the **Gaussian surface** can be any closed surface of our choice. Stress the fact that the **Gaussian surface** is not a physical surface. The proper choice of **Gaussian surface** can simplify seemingly complicated problems. Go through conceptual Example 23-3 and worked Example 23-4 to illustrate how **Gauss' law** is applied.

Section 23-3 lists problem-solving techniques that can prove useful to students. Go over this in class, and try to use these steps when working out examples in class. Students need to learn to recognize spatial symmetry of charge distributions and then choose a **Gaussian surface** based on this symmetry. Examples 23-5 through 23-8 look at situations involving a **line charge**, a **spherical shell**, a **solid sphere** and a **plane sheet**. These are all typical standard problems that students need to be familiar with. In determining the electric field inside a solid sphere, the charge enclosed will now be a ratio of the total charge on the sphere. Students will first have to calculate the charge density (which is uniform) and then find the charge enclosed within the sphere of interest. (See Example 23-7.) It is quite common for students to ignore this step. Use Fig. 23-12c to discuss the variation of the electric field inside and outside a solid sphere as you go from the center out to a great distance.

Sections 23-4 – 23-5

Section 23-4 discusses the **electric field** inside and outside a **conductor** placed in an external **electric field**. Ask students why it is safe to stay inside an automobile (and be sure to not touch any metal parts that may be connected to the chassis) during a thunderstorm. Then use their answers to start a discussion on the effects of an external field on a conductor placed in such a field. Use Figs. 23-14 through 23-18 to discuss these effects in detail. Then state the four points summarized on the next page (in the textbook) and be sure to go over these in class and emphasize the significance of these statements.

Compare the case of a conductor and a charged plane surface, both having the same charge density. Point out that in the case of the nonconducting plane the two sides have equal number of field lines and this leads to the field outside the plane being less than the field outside of a conducting surface. In fact, the field is exactly half for a nonconducting surface compared to a conducting surface.

While the last section of this chapter might be considered to be of nothing more than historical significance, this is the first time students are introduced to the concept of a **null experiment** and its significance. Discuss the meaning of a null experiment and why it is important in this particular case. **Cavendish's** experiment tries to detect small changes or no change at all, while **Coulomb's** experiment has to do with detecting small changes in comparison to large effects. Point out that the importance of **Cavendish's** experiment lies in the fact that it is more precise to look for small changes as compared to no change at all.

Finally, discuss the significance of the data shown in Table 23-1. Students may not fully appreciate the importance of the value of the deviation listed in the last column of the table. The decrease in the value of this deviation has to do with the fact that the more recent the experiment, the better the precision of the instruments used.

Textbook Resource Information

Transparency Acetates

Fig. 23-1   Representation of electric field lines through a closed surface
Fig. 23-2   Field lines through a plane of area A in a uniform electric field
Fig. 23-6   Some Gaussian surfaces in the electric field of a dipole
Fig. 23-10   Electric field due to an infinitely long line charge
Fig. 23-11   Electric field inside a spherically charged shell
Fig. 23-12   Electric field outside a uniformly charged nonconducting sphere
Fig. 23-16   A nonconducting cavity inside a conductor
Fig. 23-17   Electric field outside a conductor of arbitrary size
Fig. 23-18   The electric field in and outside a conductor in equilibrium
Fig. 23-19   Using an electroscope to test the presence of charge on a conductor

Physlet Physics Illustrations

24.1 Flux and Gaussian Surfaces
24.3 A Cylinder of Charge

Physlet Physics Explorations

24.1 Flux and Gauss' law
24.2 Symmetry and using Gauss' law
24.3 Conducting and insulating sphere
24.4 Application of Gauss' law

Physlet Physics Problems

24.3 Flux through a cylindrical Gaussian surface
24.5 Flux through spherical shells
24.6 Flux through the sides of a cube

Ranking Task Exercises in Physics, Student Edition

Page 127   Charged conducting spheres – Electric field at the center
Page 129   Charged conducting spheres – Electric field at various points

End of Chapter Problems with Solutions in the *Student Study Guide*

3, 17, 23, 29, 41, 59

Suggested Readings

Haywood, T.W., and Nelson, R.C., "Demonstration of Gauss' law for a metal surface," *The Physics Teacher* (December 1979), p. 956.

Kalotas, T.M., Lee, A.R., and Liesegang, J., "Analytical Construction of Electrostatic Field Lines with the Aid of Gauss' Law," *Am.J.Phys.* (April 1996), p. 373 – 378.

Lietz, M., "A Potential Gauss's Law Lab," *The Physics Teacher* (April 2000), p. 220 – 221

Spencer, R.L., "Electric Field Lines Near an Oddly Shaped Conductor in a Uniform Electric Field," *Amj.Phys.* (June 1988), p. 510 – 512.

Spencer, R.L., "If Coulomb's Law Were Not Inverse Square: The Charge Distribution Inside a Solid Conducting Sphere," *Am.J.Phys.* (April; 1990), p. 385 – 390.

Notes and Ideas

Preparation time: *Estimated:* _____   *Actual:* _____

Class time spent on material: *Estimated:* _____   *Actual:* _____

Related laboratory activities:

Demonstration materials:

Notes for next time:

Chapter 24: Electric Potential

Outline

Summary

The previous two chapters dealt with the study of electric charge, electric field lines, and Gauss' law. Now we learn about **electric potential energy** and the **absolute potential** at a given point due to a charge distribution. The concept of **equipotential surfaces** is introduced and the relation between **potentials** and **electric field** is discussed. The effect of **potentials** and **fields** on conductors is covered. Finally, application of **electric potentials** to technology like the **Van de Graaff generator**, the **field-ion microscope** and **quantum engineering** is discussed.

Major Concepts

- Electric potential energy

- Electric potential
    - The electric potential of a point charge
    - The electric potential of charge distributions
    - Units of electric potential
    - The potential energy of a system of charges
    - The electron-volt

- Equipotentials
    - Equipotential lines and surfaces
    - Electric field lines from equipotentials and vice versa

- Determining fields from potentials
    - Electric field as the gradient of the potential
    - How the potential determines the field in Cartesian coordinates

- The potentials of charge distributions
    - Examples

- Potentials and fields near conductors
    - Electric fields and potentials for various charge configurations
    - The role of sharp points on conducting surfaces

- Electric potentials in technology
  - The Van de Graaff accelerator
  - The field-ion microscope
  - Xerography
  - Electric potentials and quantum engineering

Teaching Suggestions and Demonstrations

Electric potential energy is associated with a conservative force as is gravitational potential energy. Students will have difficulty with the concept of work done in moving a **charge** in an **external field**. On the other hand, they will find the concept of **electric potential** and the relation between **electric field** and **electric potential** to be comparatively easy. Working as many examples as possible will certainly be beneficial to students.

Sections 24-1 –24-2

Review gravitational potential energy and remind students that this energy is associated with a conservative force. You may also have to review the definition of a conservative force. The **electric potential energy** is similarly associated with a conservative **electric force** (as given by Coulomb's law). Students will usually forget that the change in **potential energy** is the negative of the work done. It is also essential to stress that work is done because a **charge** is moved from point a to point b in an **external field**. The key here is the *external field*.

How does one determine if the change in **potential energy** is positive or negative? This is another question that is a source of confusion to many students. When two like **charges** move toward each other, they will experience a repulsive force. They will tend to slow down, which implies that the kinetic energy of the system will decrease. The law of conservation of energy tells us that the **potential energy** has to increase, so the **change** in **potential energy** has to be positive. By similar reasoning you can show that the **change** in **potential energy** will be negative when two unlike **charges** move toward each other. The opposite argument can be made for two **charges** moving away from each other.

Point out that Equation 24-7 is applicable to **point charges** only. For a **continuous charge distribution**, the **potential** can be obtained by considering the **potential** due to an **elemental charge** and then integrating. Remind students that **potential** is a scalar quantity. A sign of the **potential** at a point does not relate to a direction. A **positive charge** will produce a **positive potential** while a **negative charge** will give rise to a **negative potential**.

Equation 24-18 and its application to solving problems will be very confusing to the majority of students. It is best to start with a single **charge** and find the work done (define work done as $q \Delta V$ with V_∞ being zero) in bringing a second **charge** from infinity to a point at a distance r_{12} from the first charge. Next find the total **potential** at point c due to charges q_1 and q_2 and then find the work done in bringing q_3 from infinity to c. After you repeat this process for q_4 and then generalize the equation (which should be similar to Equation 24-18) students will get the hang of it.

Sections 24-3 – 24-4

To define **equipotential surfaces**, start with Equation 24-7. Draw a circle of radius r and ask the students to comment on the **potential** at various points on this circle. Then draw another circle of a larger radius and repeat the process. Ask them if the **potential** at a point on the first circle is the same as at a point on the second circle. The students will by now get the idea, and you can define **equipotential surfaces**. Be sure to point out that the diagram on the board is two dimensional but actually represents a three-dimensional situation.

⊃ **DEMO** Use a conducting sheet and draw a point charge. Measure the potential at different locations and join points having the same potential. Use a different color pen and draw the electric field lines. Repeat for other charge configurations such as a point charge and a charged plate or two parallel charged plates.

Three important points need to be made regarding electric field lines. First, the electric field is perpendicular to the equipotential surface everywhere. Second, the surface of a conductor is an equipotential surface. The third point to remember is that the electric field always points from a higher to a lower potential by way of the shortest distance between the two points.

Sections 24-5 – 24-6

Section 24-5 starts off by summarizing the concepts discussed thus far in this chapter. For different **charge distributions**, several examples are worked to evaluate the **electric field** when the **potential** is known or vice versa. In the case of two parallel plates, since the **field** is uniform in the space between the plates, the **electric field** is given by Equation 24-30. Be sure to point out that this is a special case. Work as many of the examples offered in the text, as is possible.

Table 24-1 lists the **electric fields** and associated **potentials** for various **charge configurations**. Be sure to go through this with students and highlight the differences and similarities if any.

After discussing the effect of a **conductor** on the **external field** and the **potential**, go through the section Think About This…How Do Lightning Rods Work. Students are sure to find this very interesting.

Section 24-7

This last section discusses the application of **electric fields** and **potentials** to the field of technology. While it may be tempting to omit this section (perhaps due to time constraints), the various technologies discussed here have very practical applications that students can relate to. If you are indeed constrained for time, try to discuss the **Van de Graaff generator** and the **tunneling** of an **electron** through a **potential barrier**. The latter will be an introduction to quantum mechanics that is sure to pique the interest of the students. Be sure to mention that they will be learning more about this in Chapter 40.

⊃ **DEMO** If you have access to a Van de Graaff generator, you can demonstrate the buildup of charges. Tie a bunch of aluminum strips at one end and place this tied end on the bulb of the generator. Turn on the generator and watch the loose ends of the aluminum strips separate out.

⊃ **DEMO** Turn on the generator so the charges build up on it. Now bring a second metal bulb (mounted on an insulated stand) close to the bulb of the generator until you see sparks between the two.

Note: When using the Van de Graaff generator, be sure to follow all of the recommended precautions.

Textbook Resource Information

Transparency Acetates

Fig. 24-4   The superposition principle for potential due to multiple charges
Fig. 24-5   Potential due to a continuous charge distribution
Fig. 24-9   Equipotential surfaces for a point charge
Fig. 24-11   Electric field lines and equipotentials for charged parallel plates
Fig. 24-14   Two equipotentials with a potential difference of dV
Table 24-1   Electric fields and potentials for various charge configurations
Fig. 24-27a   Schematic diagram of a Van de Graaff generator
Fig. 24-28   Schematic diagram of a field-ion microscope
Fig. 24-31   Schematic diagram of xerography
Fig. 24-33   Schematic diagram of a scanning tunneling microscope

Physlet Physics Illustrations

25.2   Work and Equipotentials
25.3   Electric Potential of Charged Spheres

Physlet Physics Explorations

25.1   Investigate equipotential lines
25.2   Electric field lines and equipotentials
25.3   Electric potential around conductors
25.5   Spherical conductor and insulator

Physlet Physics Problems

25.1   Investigating potential energy
25.2   Work done in moving an electron
25.9   Electric field and potential due to three charges

Ranking Task Exercises in Physics, Student Edition

Page 123   Two electric charges – electric potential
Page 124   Three electric charges – electric potential energy
Page 128   Charged conducting spheres – electric potential at the center
Page 130   Charged conducting spheres – electric potential at various points
Page 139   Uniform electric field/potential lines – force on charge at rest
Page 145   Nonuniform electric field – electric potential
Page 147   Uniform electric field – potential difference
Page 151   Uniform electric field – electric potential at different points
Page 152   Uniform electric field – change in potential energy of a positive charge
Page 153   Uniform electric field – change in potential energy of a negative charge

End of Chapter Problems with Solutions in the *Student Study Guide*

7, 15, 21, 33, 51, 65

Suggested Readings

Amann, G., "'Crying' Electrostatics," *The Physics Teacher* (January 1999), p. 10.

Beichner, R., "Visualizing Potential Surfaces with a Spreadsheet," *The Physics Teacher* (February 1997), p. 95 – 97.

Bracikowski, C., Schneider, R., Singley, J., and Madara, R., "Faster Electrostatics Plots," *The Physics Teacher* (September 1998), p. 323.

Cleaver, T.G., "Supercharge, a Game to Help Students Visualize Equipotential Surfaces," *The Physics Teacher* (October 1978), p. 484 – 486.

De Jong, M.L., "Graphing Electric Potential," *The Physics Teacher* (May 1993), p. 270 – 272.

Horn, J., "Electrostatic Landscapes," *The Physics Teacher* (November 1997), p. 499 – 501.

Kristjansson, L., "On the Drawing of Lines of Force and Equipotentials," *The Physics Teacher* (April 1985), p. 202 – 206.

Thomas, B.R., "Easy Equipotentials," *Am.J.Phys.* (June 1996), p. 815 – 816.

Touger, J., "Bigger Gap — Bigger Spark," *The Physics Teacher* (November 1992), p. 454.

Shaw, D.E. and Dallas, J.L., "An Updated Equipotential Apparatus," *Am.J.Phys.* (December 1986), p. 1146 – 1147.

Notes and Ideas

Preparation time: *Estimated:* _____   *Actual:* _____

Class time spent on material: *Estimated:* _____   *Actual:* _____

Related laboratory activities:

Demonstration materials:

Notes for next time:

Chapter 25: Capacitors and Dielectrics

Outline

Summary

Capacitors as energy-storage devices and how **capacitors** are used in electrical circuits are the main topics of this chapter. The method of calculating the **equivalent capacitor** for **parallel** and **series** connections is discussed. The effects of introducing a **dielectric** in a **capacitor** and the study of **dielectrics** from a microscopic point of view are also studied.

Major Concepts

- Capacitance
    - Definition of capacitance
    - Calculating capacitance
    - Units of electric potential

- Energy in capacitors
    - Energy stored in a capacitor
    - Batteries vs. capacitors

- Energy in electric fields
    - Energy in electric fields
    - Energy density

- Capacitors in parallel and in series
    - Circuits
    - Parallel connection
    - Series connection

- Dielectrics
    - Dielectric constant
    - Experimental evidence for the behavior of dielectrics
    - Real capacitors

- The microscopic description of dielectrics
    - Microscopic description
    - Gauss' law and dielectrics
    - Consequences of the microscopic model of dielectrics

Teaching Suggestions and Demonstrations

The concepts discussed in this chapter are straightforward; however, students will encounter some difficulty in recognizing the difference between **parallel** and **series** connections. Use as many different examples as possible to give them practice in this area.

Sections 25-1 –25-3

Start off by defining **capacitance** and discuss the relationship between the voltage and charge in terms of the **capacitance**.

> ⟳ **DEMO** Bring in different kinds of capacitors (parallel plate, coaxial and variable capacitors) and let the students familiarize themselves with them.

> ⟳ **DEMO** Construct a parallel plate capacitor.

Emphasize that Equation 25-4 is valid only for **parallel plate capacitors**, while Equation 25-2 is generic and applicable regardless of the kind of **capacitor**.

The derivation of Equation 25-8 is straightforward. However, point out that this **energy** is due to the work needed during the **charging process** to move **charges** from one plate to the other across the **electric field** that exists between the plates. The important point here is that the **energy** is stored in the **electric field**. Students will often forget the presence of this **electric field** and will not consider the space between the plates to be of any significance. Point out that Equations 25-9 and 25-10 are the same as Equation 25-8 but expressed in terms of other variables.

Be sure to discuss the advantage or disadvantage of using a battery vs. a **capacitor**. It is useful to know the practical uses of a **capacitor** as an **energy storage** device and also when and why a battery is preferable.

Sections 25-4

Students are introduced to **electric circuits** here for the first time. Take a little time to talk about the conventional symbols used for depicting a battery (or voltage source) and **capacitor** in a **circuit diagram**. Tell them that they will be coming across other circuit elements in later chapters and to learn the symbols for those elements as they get to them.

One of the biggest misconceptions students have is in the interpretation of a **circuit diagram**. Emphasize that the straight lines between the elements in a circuit diagram represent connecting wires and the lengths of these lines have no significance.

> ⟳ **DEMO** Draw a simple circuit diagram with a battery, switch and capacitor in series. Now take a capacitor, battery, and switch and show students how the connections are made. Compare the actual circuit to the diagram and point out that in the actual circuit the wires are not really perfectly straight lines. In fact, each wire can be of a different length.

Use Figs. 25-12 and 25-13 to discuss the definition of **parallel** and **series** connections. Three major points have to be recognized with regard to the differences between the two kinds of connections. First, the **potential difference** across the **capacitors** is the same in a **parallel** connection, while **capacitors** in series will have the same **charge**. Secondly, in a **parallel** connection the **charge** on each **capacitor** adds up while the **potentials** across each **capacitor** will add up for a **series** connection. Finally, as a consequence of Equations 25-14 and 25-17, we see that the total **capacitance** will be larger than the largest of the individual **capacitors** for a **parallel** connection, while the **equivalent capacitance** will be smaller than the smallest of the individual **capacitor** for a **series** connection.

While students will be able to find the **equivalent capacitance** for simple **parallel** or **series** circuits, a more complicated **circuit** with combined **series** and **parallel** connections will cause confusion. To minimize this, encourage students to redraw the **circuit diagram** so it looks progressively simpler with each **equivalent capacitance** that they evaluate. Remind students that Equation 25-17 gives the reciprocal of the **equivalent capacitor** and not the **equivalent capacitance** itself. Quite often students will forget this last step in their calculation. Students will need lots of practice in working **series** and **parallel** connections, so allow time in your schedule for this.

Sections 25-5 – 25-6

Section 25-5 introduces the concept and purpose of **dielectrics**. Start the discussion by considering Fig. 25-15. Point out that aligned dipoles will create its own **electric field**, which will oppose the existing **electric field**. This point is important as it helps to understand why the introduction of a **dielectric** reduces the **electric field** between the plates of a **capacitor**.

When discussing the experimental evidence for the behavior of **dielectrics**, stress the difference between the behavior of a charged isolated **capacitor** as compared to one where the battery is left in the circuit as the **dielectric** is introduced. In the first case, the voltage across the **capacitor** will reduce by a factor equal to the **dielectric constant**. However, when the battery is left intact in the circuit, it will maintain a steady voltage across the **capacitor**, and now the **capacitor's** charge will increase by a factor equal to that of the **dielectric constant**. Go through worked Examples 25-10, 25-11 and 25-12.

The last section of this chapter considers a **microscopic model** to look at how **dielectrics** work. This is very informative and useful in understanding why the **potential, charge** and **electric field** are affected when a **dielectric** is introduced. Use Figs. 25-22 and 25-23 when discussing this model because they help to visualize the ideas discussed here.

Textbook Resource Information

Transparency Acetates

Fig. 25-9	Energy in electric fields
Fig. 25-12	Capacitors in parallel
Fig. 25-13	Capacitors in series
Fig. 25-15	Dipoles in an external electric field
Fig. 25-16	Schematic diagram of a stud finder
Fig. 25-17	Effect of dielectric on the voltage of a capacitor
Fig. 25-18	Effect of dielectric on the charge of a capacitor
Fig. 25-21	Polar and nonpolar molecules in external field
Fig. 25-22	Effect of dielectric on field between the plates

Physlet Physics Illustrations

26.2   Work and Equipotentials
26.3   Electric Potential of Charged Spheres

Physlet Physics Explorations

25.1   Investigate equipotential lines
26.2   Electric field lines and equipotentials
26.3   Electric potential around conductors
26.5   Spherical conductor and insulator

Physlet Physics Problems

26.1   Investigating potential energy
26.2   Work done in moving an electron
26.9   Electric field and potential due to three charges

Ranking Task Exercises in Physics, Student Edition

Page 123	Two electric charges – electric potential
Page 125	Three electric charges – electric potential energy
Page 128	Charged conducting spheres – electric potential at the center
Page 130	Charged conducting spheres – electric potential at various points
Page 139	Uniform electric field/potential lines – force on charge at rest
Page 145	Nonuniform electric field – electric potential
Page 147	Uniform electric field – potential difference
Page 151	Uniform electric field – electric potential at different points
Page 152	Uniform electric field – change in potential energy of a positive charge
Page 153	Uniform electric field – change in potential energy of a negative charge

End of Chapter Problems with Solutions in the *Student Study Guide*

9, 17, 25, 37, 55, 73

Suggested Readings

Brown, R., "Series and Parallel Resistors and Capacitors," *The Physics Teacher* (November 2003), p. 483 – 485.

Doerr, T.P., and Yu, Y., "Electrostatics in The Presence of Dielectrics: The Benefits of Treating The Induced Surface Charge Density Directly," *Am. J. Phys.* (February 2004), p. 190 – 196.

Greenslade, Jr., B., "From Our Files," *The Physics Teacher* (February 2003), p. 123.

Gluck, P., "Force on the Dielectric in a Parallel Plate Capacitor," *The Physics Teacher* (December 2003), p. 521 – 523.

Parker, G.W., "Electric Field Outside a Parallel Plate Capacitor," *Am.J.Phys.* (May 2002), p. 502 – 507.

Powell, R.A., "Two-Capacitor Problem: A More Realistic View," *Am.J.Phys.* (May 1979), p. 460 – 462.

Notes and Ideas

Preparation time: *Estimated:* _____   *Actual:* _____

Class time spent on material: *Estimated:* _____   *Actual:* _____

Related laboratory activities:

Demonstration materials:

Notes for next time:

Chapter 26: Currents in Materials

Outline

Summary

So far we have studied static electricity. This chapter discusses the **motion** of **charges** and how a **material's structure** affects the flow of **electric current**. **Ohm's law** is defined, and **resistors** in **series** and **parallel,** as well as the temperature **dependence** of **resistance,** are studied. The **free-electron model** of **resistivity** and the **conductivity** of **materials** are also discussed. Finally, the concept of **electric power** is introduced.

Major Concepts

- Electric current
    - Definition of electric current
    - The direction of current
    - Current density
    - Current density of moving charges

- Currents in materials
    - Currents in materials
    - Current and conservation of charge

- Resistance
    - Definition of resistance
    - Ohm's law
    - Resistors
    - Resistivity and conductivity
    - Temperature dependence of resistivity

- Resistances in series and parallel
    - Resistors in series
    - Resistors in parallel

- Free electron model of resistivity
    - The free electron model
    - The failure of the free electron model

- Materials and conductivity
  - Conductivity in materials

- Electric power

Teaching Suggestions and Demonstrations

This chapter lays the foundation for the study of **circuits**, so a good understanding of **Ohm's law** and the relation between **voltage** and **current** is essential. Most students will find **electricity** to be abstract because they are unable to "see" what happens in a wire when the switch is closed in a **circuit**. One way to get around this difficulty is to use as many demos as possible, and to make use of thought questions and analogies wherever possible.

Sections 26-1 – 26-2

Start by discussing the definition of **electric current**. The analogy of the balls passing through a pinball machine under the influence of gravity is useful in presenting a picture of the motion of electrons inside a conductor. Most students will have had at least a semester of chemistry and are familiar with the electrons as the **current carrier**. Go through the discussion on the **direction of current** and point out that the convention is to take the **current** direction as opposite to the motion of the electrons.

The concept of **current density** is important because it will feature in the study of **flow** of **charges** in nonuniform materials or in gases and plasma. Go through the derivation of Equations 26-4, 26-7 and 26-10 for the same reason. In considering the **drift speed**, point out that the **charge carriers** are now the electrons. This seeming contradiction is a common source of confusion; however, just remind students that the **drift speed** is considered as being opposite to the direction of the **current density**.

Sections 26-3 – 26-4

Section 26-3 introduces the concept of **resistance** and states **Ohm's law**. Point out that the **voltage** and **current** are directly proportional and the slope of a **current** vs. **voltage** graph is the reciprocal of the **resistance** (see Fig. 26-8). Introduce the symbol for a resistor as used in circuit diagrams. Remind students that connecting wires have negligible resistance.

Be sure to stress the difference between **resistance** and **resistivity**. Discuss the fact that **resistivity** is an inherent property of the material. Point out that a wire is like a cylinder and has a circular cross-sectional area. Quite often, problems will give the diameter of a wire in millimeters, and students will need to remember to convert it to the metric system. Briefly discuss the **temperature dependence of resistance**.

> **DEMO** Bring in several different kinds of wires, some standard resistors (color-banded), a variable resistor, as well as some lightbulbs, and discuss the fact that each of them has a certain resistance. Point out that electrical appliances like hair dryers and toaster ovens also have electrical resistance.

> **DEMO** Connect a variac (or power supply), switch and a 100 W lightbulb in series. Use an ammeter to measure the current through the lightbulb. Plot the voltage and current to show the relation between them. If you use a large current meter, it will be visible to most of the class.

⊃ **DEMO** Repeat the above demo with the following variation: keep the voltage on the power supply constant and measure the current for different resistors. The product of the current and resistance will be constant, proving Ohm's law.

⊃ **DEMO** Use a digital multimeter to measure the resistance of a coil of nickel wire. Now lower the coil into liquid nitrogen and once again measure the resistance. You will notice the resistance drop, showing the effect of temperature on the resistance.

In Chapter 25, you discussed the rules for finding the **equivalent** value for **capacitors** connected in **series** and **parallel**. **Resistors** in **series** and **parallel** will have similar rules, but with some differences. Discuss the rules and be sure to point out these differences. Work as many examples with different **parallel** and **series** connections so students get sufficient practice. Remind students to draw the circuit diagram for each intermediate step as in the case of series and parallel capacitors.

⊃ **DEMO** Connect a 9-volt battery and two resistors in series. Measure the voltage across the battery and across each of the two resistors. The voltage across the battery will equal the sum of the voltages across the two individual resistances.

⊃ **DEMO** Connect a 9-volt battery and two resistors in parallel. Measure the voltage across the battery and across each of the two resistors. They will all be the same.

⊃ **DEMO** Connect a 9-volt battery and two resistors in parallel. Measure the current coming out of the battery and the current through each resistor using an ammeter. The sum of the currents through the two resistors will equal the current coming out of the battery.

⊃ **DEMO** Connect two identical lightbulbs in parallel and then in series. Compare the brightness of the two bulbs in the two cases and use it to discuss the voltage across each bulb and the current through each bulb. Repeat the process by introducing a third identical bulb. Have the students make some predictions before you make the connections. Use this to discuss what happens to the equivalent resistance when the third bulb is added. Show that the current coming from the battery is dependent on the equivalent resistance in a circuit.

Section 26-5 – 26-7

The **free-electron model** discussed in Section 26-5 will help in the understanding of the concept of **resistivity**. Be sure to discuss the reasons for the failure of this model and the significance of learning from failed models.

Section 26-6 used minimal quantum physics to discuss the differences in the **resistivity** of conductors, semiconductors, superconductors, and insulators. Students will need an introduction to the concepts of energy diagrams and energy quantization. Use Figs. 26-16 through 26-20 to discuss why some bands are completely empty and others are partially filled or completely filled.

⊃ **DEMO** Connect a battery to a lightbulb. Leave a gap in the circuit. Introduce different materials (both good and bad conductors) in the gap and compare their conducting properties.

The last section of this chapter looks at **electric power** and how the **power** dissipated in a circuit depends on the **voltage** and the **current**. Point out that Equation 26-27 is a general one and can be used for any material. On the other hand, Equation 26-28 is applicable to **ohmic materials** alone.

Textbook Resource Information

Transparency Acetates

Fig. 26-3	Current density vector
Fig. 26-4	Total charge flowing through area
Fig. 26-5	Motion of electron in a metal
Fig. 26-7	Current through wire with varying areas
Table 26-2	Resistivities, conductivities and temperature coefficients
Fig. 26-17	Energy diagrams with possible energy levels
Fig. 26-18	Energy diagram for conductors, and insulators
Fig. 26-19	Energy diagram for a semiconductor
Fig. 26-20	Lattice structure for n- and p-type semiconductors

Physlet Physics Illustrations

30.5 Ohm's Law

Physlet Physics Explorations

30.2 Lightbulbs

Physlet Physics Problems

30.1 Examining identical lightbulbs in different circuits
30.2 Examining current and voltage by varying resistance
30.3 Ranking resistors

Ranking Task Exercises in Physics, Student Edition

Page 160	Current carrying wires with different lengths – net charge
Page 161	Batteries and bulbs – bulb brightness
Page 162	Simple resistor circuits – resistance
Page 163	Simple resistor circuits – current
Page 164	Simple resistor circuits – voltage
Page 166	Simple resistor circuits – bulb brightness
Page 170	Simple circuits – equivalent resistor

End of Chapter Problems with Solutions in the *Student Study Guide*

7, 17, 35, 51, 55, 89

Suggested Readings

Amengual, A., "The Intriguing Properties of the Equivalent Resistances of n Equal Resistors Combined in Series and in Parallel," *Am.J.Phys.* (February 2000), p. 175 – 179.

Brown, R., "Series and Parallel Resistors and Capacitors," *The Physics Teacher* (November 2003), p. 483 – 485.

Denardo, B., "Temperature of a Lightbulb Filament," *The Physics Teacher* (February 2002), p. 101 – 105.

Denardo, B., Earwood, J., and Sazonova, V., "Experiments with Electrical Resistive Networks," *Am.J.Phys.* (November 1999), p. 981 – 986.

Derman, S., and Goykadosh, A., "A Pencil-and-Tape Electricity Experiment," *The Physics Teacher* (October 1999), p. 400 – 402.

Fisher, K., "Conjugate Relationships in Basic Electricity," *The Physics Teacher* (November 1999), p. 458 – 459.

Greene, N.R., "Lightbulbs with a Memory," *The Physics Teacher* (May 2002), p. 275.

Greenslade, Jr., B., "A Nomograph for Resistors in Parallel," *The Physics Teacher* (November 2002), p. 458 – 459.

Greenslade, Jr., B., "The Hydraulic Analogy for Electric Current," *The Physics Teacher* (November 2003), p. 464 – 466.

Livelybrooks, D., "'Feel' the Difference Between Series and Parallel Circuits," *The Physics Teacher* (February 2003), p. 102 – 103.

Priest, J., "Meter Resistance: Don't Forget It!," *The Physics Teacher* (January 2003), p. 40 – 41.

Reif, F., "Generalized Ohm's Law, Potential Difference, and Voltage Measurements," *Am.J.Phys.* (November 1982), p. 1048 – 1049.

Schuetze, A.P., Lewis, W., Brown, C., and Geerts, W.J., "A Laboratory on the Four-Point Probe Technique," *Am.J.Phys.* (February 2004), p. 149 – 153.

Vreeland, P., "Analyzing Simple Circuits," *The Physics Teacher* (February 2002), p. 99 – 100.

Notes and Ideas

Preparation time: *Estimated:* _____   *Actual:* _____

Class time spent on material: *Estimated:* _____   *Actual:* _____

Related laboratory activities:

Demonstration materials:

Notes for next time:

Chapter 27: Direct Current Circuits

Outline

27-1   EMF
27-2   Kirchhoff's Loop Rule
27-3   Kirchhoff's Junction Rule
27-4   Measuring Instruments
27-5   RC Circuits

Summary

The main topic in this chapter is the study of **multiloop circuits** using **Kirchhoff's loop** and **junction rules**. The use of **measuring instruments** and the meaning of **emf** is briefly discussed. *RC* **circuits** and the **charging** and **discharging** of a **capacitor** through a **resistor** are studied. Finally the **energy stored** in *RC* **circuits** is considered.

Major Concepts

- emf
    - Circuits
    - The meaning of emf
    - Internal resistance
    - Electric Power and batteries

- Kirchhoff's loop rule

- Kirchhoff's junction rule

- Solving for the behavior of multiloop circuits

- Measuring instruments
    - Ohmmeters, voltmeters and ammeters
    - How to construct analog measuring devices

- RC circuits
    - Charging and discharging processes
    - Energy in *RC* circuits

Teaching Suggestions and Demonstrations

Analyzing **multiloop circuits** is a difficult topic. It is important that students understand the application of **Kirchhoff's rules** to solving problems involving **multiloop circuits**. Work as many examples as possible to make this process easier.

Sections 27-1 –27-4

Section 27-1 is simple and straightforward in its discussion of the concept of **electromotive force**. Stress that **emf** is not a force but a potential difference. This is the only place that the internal resistance of a battery is considered. So be sure to discuss this and work some problems involving internal resistance of a battery. Students need to be familiar with terms such as load resistance and terminal voltage. Use Fig. 27-3 to show why there is a voltage drop when a battery is connected to a circuit with a load resistance.

State Kirchhoff's loop rule and then use Fig. 27-5 to stress the importance of learning the rules for potential differences across various circuit elements. Students will be confused over the **loop direction** and the **current direction**. Point out that the **loop direction** is arbitrary and is one chosen by the student. On the other hand, the **current direction** is based on what is happening in the circuit. However, there is no need for them to agonize over the **current direction**. If they choose an incorrect direction for the current, this will be indicated by a negative sign for the solved value of the current.

Compared to the loop rule, **Kirchhoff's junction rule** is very easy to understand. However, students should not minimize the importance of this rule in solving complex circuit problems. Take the example shown in Fig. 27-9 to point out that both junction a and d will give the same equation and hence will yield no new information.

Start with a simple circuit to show how the loop rule is applied and then increase the complexity of the circuit. Use the problem-solving techniques outlined in Section 27-3 to solve **multiloop** problems. Some students might need a quick refresher on how to solve for the unknown quantities using a system of equations.

⮑ **DEMO** Build a multiloop circuit with a couple of batteries and several resistances. Use a voltmeter to measure the voltages across each of the circuit elements. Show that the sum of the voltages is zero.

⮑ **DEMO** Repeat the above demo, but now measure the current through each branch of the circuit and show that Kirchhoff's junction rule works.

Section 27-4 discusses the use of **measuring instruments** such as the ammeter, voltmeter and ohmmeter. Point out that a voltmeter is always connected across the two points for which the potential difference is to be measured, and the ammeter is always connected in series with the circuit through which the current is to be determined. Emphasize that voltage is measured across whereas current is through a certain element.

Discuss why an ammeter should have a small resistance while a voltmeter should have a large resistance. Remind students that a measuring device such as a voltmeter or an ammeter should not cause any major change in the working of a circuit.

⮑ **DEMO** Connect a battery and a lightbulb in series with an analog ammeter. Connect a voltmeter across the lightbulb. Show how these two instruments are used to measure the current through and the voltage across the bulb. Now use a digital meter to show how that works. Finally use a multimeter to illustrate how it can be used as a voltmeter and an ammeter.

Section 27-5

In learning about **RC circuits**, emphasize the differences between the **charging** and **discharging** processes. Make the distinction between phrases like 'immediately after the switch is closed' and 'a long time after the switch is closed'. Discuss the graphs shown in Fig. 27-20 in detail. Point out the difference between Fig. 27-20a and 27-20b so students can make the connection between the charge on the

capacitor and the current through the resistor. Remind them that current is the derivative of the charge with respect to time.

Define **time constant** and explicitly mark it on the graph. Students will not be convinced that the **time constant** is indeed a measurement of time. Work the units for the time constant and show that it has the dimensions of time measurement.

Students will often forget that during the **discharging** process the source of **emf** is removed from the circuit. Be sure to draw the circuit diagram for the **discharging** process (rather than merely stating it verbally) and describe the process. Figure 27-22 shows the behavior of the charge on the **capacitor** as time progresses. Emphasize the fact that the **time constant** is the time needed for the **capacitor** to lose two-thirds of its charge.

⊃ **DEMO** Connect a resistor, capacitor, power supply and an ammeter in series. As the capacitor charges up, measure the current and plot current vs. time to show the time dependence of the charging process. Once the capacitor is charged, remove the power supply and illustrate the discharging process. To make sure that you get a useable charging rate, test several resistors ahead of time.

In solving problems, it is quite common for students to forget which of the two Equations 27-22 and 27-26 is for the **charging** process and which is for the **discharging** process. Have them calculate the value of the exponential term in the two equations for time $t = 0$. (I insist that they actually go through this operation using their calculator because they are then more likely to remember it than if I were to just mention it in passing.) Then point out that Equation 27-22 will yield a value of zero for the charge Q at time $t = 0$ which corresponds to a **capacitor** starting off with no charge and hence indicates the **charging** process of a capacitor. On the other hand, Equation 27-26 will yield a value of Q_0 for the charge at time $t = 0$ which indicates a fully charged **capacitor** that is starting the **discharging** process. As obvious as this may seem to us, this simple exercise will help students when faced with this situation during an exam.

The **energy stored** in an *RC* **circuit** is due to the work done by the battery in **charging** the **capacitor**. Point out that half of this work done is stored as **energy** in the electric field that exists between the plates of the **capacitor**. The rest of the work done is converted into Joule heating of the resistor.

Textbook Resource Information

Transparency Acetates

Physlet Physics Illustrations

Physlet Physics Explorations

30.1 Circuit analysis
30.4 Galvanometers and ammeters
30.5 Voltmeters
30.6 *RC* time constant

Physlet Physics Problems

30.11 *RC* circuit – ranking resistors
30.12 *RC* circuits – finding capacitance
30.13 *RC* circuit – voltage across capacitor

Ranking Task Exercises in Physics, Student Edition

Page 159   Circuits with resistors and capacitors – current

End of Chapter Problems with Solutions in the *Student Study Guide*

7, 19, 29, 47, 53, 59

Suggested Readings

Bartlett, A.A., and Braun T.J., "Death in a Hot Tub: The Physics of Heat Stroke," *Am. J. Phys.* (February 1983), p. 127 – 132.

Cleveland, J.R., and Hirschi, S., "Discharge Time for a Capacitor," *Am. J. Phys.* (September 1979), p. 776 – 778.

Denardo, B., Earwood, J., and Sazonova, V., "Experiments with Electrical Resistive Networks," *Am.J.Phys.* (November 1999), p. 981 – 986.

Hart, F., "Computer-Based Experiments to Measure RC," *The Physics Teacher* (March 2000), p. 176 – 177.

Preyer, N.W., "Transient Behavior of Simple RC Circuits," *Am. J. Phys.* (December 2002), p. 1187 – 1193.

Priest, J., "Meter Resistance: Don't Forget It!," *The Physics Teacher* (January 2003), p. 40 – 41.

Sorenson, R.A., "The Random Walk Method for DC Circuit Analysis," *Am. J. Phys.* (November 1990), p. 1056 – 1059.

Van Baak, D.A., "Variational Alternatives to Kirchhoff's Loop Theorem in DC Circuits," *Am. J. Phys.* (January 1999), p. 36 – 44.

Notes and Ideas

Preparation time: *Estimated:* _____   *Actual:* _____

Class time spent on material: *Estimated:* _____   *Actual:* _____

Related laboratory activities:

Demonstration materials:

Notes for next time:

Chapter 28: The Effects of Magnetic Fields

Outline

Summary

Magnets, **magnetic fields**, and the effect of **magnetic fields** are the topics introduced in this chapter. The **force** on **moving charges** in a **magnetic field** is studied, and the **Lorentz force** is briefly touched on. Consequences of **magnetic force** on a **moving charge**, such as the **cyclotron**, **velocity selector**, and the **mass spectrometer** are examined. Included are topics such as **magnetic fields** in outer space and the effect of combining **magnetic** and **electric fields**. The **force** on **straight wires** and **current loops** and the **torque** on **current loops** are considered. Finally, the **Hall effect** is discussed.

Major Concepts

- Magnets and magnetic fields

- Magnetic force on an electric charge
    - Magnetic force law
    - The Lorentz force

- Consequences of the magnetic force on a charge
    - Energy of a charged particle in a static magnetic field
    - Circular motion in a constant magnetic field
    - Velocity selectors
    - The charge-to-mass ratio of the electron
    - The mixing of electric and magnetic fields
    - Magnetic fields in outer space

- Magnetic forces on currents
    - Magnetic forces on infinitesimal wires with currents
    - Magnetic forces on finite wires with currents

- Magnetic force on current loops
    - Torque on a current loop
    - Galvanometers
    - Energy and the torque on loops

- The Hall effect

Teaching Suggestions and Demonstrations

Chapter 28 introduces the concept of **magnets** and **magnetic fields** and as such lays the foundation for the study of **electromagnetic** phenomena that are discussed in the next seven chapters; thus a sound understanding of **magnetic fields** and **magnetic forces** on **charges** and **currents** is essential. Students will have a difficult time visualizing these concepts since they are fairly abstract. Using conceptual questions and demos (wherever possible) will help.

Section 28-1

Start by discussing properties of a **magnet**. In electricity we talk in terms of a single charge. However, in the case of a **magnet**, it is not possible to isolate a single **pole**. If you break a **magnet** into two pieces, you will get two **magnets**, each with a north and a south pole, however small the pieces may be.

⟳ **DEMO** Bring in different kinds of magnets such as bar, cylindrical, horseshoe, and refrigerator magnets. Illustrate that like poles will repel and unlike poles will attract.

⟳ **DEMO** To show the repulsion between like poles place some ring magnets on a wooden dowel. If the magnets are placed with like poles facing each other, they will levitate due to the repulsive forces.

⟳ **DEMO** This demo illustrates how to determine if a piece of iron is a magnet. Get a piece of iron bar that is identical (in shape and size) to a bar magnet. Place the magnet flat on the table. Now bring one end of the nonmagnetized bar near the center of the magnet without any effect. Reverse the two bars and repeat, and you will see the magnet lift up the nonmagnet.

When studying electric fields, we use a test charge to map the field lines. To map **magnetic fields**, we use a compass. Electric field lines begin and end on charges; however, **magnetic field lines** form closed loops. Figure 28-2 shows the **magnetic field lines** for some typical situations.

⟳ **DEMO** Fashion an arrow with a paper clip and suspend it by a light string. Bring the arrow near a large magnet, and the arrow will align itself in the direction of the magnetic field.

⟳ **DEMO** Place a bar magnet on a sheet of paper. Place a small compass near the north pole of the magnet. The compass needle will align itself along the direction of the field line at that location with the north pointing away. Mark the two ends of the compass needle on the paper. Now move the compass needle so the south of the compass is on the mark you just made and once again mark the orientation of the needle on the paper. You can trace the field lines in this manner.

⟳ **DEMO** Place a bar magnet under a piece of Plexiglas. Sprinkle iron filings on the glass and gently tap the glass. The iron filings will arrange themselves to show the field lines. Repeat using different kinds of magnets, as well as two bar magnets with like poles facing each other and then with unlike poles facing each other. Discuss the pattern obtained in each case and point out the regions of strongest field is where the lines are crowded closer.

Look at Table 28-1 to get some idea of the strengths of some typical magnetic fields.

Sections 28-2 – 28-3

Magnetic fields affecting **moving charges** have several practical applications. The demo described below will illustrate the **force** exerted on **charges** by **magnetic fields** in a very concrete way, that students are apt to remember for a long time.

⮕ **DEMO** Set up an oscilloscope and use a bar magnet to deflect the electron beam. (See Figs. 28-4f and 28-4g.)

The **magnetic force law** (Equation 28-1) gives the relationship between the **force**, the **velocity** and the **field** vectors, and Figs. 28-4b through 28-4e illustrate this dependence for a positive charge. The cross product tells us that the **force** on the **charge** is perpendicular to the plane containing the **field** and **velocity** vectors. This is a point often forgotten by students. You may have to also review the cross product of two vectors and the right-hand rule (Chapter 10) for determining the cross product of two vectors. Point out that the **charge** will experience no **force** if it is moving parallel to the **magnetic field** or if it is stationary. Use examples similar to those shown in Fig. 28-4 to give students sufficient practice in determining one of the vectors given the other two. In the case of a **negative charge**, the right-hand rule still applies, but the **force** will be opposite that for a **positive charge**. Discuss the convention for depicting vectors that go into or out of the page.

Section 28-3 discusses some very interesting applications of the **force** exerted by a **magnetic field** on **moving charges**. When a **charge** enters a constant **magnetic field** with a velocity perpendicular to that **field**, the charge will follow a circular path. This forms the basis of the working of a **cyclotron**. In the case of the **velocity selector**, the **forces** exerted by a **magnetic** and an electric **field** are balanced so only **charges** within a certain velocity range go through without any deflection. The discussion on the determination of the **charge-to-mass** ratio is interesting from a historical perspective while the treatment of **magnetic fields** in outer space is very relevant today. The section Think About This… How Does **Earth's Magnetic Field** Create the Northern Lights? will be interesting to students because some of them may have witnessed this phenomenon.

Sections 28-4 – 28-6

Now that students are familiar with the **force** on a single **moving charge** in a **magnetic field**, extend this idea to a collection of **moving charges** and hence to the idea of a **magnetic field** exerting a **force** on a **current-carrying wire**. Section 28-4 looks at an **infinitesimal wire** first and then at **finite wires** with currents flowing in them. Equations 28-19 and 28-1 are similar in that they both have to do with the cross product of the **magnetic field** and the velocity of the moving charge. In the case of the wire, however, the students will not recognize that the product qv in the case of a **single moving charge** translates into the product IL for a collection of **moving charges** (a flow of current). Remind them that the current I is the rate of flow of charge.

⮕ **DEMO** Set up three or four strong horseshoe magnets in a row (and parallel to each other) with the north poles facing the same way. Take a long strip of aluminum foil and stretch it in the space between the poles of the horseshoe magnets. (The horseshoe magnets are like arches with the aluminum strip running between the "feet" of the magnets). Connect the two ends of the aluminum strip to the terminals of a power supply using alligator clips. Turn the voltage up, and the aluminum strip will be deflected upwards. Reverse a few of the magnets and the foil will be pushed flat against the table at these points. Have students use the right-hand rule to determine which end of the magnets is the north pole.

For many students, the **magnetic force** on **current loops** and hence the **torque** on the **loops** are difficult concepts to grasp. The following demo will give them a good visualization of the phenomenon.

⊃ **DEMO** Stack up a couple of books about a foot apart. Place six to eight long skewers (you can get some inexpensive disposable ones from the grocery store) parallel to each other and with their ends resting on the two stacks of books. The skewers now represent magnetic field lines in the space between the two stacks of books. Designate one stack as the north pole of the magnet and the other as the south pole of the magnet. Take a sheet of stock card and cut out a rectangle from the center so you have a window. The stock card is now a loop of area A. (Alternately, you could use a wire coat hanger that has been bent into the shape of a rectangular loop.) Mark the direction of the current on the loop so it is visible to the class. Hold the loop perpendicular to the field lines (skewers). Have the students determine the force direction (by using the right-hand rule) on each straight section of the loop. Discuss the fact that there is (maximum) torque on the loop due to equal but opposite forces on the vertical sections of the loop. Next hold the loop so its surface is parallel to the skewers and show that the torque on the loop is zero.

⊃ **DEMO** You will need a large coil and a powerful magnet, both of which can be purchased. Suspend the coil above the magnet and connect the two ends of the coil to a power supply. When the power supply is turned on the coil will rotate.

Point out that the **galvanometer** works on the above principle, as does the **electric motor**.

⊃ **DEMO** You can construct a motor without too much trouble. Drive two small nails on the end faces of a small wooden dowel to form a shaft. Wrap several turns of coil on to the dowel. Place the dowel so the two end nails rest on two supports in such a way that the dowel is free to rotate. Connect the two free ends of the coil to a battery and place the coil near a powerful magnet. When the current flows through the coil it will rotate. You may have to give the shaft a slight turn to get it going.

The **torque** on a **loop** is defined in terms of the cross product of the **magnetic dipole moment** and the **magnetic field**. There are three points to keep in mind with regard to this. First, the perpendicular to the plane of the area of the **loop** gives the direction of the area vector. Second, the direction of the **magnetic dipole moment** vector is determined by using the right-hand rule. Finally, the **magnetic dipole moment** is analogous to the electric dipole moment.

Section 28-6

Many curricula tend to omit discussion of the **Hall effect**. One very practical application of the **Hall effect** is in computer keyboards. Students are bound to find this illuminating, so keep this in mind when planning your syllabus.

Textbook Resource Information

Transparency Acetates

Fig. 28-2   Magnetic fields for different types of magnets
Fig. 28-5   Vector product and right-hand rule
Fig. 28-6   Right-hand rule for magnetic force law

Physlet Physics Illustrations

27.1 Magnets and Compass Needles
27.2 Earth's Magnetic Field
27.3 A Mass Spectrometer
27.4 Magnetic Forces on Currents

Physlet Physics Explorations

27.1 Map field lines and determine forces
27.2 Velocity selector
27.3 Mass spectrometer

Physlet Physics Problems

27.6 Motion of an electron in a magnetic field
27.7 Motion of charged particles in a magnetic field
27.8 Mass spectrometer
27.9 Velocity selector
27.10 Magnetic force on a wire

Ranking Task Exercises in Physics, Student Edition

Page 180   Moving charges in uniform magnetic field – acceleration
Page 181   Moving charges in uniform magnetic field – change in kinetic energy
Page 185   Charged particle and a uniform magnetic field – acceleration
Page 186   Charged particle and a uniform magnetic field – force

End of Chapter Problems with Solutions in the *Student Study Guide*

1, 19, 31, 47, 59, 67

Suggested Readings

Berger, R., and Schmitt, M., "Estimating the Earth's Magnetic Field Strength with an Extension Cord," *The Physics Teacher* (May 2003), p. 295 – 297.

Bichsel, E.S., Wilson, B., and Geerts, W.J. "Magnetic Domains of Floppy Disks and Phone Cards Using Toner Fluid," *The Physics Teacher* (March 2002), p. 150 – 153.

Butcher, F., "Remagnetizer/Degausser," *The Physics Teacher* (March 2003), p. 185.

Capitolo, M., and Lonc, W., "Trick of the Trade: Magnetic Deflection Demonstrator," *The Physics Teacher* (May 2000), p. 277.

Connors, M., "Apparatus for Teaching Physics: Measurement and Analysis of the Field of Disk Magnets," *The Physics Teacher* (May 2002), p. 308 – 311.

Fletcher, K.A., Iyer, S.V., and Kinsey, K.F., "Some Pivotal Thoughts on the Current Balance," *The Physics Teacher* (May 2003), p. 280 – 284

Gottlieb, H.H., "Ceramic Magnets," *The Physics Teacher* (March 1976), p. 181.

King, J.G., Morrison, P., Morrison, P., and Pine, J., "ZAP! Freshman Electricity and Magnetism Using Desktop Experiments: A Progress Report, " *Am. J. Phys.* (November 1992), p. 973 – 978.

Klittnick, A.F., and Rickard, M.J., "Apparatus for Teaching Physics: Mystery Motor Demystified," *The Physics Teacher* (March 2001), p. 174 – 175.

Norton, F., "Reversing Compass Needles," *The Physics Teacher* (October 2003), p. 434.

Rabchuk, J.A., "The Gauss Rifle and Magnetic Energy," *The Physics Teacher* (March 2003), p. 158 – 161.

Schmidt, Jr., M.F., "Investigating Refrigerator Magnets," *The Physics Teacher* (April 2000), p. 248 – 249.

Sinacore, J., and Graf, E.H., "Precision Laboratory Apparatus for the Study of Magnetic Forces," *The Physics Teacher* (May 2000), p. 296 – 298.

Stewart, G., "Measuring Earth's Magnetic Field Simply," *The Physics Teacher* (February 2000), p. 113 – 114.

Van Heuvelen, A., Allen, L., and Mihas, P., "Experiment Problems for Electricity and Magnetism," *The Physics Teacher* (November 1999), p. 482 – 485.

Weichman, F., "Force on Current-Carrying Wire," *The Physics Teacher* (December 2003), p. 547.

Notes and Ideas

Preparation time: *Estimated:* _____   *Actual:* _____

Class time spent on material: *Estimated:* _____   *Actual:* _____

Related laboratory activities:

Demonstration materials:

Notes for next time:

Chapter 29: The Production and Properties of Magnetic Fields

Outline

Summary

In the last chapter we saw the effects of **magnetic fields** on **moving charges** and **currents**. This chapter looks at how **moving charges** and **currents** can themselves produce a **magnetic field** and what the properties of these **magnetic fields** are. Three important laws, **Ampère's law**, **Gauss' law** for **magnetism**, and the **Biot – Savart law** and their applications are discussed. A look at the **Maxwell displacement current** completes this chapter.

Major Concepts

- Ampère's Law
    - The magnetic field of a straight wire
    - Ampère's
    - Using Ampère's law to find the magnetic field

- Gauss' law for magnetism
    - Magnetic flux and Gauss' law for magnetism
    - The field lines of a bar magnet
    - Using Gauss' law to find magnetic fields

- Solenoids
    - Using Ampère's law to find the magnetic field in a solenoid
    - A toroidal solenoid

- The Biot – Savart law
    - The Biot – Savart law
    - Using the Biot – Savart law
    - Magnetic dipoles

- The Maxwell displacement current

Teaching Suggestions and Demonstrations

This chapter builds on the concepts studied in the previous chapter, and students should be a bit more comfortable with the abstract ideas presented earlier; however, the use of plenty of conceptual examples and visual aids are still recommended.

Sections 29-1 – 29-3

Begin your presentation with the **magnetic field** produced by a single **current-carrying wire** and then discuss the **force** between **two parallel current**-carrying wires. Draw two parallel vertical lines on the board to depict the two wires. Consider four different situations: both currents going up, both currents going down, current one going up and current two going down, current one going down and current two going up. For each of these situations, have the students figure out the direction of the **force** each wire exerts on the other. The **force** on a wire is due to a **field** external to the wire. This is a major source of confusion to students. Explain that the **force** experienced by each wire is due to the **field** produced by the other wire. Since the **magnetic field lines** are concentric circles around a straight wire, remind them that the **field** direction at any point is tangential to the circle.

In doing the three demos described below, have students predict the outcome. This will give them some practice with the right-hand rule for finding the direction of the **magnetic field** as well as the **force** exerted by the **field** on a wire.

➲ **DEMO** A long, straight wire is stretched (horizontally) between two vertical supports. The wire should not sag, but at the same time it should not be taut, either. Connect the two ends of the wire to a power supply and a switch. Place a compass below the wire. The compass needle will align itself in the north-south direction. Now close the switch and turn on the power supply. The magnetic needle of the compass will swing in the direction of the magnetic field produced by the current. (See Fig. 29-1.)

➲ **DEMO** Bore a hole through a Plexiglass plate. Pass a straight wire through the hole. (You may have to use supports to keep the wire vertical and the plate horizontal.) Connect the two ends of the wire to a power supply. Sprinkle iron filings on the Plexiglass and turn on the power supply. Gently tap the plate, and the filings will arrange themselves in concentric circles around the wire.

➲ **DEMO** This demo shows that two parallel wires exert a force on each other. Two long straight wires are stretched (horizontally) between two sets of vertical supports. (See Fig. 29-2.) The wires should not sag, but at the same time they should not be taut either. Connect each wire to a power supply so the currents flow in the same direction in both wires. When the power supplies are turned on, the wires will be attracted to each other. Now change the connection so the currents flow in opposite directions and the wires will experience a repulsive force.

Equation 29-5 gives us a way to evaluate the **magnetic field** due to a **straight wire**. The r in the denominator is the perpendicular distance of the point under consideration from the wire. Points on a circle of the same radius will have the same magnitude of the **magnetic field**, which once again reinforces the concept of concentric field lines.

Ampère's law is used to find the **magnetic field** for situations with symmetry properties. Point out that this is similar to using **Gauss' law** in electricity. But there is one difference between the two methods. **Gauss' law** has to do with the integration over a closed surface, while in **Ampère's law** the integral is over a closed path. Go through Example 29-2 to show how the path of integration is chosen for a given situation.

Section 29-2 introduces **Gauss' law** for **magnetism**. Four main points need to be considered when comparing **Gauss' law** for electricity with that for **magnetism**. First, unlike electricity (where we have single charges), there are no monopoles in magnetism, as discussed in Chapter 28. Second, the **magnetic field lines** do not start and end at the poles, but are closed curves. Third, as a consequence of this, the number of **field lines** entering a surface should equal the number leaving the surface. This leads to the fourth and last point, which is the integral of *B.dA* over a closed surface is zero here. Worked Example 29-3 in the text is a good exercise to go through in class.

In considering a **solenoid**, go through Fig. 29-16 in detail because students will not be easily convinced that the **field** outside the **solenoid** is zero and is uniform inside. Emphasize the difference between the total number of turns and the turn density of a **solenoid**. Go over Examples 29-4 and 29-5. Point out that a **toroid** is essentially a **solenoid** bent into a circle to form a donut. In the case of the **toroid,** however, the field changes across the cross-sectional area.

> ➲ **DEMO** If you are handy with tools, construct the setup described in Fig. 29-17a to show the magnetic field lines for a solenoid.

Section 29-4

To use **Ampère's law**, we need to have symmetry of the system. The **Biot – Savart law**, on the other hand, requires no symmetry. Go through the derivation of Equation 29-19. At first glance, the integral of this equation can be intimidating to students. Go through Examples 29-7 and 29-8 to show how this law is used when solving problems. The section on problem-solving techniques is very useful. Take time to go over this in class.

Section 29-5

The last section in this chapter discusses the Maxwell displacement current. Discuss the drawbacks of Ampere's law and how Maxwell addressed this by introducing the concept of a displacement current.

Textbook Resource Information

Transparency Acetates

Fig. 29-3	Magnetic field at wire 2 due to current in wire 1
Fig. 29-4	Another view of field due to a current in a wire
Fig. 29-6	Right-hand rule to find field direction due to current
Fig. 29-12	Comparing electric and magnetic field lines
Fig. 29-16	Magnetic field lines of a solenoid
Fig. 29-18	Applying Ampère's law to a solenoid
Fig. 29-20	A toroid
Fig. 29-21	Using Biot – Savart law to find field due to a current
Fig. 29-26	Magnetic field lines of a circular loop
Fig. 29-28	Two surfaces bounded by same closed path

Physlet Physics Illustrations

28.1 Fields from Wires and Loops
28.2 Forces between Wires
28.3 Ampère's Law and Symmetry
28.4 Path Integral

Physlet Physics Explorations

28.1   A long wire with uniform current
28.3   Wire configurations for a net force of zero

Physlet Physics Problems

28.2   Wire configurations for zero net force
28.4   Path integral
28.5   Coaxial cable
28.8   Ampère's path and symmetry
28.9   Magnetic field for a solenoid

Ranking Task Exercises in Physics, Student Edition

End of Chapter Problems with Solutions in the *Student Study Guide*

3, 9, 33, 47, 51, 61

Suggested Readings

Baker, B., "Demonstrating Forces between Parallel Wires," *The Physics Teacher* (May 2000), p. 299.

Chia, C., and Wang, Y., "The Magnetic Field along the Axis of a Long Finite Solenoid," *The Physics Teacher* (May 2002), p. 288 – 289.

D'Amario, J.J., and Rodano, S., "Displaying Magnetic Forces Produced by Currents," *The Physics Teacher* (May 2003), p. 307.

Dindorf, T., and Dindorf, W., "Trick of the Trade: A Useful Multipurpose Instrument," *The Physics Teacher* (October 2002), p. 440.

Erlichson, H., "The Experiments of Biot and Savart Concerning the Force Exerted by a Current on a Magnetic Needle," *Am. J. Phys.* (May 1998), p. 385 – 391.

French, A.P., "Is Maxwell's Displacement Current a Current?," *The Physics Teacher* (May 2000), p. 274 – 276.

Notes and Ideas

Preparation time: *Estimated:* _____   *Actual:* _____

Class time spent on material: *Estimated:* _____   *Actual:* _____

Related laboratory activities:

Demonstration materials:

Notes for next time:

Chapter 30: Faraday's Law

Outline

Summary

Continuing with the concept of how electricity and magnetism are closely related, this chapter discusses **induced emf** and **induced current** produced by changing magnetic fields. **Faraday's law** and **Lenz's law** are introduced, and the different ways in which induced current can be produced is considered. The application of **induced current** to **generators** is studied. **Time-varying magnetic fields** and the **frame dependence** of **magnetic fields** are also discussed.

Major Concepts

- Faraday's discovery and the law of induction
    - Magnetic induction
    - Faraday's law of magnetic induction
    - Lenz's law and the direction of the induced current
    - What sets the surfaces used in Faraday's law
    - More on magnetic induction

- Motional emf
    - Motional emf
    - Eddy currents

- Forces and energy in motional emf
    - Energy in motional emf
    - Forces and Lenz's law

- Time-varying magnetic fields
    - A new way to make an electric field
    - Is a magnetic field present where a current is induced

- Generators

- The frame dependence of fields

Teaching Suggestions and Demonstrations

By now students will be comfortable with magnetic fields as well as forces on wires and moving charges in **magnetic fields**. **Electromagnetic induction** can be confusing, so take time to go over **Faraday's law** and **Lenz's law** in detail. Use lots of demos to reinforce the two laws. Students will relate to the practical applications of induction like magnetic levitation, so discuss these applications in class.

Sections 30-1 – 30-4

To catch students' interest, introduce the concept of **induced emf** and **induced current** by using the following demos.

⮑ **DEMO** Connect a solenoid to a galvanometer. (Use an overhead projector to show the deflection of the galvanometer needle). Slowly push the north pole of a bar magnet into the coil of the solenoid. The galvanometer needle will deflect as long as the magnet is moving. Stop the motion of the magnet, and the needle will come back to zero. Now pull the magnet out and again you will notice the deflection of the needle, but in the opposite direction. Illustrate that this deflection is also dependent on the speed with which the magnet is pushed into the coil. Reverse the process by keeping the magnet stationary and moving the coil closer to and further away from the magnet. (See Figs. 30-2b and 30-2c.)

⮑ **DEMO** This demo needs two solenoids, one bigger than the other. Connect the smaller one to a power supply and the larger one to a galvanometer. Insert the smaller coil into the larger one and then pull it out. Again, as long as the coil is in motion, the galvanometer will deflect, thus showing the presence of an induced current in the larger coil.

⮑ **DEMO** A variation of the above demonstration is to keep the two coils side by side. When the switch is closed on the first coil, an induced current will be noticed in the second coil. Once the current in the first coil reaches a steady state, there will be no induced current in the second coil. Again, soon after the switch is open (as the current in the first coil reduces to zero) there will be an induced current in the second coil.

The above demos should clue students to the fact that a changing **magnetic field** produces a current. Now introduce **Faraday's law** of **magnetic induction** and **Lenz's law**. Point out that Equation 30-2 is **Faraday's law** for evaluating the **induced emf**, while **Lenz's law** helps to find the direction of the **induced emf** and hence the **induced current**. The use of **Lenz's law** requires lots of practice. Point out that it is the change in the magnetic flux that is being opposed. Show situations where the original field decreases and remind students that according to **Lenz's law**, the induced field will now be in the same direction as the original field in order to maintain the status quo.

It is important for students to recognize that a changing flux does not automatically mean a changing magnetic field. Consider Equations 30-2 and 29-11, and discuss the fact that the flux can change by changing the magnetic field (moving a magnet into or out of a coil), by changing the area (moving a coil into or out of a constant magnetic field, which introduces the concept of **motional emf**), and by changing the angle between the magnetic field vector and the area vector (rotating a coil in a magnetic field). Remind students that the angle in the dot product (in Equation 29-11) is by definition the angle between the normal to the plane of the area and the magnetic field direction. The textbook has plenty of good numerical and conceptual examples that should help in reinforcing these ideas.

Discuss the application of these concepts, especially magnetic levitation and magnetically levitated trains. Students will find this interesting.

Section 30-4 looks at **Faraday's law** in cases where there is symmetry. To understand this, review Example 30-10.

Section 30-5

The principle of a **generator** is a direct consequence of **Faraday's law**. A **generator** is the opposite of a motor. In a motor, (as seen in Chapter 28), electrical energy is converted to mechanical energy because a current-carrying loop experiences a torque when placed in a magnetic field. In the case of a **generator**, the coil is made to rotate in a magnetic field by an external force (usually a motor). The **induced current** will be sinusoidal in nature.

> ⊃ DEMO Use the demo described in Chapter 28 for a motor. Here, however, there is no current flowing through the loop and hence there is no torque on the loop. The coil is rotated by an external force. Show the students how the flux changes as the coil is rotated. Show that the induced current changes direction every half a cycle and this gives rise to an alternating current.

Section 30-6

This section looks at the dependence of the **electric** and **magnetic fields** on the **frame of reference**. Equation 30-20 shows the relationship between the **electric** and **magnetic fields** due to the transformation from one **reference frame** to another. While this section is optional, it sets the stage for Chapter 39, where the theory of special relativity is discussed. So if time permits, briefly discuss this concept.

Textbook Resource Information

Transparency Acetates

Fig. 30-3	Ways to change magnetic flux and induce a current
Fig. 30-4	Direction of surface element – right-hand rule
Fig. 30-5	Induced current and induced magnetic field
Fig. 30-8	Magnetic field lines through two surfaces bounded by a closed loop
Fig. 30-12	Conductor moving in a constant magnetic field
Fig. 30-15	Formation of eddy currents
Fig. 30-20	Magnetically levitated trains – schematic diagram
Fig. 30-21	Magnetic flux through a conducting ring due to a moving magnet
Fig. 30-23	Rotating coil in a uniform magnetic field

Physlet Physics Illustrations

29.1 Varying Field and Varying Area
29.2 Loop in a Changing Magnetic Field
29.3 Electric Generator

Physlet Physics Explorations

29.1 Lenz's law
29.2 Force on a moving wire in a uniform field
29.4 Loop in a time-varying magnetic field

Physlet Physics Problems

29.3 Motional emf
29.4 Induced emf in a loop
29.7 Moving magnets and induced emf
29.10 Magnetic field from induced current
29.11 Inductance of a solenoid

Ranking Task Exercises in Physics, Student Edition

Page 195   Graphs of current vs. time – induced current

End of Chapter Problems with Solutions in the *Student Study Guide*

7, 9, 25, 33, 47, 53

Suggested Readings

Edge, R., "A Simple Diamagnetic Levitation Experiment," *The Physics Teacher* (February 2003), p. 122.

Hinaus, B., and Veum, M., "The Hard Drive: an Experiment for Faraday's Law," *The Physics Teacher* (September 2002), p. 339 – 341.

Ivanov, D.T., "Another Way to Demonstrate Lenz's law," *The Physics Teacher* (January 2000), p. 48 – 49.

Kingman, R., and Popescu, S., "Motional EMF Demonstration Experiment," *The Physics Teacher* (March 2001), p. 142 – 144.

Kingman, R., Rowland, S., and Popescu, S., "An Experimental Observation of Faraday's Law of Induction," *Am J.Phys.* (June 2002), p. 595 – 598.

Lan, B.L., and Lim, J.B.S., "Michael Faraday: Prince of Lecturers in Victorian England," *The Physics Teacher* (January 2001), p. 32 – 36.

Nicklin, R.C., "Faraday's Law —Quantitative Experiments," *Am.J.Phys.* (May 1986), p. 422 – 486.

Sawicki, C.A., "A Lenz's Law Experiment Revisited," *The Physics Teacher* (October 2000), p. 439 – 441.

Sawicki, C.A., "Apparatus for Teaching Physics: Small Inexpensive Diamagnetic Levitation Apparatus," *The Physics Teacher* (December 2001), p. 556 – 558.

Tanner, P., Loebach, J., Cook, J., and Hallen, H., "A Pulsed Jumping Ring Apparatus for Demonstration of Lenz's Law," *Am.J.Phys.* (August 2001), p. 911 – 916.

Zhang, C.G., and Hu, S.F., "Apparatus for Teaching Physics: Another Way to Demonstrate Lenz's Law," *The Physics Teacher* (April 2002), p. 249.

Notes and Ideas

Preparation time: *Estimated:* _____   *Actual:* _____

Class time spent on material: *Estimated:* _____   *Actual:* _____

Related laboratory activities:

Demonstration materials:

Notes for next time:

Chapter 31: Magnetism and Matter

Outline

31-1   The Magnetic Properties of Bulk Matter
31-2   Atoms as Magnets
31-3   Ferromagnetism
31-4   Diamagnetism and Paramagnetism
31-5   Magnetism and Superconductivity
31-6   Nuclear Magnetic Resonance

Summary

To explain why **magnets** behave as they do is the main topic of this chapter. Starting with a discussion of the **bulk properties** of matter, topics that are discussed here include **atoms as magnets**, **ferromagnetism**, **diamagnetism**, and **paramagnetism**. The phenomenon of **hysteresis** as well as **superconductivity** and **nuclear magnetic resonance** are also considered.

Major Concepts

- The magnetic properties of bulk matter

- Atoms as magnets
    - o   The magnetic dipole moment of atoms
    - o   Bulk effects due to the alignment of atomic magnetic dipoles
    - o   Connection between microscopic and macroscopic quantities

- Ferromagnetism
    - o   Ferromagnets
    - o   Hysteresis

- Diamagnetism and paramagnetism
    - o   Diamagnetism
    - o   Paramagnetism

- Magnetism and superconductivity

- Nuclear magnetic resonance

Teaching Suggestions and Demonstrations

Very often textbooks look at how **magnets** behave and not why they behave so. The topics in this chapter are all fairly straightforward, but several new terminologies and definitions are introduced. There is also a switch in the notations used from an earlier chapter that can lead to some confusion. Furthermore, there are not many demonstrations that can help with the visualization of the abstract concepts discussed here. Keep all of this in mind when preparing to teach this chapter.

Section 31-1

To show that **magnetic properties** depend on the material, start of with the following demos.

> ↪ **DEMO** Connect a solenoid to a power supply. Turn on the power supply and introduce a wooden or copper core into the solenoid. Remove the core and test to see if it is magnetized and you will find that it is not. Now introduce an iron core and repeat the process. You will find that the iron core is indeed magnetized.

> ↪ **DEMO** You can make a very simple electromagnet without any difficulty. Wind a coil of wire around a metal bolt and connect the two ends of the coil to a power supply. Turn on the power supply and watch the bolt pick up metal paperclips. Now turn off the power supply and the paper clips will fall on to the table from the bolt that is not magnetized anymore.

The magnetic dipole moment introduced in Chapter 29-4 was referred to by the symbol μ. However, in this chapter this notation has been switched from μ to m, reserving the symbol μ for the magnetic permeability. Remind students that m is now the magnetic dipole moment and not the mass of a substance and that μ is the magnetic permeability as given by Equation 31-7.

This section introduces several new definitions and terminologies. Go through the definition of terms such as magnetic intensity, magnetic susceptibility, permeability, **ferromagnetism**, **diamagnetism** and **paramagnetism**. Equation 31-5 defines the magnetic susceptibility in terms of the magnetization and the magnetic intensity. Quite often students place greater importance on an equation and fail to recognize the physical significance of it. Go through Table 31-1 and discuss how the susceptibility value defines the kind of magnetic material. **Diamagnetic** materials have a low negative susceptibility; a small positive value is indicative of a **paramagnet** while **ferromagnets** have large positive susceptibilities. Point out that a positive susceptibility also implies that the magnetization is parallel to the external magnetic field, while in a material with a negative susceptibility, the two are antiparallel. These facts are not to be gleaned by merely considering the equation.

Table 31-2 lists and is a good overview of the **magnetic bulk properties** and the relation between these properties. Review this table with students in class and once again remind them of the change in notation for the magnetic dipole moment.

Conceptual Example 31-2 illustrates the difference between a **paramagnetic** substance and a **diamagnetic** substance and makes up for lack of visual demonstrations.

Sections 31-2 – 31-4

Section 31-2 looks at the concept of **atoms as magnets**. Remind students that a moving charge can produce a magnetic field and this forms the basis for the characterization of **atoms as magnets**. Show how the expression (Equation 31-11) for the orbital magnetic dipole moment (of an electron in orbit) is arrived at. Point out that the direction of this is given by the right-hand rule.

The idea of quantization is introduced in this course for the first time here. Discuss the effect of the quantization of the **magnetic moment** and the concept of the Bohr magneton. Inform students that they will learn more about this later on in the course. Besides the orbital **magnetic moment**, point out that the electron also has an intrinsic **magnetic moment**. The significance of the magnetic field of an individual atom lies in the fact that the alignment of the **magnetic moments** of individual atoms produces noticeable effects on a macroscopic scale. It is good to make this connection between the micro and macro worlds whenever possible. Keep in mind that these ideas are abstract and can be strange and confusing to students.

Sections 31-3 and 31-4 discuss in detail the properties of **ferromagnetic**, **diamagnetic** and **paramagnetic** materials as well as the phenomenon of **hysteresis**. The concept of domain formation is important to the understanding of the behavior of **ferromagnetic materials**. So be sure to discuss this idea and how it is affected by an external magnetic field. The electrons in a **ferromagnet** tend to align themselves so there magnetic moments are parallel. This corresponds to a lower energy state. Interestingly this is brought about by electrostatic rather than magnetic forces.

Ferromagnets exhibit the phenomenon of **hysteresis**. Use Fig. 31-9 to explain how the magnetization process is irreversible. The importance of **hysteresis** lies in the fact that **ferromagnets** can be categorized as magnetically hard or soft based on their **hysteresis** loops. A broader loop indicates that the material is not as easily affected by changes in nearby magnetic fields and hence are typically considered good for making magnetic tapes or memory disks. On the other hand, magnetically soft materials are not as stable in the presence of changing magnetic fields and hence are suitable for use in transformer cores.

Discuss the differences between **dia** and **paramagnetic** materials in terms of their response to an external magnetic field. **Diamagnetic** materials reduce the external magnetic field while **paramagnetic** materials reinforce the external magnetic field. The other difference is that **diamagnetism** is to be found in all materials while that is not the case with **paramagnetism**.

Sections 31-5 – 31-6

Superconductors have zero resistance and students are aware of this fact. Now they learn that **superconductors** have zero magnetic field inside. This is known as the Meissner effect. Discuss the difference between Type I and Type II **superconductors** and why Type II **conductors** are preferable for use in electromagnets.

➲ **DEMO** You need a superconducting disk and some liquid nitrogen to demonstrate the Meissner effect. Take a Styrofoam cup and cut off part of the side. This will enable the class to see what is happening inside the cup. Place a superconducting disk inside and then a magnet on top of the disk. Nothing will happen. Now remove the magnet and pour liquid nitrogen into the cup. When it has stopped boiling, place the magnet on top of the disk. You will need a pair of tweezers to handle the magnet.

A discussion of **nuclear magnetic resonance** completes this chapter. Once again, the concept of spin will be hard to fathom for many students. Point out that both the electron and proton can have a spin value of $\frac{1}{2}\hbar$ that can be oriented either up or down. There are two main points to keep in mind here. First, the atom is considered as an oscillating magnetic field. Second, when this field supplies a specific amount of energy to the proton, the proton spin will flip from up to down, and when this energy transfer is in the other direction (from the proton to the field) the spin flip will be opposite. This spin flip is accompanied by a signal that can be measured. Go through the section (at the very end of the chapter) titled Think About This… What Is **Magnetic Resonance** Imaging. Students will find this application interesting as they can relate to it.

Textbook Resource Information

Transparency Acetates

Fig. 31-2   Diamagnetic and paramagnetic substances near a magnet
Table 31-3   Magnetic forces on materials near a large electromagnet
Fig. 31-5   Magnetic field produced by orbiting electrons
Fig. 31-12   Magnetic moment of a two-electron atom
Fig. 31-14   Meissner effect in Type I superconductor
Fig. 31-15   Meissner effect in Type II superconductor
Fig. 31-16   Precession of magnetic moment of a proton

Physlet Physics Illustrations

27.5   Permanent Magnets and Ferromagnetism

Ranking Task Exercises in Physics, Student Edition

Page 191   Pairs of equal current electromagnets - force
Page 192   Pairs of equal current electromagnets – magnetic field between
Page 193   Unequal current electromagnets – magnetic field at ends
Page 194   Unequal current electromagnets – magnetic field between

End of Chapter Problems with Solutions in the *Student Study Guide*

7, 13, 17, 23, 25, 49

Suggested Readings

Brahmia, B., and Horton, G., "Induction or Hysteresis: That is the Cooktop Question," *The Physics Teacher* (February 2001), p. 80 – 83.

Brown, R., "Demonstrating the Meissner Effect and Persistent Current," *The Physics Teacher* (March 2000), p. 168 – 169.

Conery, C., Goodrich, L. F., and Stauffer, T. C., "More Diamagnetism Demonstrations," *The Physics Teacher* (February 2003), p. 74 – 75.

Edge, R., "A Simple Diamagnetic Levitation Experiment," *The Physics Teacher* (February 2003), p. 122.

Gavrin, A., "Induction or Hysteresis: No Longer a Burning Issue," *The Physics Teacher* (September 2001), p. 354 – 355.

Sawicki, C.A., "Apparatus for Teaching Physics: Small Inexpensive Diamagnetic Levitation Apparatus," *The Physics Teacher* (December 2001), p. 556 – 558.

Schreiner, M., and Palmy, C., "Why Does a Cylindrical Permanent Magnet Rotate When Levitated Above a Superconducting Plate?," *Am. J. Phys.* (February 2004), p. 243 – 248.

Stacey, J.E., "String & Sticky Tape Experiments: The Mechanic's Electromagnet, *The Physics Teacher* (November 2002), p. 505.

Welsh, G.S., "Magnetic Therapy in Physics?," *The Physics Teacher* (March 2000), p. 181 – 182.

Zaspel, C.E., Dahle, A.B., Given, L.D. and Weinert, J.L., "A Simple Apparatus for Illustration of Magnetic Hysteresis Effects," *Am. J. Phys.* (February 2004), p. 284 – 285.

Notes and Ideas

Preparation time: *Estimated:* _____   *Actual:* _____

Class time spent on material: *Estimated:* _____   *Actual:* _____

Related laboratory activities:

Demonstration materials:

Notes for next time:

Chapter 32: Inductance and Circuit Oscillations

Outline

Summary

Self and **mutual inductance** and **energy** in **inductors** and **magnetic fields** are studied in this chapter. **Inductors** play a useful role in controlling the **time dependence** in circuits. **RL circuits** and **time dependence** in such circuits are considered. **Oscillations** in **LC circuits, damped oscillations** in **RLC circuits,** and **energy** in **LC** and **RLC circuits** are also discussed.

Major Concepts

- Inductance and inductors
  - Self-inductance
  - Mutual inductance
  - Finding the inductance
  - The effects of magnetic materials on inductance

- Energy in inductors

- Energy in magnetic fields

- Time dependence in RL circuits

- Oscillations in LC Circuits

- Damped oscillations in RLC circuits

- Energy in LC and RLC circuits

Teaching Suggestions and Demonstrations

RC circuits and the energy stored in the electric field of a capacitor were treated in Chapter 27 of this textbook. Here students will learn how energy can be stored in the magnetic field of an **inductance coil**. The behavior of **LC, RLC** and **damped RLC circuits** are similar to that of an oscillating spring-mass system. Make sure that you emphasize this analogy at every turn so students will get a better grasp of such circuits. Again, due to absence of demos, use the figures in the textbook to reinforce the concepts.

Sections 32-1 – 32-3

Begin by reminding students of Faraday's law and Lenz's law. Discuss the difference between **self-** and **mutual inductance**. Use Fig. 32-1 to illustrate the behavior of the current and induced emf over time in a coil. In the case of **mutual inductance**, stress that each coil will induce an emf in the other and the **mutual inductance** of the two coils will be equal. When the current reaches the steady state (be it in the case of **self-inductance** or **mutual inductance**), the induced emf will no longer be present. This is a point that needs to be stressed.

➤ **DEMO**   This demo is the same as one described in Chapter 30. Two solenoids (or coils) are placed side by side. Connect one coil to a power supply and the other to a galvanometer. When the switch is closed on the first coil, an induced current will be noticed in the second coil. Once the current in the first coil reaches a steady state, there will be no induced current in the second coil. Again, soon after the switch is open (as the current in the first coil reduces to zero) there will be an induced current in the second coil

Remind students that Kirchhoff's law can still be applied when an **inductance coil** is included in a circuit, and the potential change across the **inductor** is given by Equation 32-2. Cite the chiming doorbell as one application of **self-inductance**. Figure 32-8 shows a schematic of a doorbell. Go through conceptual Example 32-5 to show how the induced emf in a coil is affected as a ferromagnetic cylinder moves through a coil.

Sections 32-2 and 32-3 discuss the **energy stored** in **inductors**. Remind students that the rate at which work is done is the power. Compare Equation 25-8 and Equation 32-13 and comment on the similarities between the two. Remind students that in the case of a capacitor, this energy is stored in the electric field that exists within the capacitor. In the case of an **inductor**, the energy is stored in the magnetic field within the **inductor**.

Section 32-4

Because the potential drop across an **inductor** is dependent on the rate of change of the current (as well as the sign of this change), it introduces a **time-dependence** factor into circuits that contain **inductors**. This is discussed in detail in Section 32-4. Begin by drawing a simple *RL* **circuit**. Go through each element to show how the potential drop is determined and write down Kirchhoff's loop rule. Compare this to Equation 27-21 to show how Equation 32-19 gives the solution to the differential Equation 32-18.

The analogous behavior of *RC* and *RL* **circuits** is shown in Table 32-1. Point out that the time constant in the case of an *RL* **circuit** is given by the ratio of the inductance to the resistance. Again use dimensional analysis to show how L/R does indeed measure time.

The most important point to remember here (in the case of an *RL* **circuit**) is that once the current in the circuit reaches a steady state, the **inductor** has no role in the circuit. Figure 32-12 shows the current increasing from zero to a steady value, and this behavior is expressed in mathematical form by Equation 32-19. Again point out the exponential nature of this expression. Example 32-8 clearly shows the potential across the **inductor** and the resistor as a function of time. Be sure to point out that this agrees with the statement that the **inductor** plays no role in the circuit once the steady state is reached.

Sections 32-5 – 32-6

Both *LC* **circuits** and **damped** *RLC* **circuits** show behavior similar to the oscillations of a spring-mass system. It is important that you start from Equation 32-21 and compare it to Equation 32-22, to stress the significance of this comparison. This gives credence to the claim that the solution to Equation 32-21 is of the form given by Equation 32-25. In the case of an *LC* **circuit**, Equation 32-25 and 32-26 show the **time-dependence** of the charge and current. Point out that the current will be a maximum when the charge on the capacitor is a minimum and vice versa. Use Table 32-2 to compare a spring-mass system to the behavior of the *LC* **circuit**.

Discuss how the oscillations of a spring-mass system would be affected by the presence of a drag force. Compare this to the addition of a resistance to an *LC* **circuit**. Use Figs. 32-16, 32-17, and Table 32-3 to emphasize this fact. In Chapter 13, students learned about **damped oscillations** and the concept of **critical damping**. *LRC* **circuits** can also be subjected to **critical damping** by choosing an appropriate value for the resistance (as given by Equation 32-33). Point out the practical application of this to situations where there is a need to eliminate oscillations in the current.

Section 32-7

To understand the effect on the **energy** when a resistance is added to an *LC* **circuit**, consider a circuit with no resistance (as discussed in the textbook). Take the students step by step through the treatment shown in Section 32-7. Remind students that the current and charge in an *LC* **circuit** do not peak at the same time (see Fig. 32-19) and neither does the energy stored in the **capacitor** and **inductor** (see Fig. 32-20). Be sure to point out that these energies are always positive. It is very easy for students to represent the energy curve to oscillate between positive and negative values as well.

Figure 32-21 shows very clearly how the **energy** oscillates between the **capacitor** and the **inductor** (between the **electric field** and the **magnetic field**) just as an oscillating mass has its energy changing between potential and kinetic energies.

Now discuss what happens when a resistor is introduced into an *LC* **circuit** and damping takes place. Remind students that in the case of a resistor, energy will always be lost due to Joule heating. This is what causes the exponential damping in the case of an *RLC* **circuit**.

Textbook Resource Information

Transparency Acetates

Fig. 32-3	Mutual inductance
Fig. 32-6	Single loop inside a solenoid – mutual inductance
Fig. 32-8	Chiming doorbell – application of inductance
Table 32-1	Analogy between *RC* and *RLC* circuits
Table 32-2	Analogy between *LC* circuits and mass on a spring
Fig. 32-16	*RLC* circuit with and without damping
Fig. 32-17	*RLC* circuit for different *R* values
Fig. 32-19	Current and charge vs. time plots for an *LC* circuit
Fig. 32-20	Inductor and capacitor energies for an *LC* circuit
Fig. 32-21	Time sequence of electric and magnetic fields and energies for an *LC* circuit

Physlet Physics Explorations

29.5 Self-inductance

End of Chapter Problems with Solutions in the *Student Study Guide*

7, 21, 29, 49, 55, 67

Suggested Readings

Crawford, F.S., "Mutual inductance $M_{12} = M_{21}$: An Elementary Derivation," *Am.J.Phys.* (February 1992), p. 186.

Notes and Ideas

Preparation time: *Estimated:* _____   *Actual:* _____

Class time spent on material: *Estimated:* _____   *Actual:* _____

Related laboratory activities:

Demonstration materials:

Notes for next time:

Chapter 33: Alternating Currents

Outline

Summary

Alternating current is the theme in this chapter. First the working of a **transformer** is considered. **Single element circuits** and then ***RLC* circuits** are discussed. **Phasor diagrams** are used to analyze the relationship between voltage, current and **impedance**/resistance of the different circuits. The **power** in AC circuits and some applications (such as **filters, diodes** and **rectifiers**) of alternating currents are considered.

Major Concepts

- Transformers

- Single elements in AC circuits
    - Resistive circuit
    - Capacitive circuit
    - Inductive circuit
    - Some mathematical devices

- AC in series *RLC* circuits
    - Driven *RLC* circuits
    - Impedance
    - Resonance in driven *RLC* circuits

- Power in AC circuits
    - Power in AC circuits
    - The power factor

- Some applications
    - Diodes and rectifiers
    - Filters
    - Impedance matching

Teaching Suggestions and Demonstrations

Chapter 30 looked at the working of a generator and how it produced an **alternating current**. The generator now serves as the power source for the circuits considered in this chapter. Students will not have much trouble understanding the behavior of **single-element circuits**. However, ***RLC* circuits**, the concept of **impedance,** and the use of **phasor diagram** are always a source of confusion. Use of diagrams and graphs will help dispel some of this confusion.

Section 33-1

⮌ **DEMO** Bring in an assortment of transformers and point out the primary and secondary coils of the transformer.

⮌ **DEMO** Connect the primary coil of the transformer to an AC power source. Turn on the power source and measure the voltage output of the secondary coil. Now reverse the process by connecting the secondary coil of the transformer to the power source and measure the voltage output of the second coil.

Use the above demo to illustrate that the ratio of the input-to-output voltage is dependent on the ratio of the number of turns in the primary and the secondary coils. Point out the various uses of step-up and step-down **transformers**. Ask students what would happen if they were to use an electrical appliance that was manufactured in Europe, here in the United States and vice versa. You may have to remind them that wall outlets in European countries supply power at 220V. The discussion Think About This…Why Is Electric Power Transmitted Along High-Voltage Lines' will be very informative to them.

⮌ **DEMO** Connect a lightbulb in series with the primary coil and a variable resistor in series with the secondary coil of the transformer. Increase the resistance in the secondary circuit. The current in the primary coil will decrease and the brightness of the lightbulb will also diminish.

Sections 33-2 – 33-4

For each of the **single-element circuits**, draw a circuit diagram and show a plot of the voltage and current vs. time. Point out that since the source voltage is sinusoidal, the current will also be sinusoidal. Define the terms **capacitive reactance** and **inductive reactance** and draw students' attention to the similarity of Equations 33-16 and 33-19 to Ohm's law. Introduce the concept of voltage and current being in phase or out of phase as the case may be and show them how the phase difference is expressed in degrees or as a fraction of π radians. Discuss the difference between Figs. 33-4b and 33-5b so they will learn to tell whether the voltage leads the current or lags behind the current. This is always a source of confusion to many students.

For each of the three **single-element circuits**, draw the **phasor diagram** (see Fig. 33-7). Point out that **phasor diagrams** are just another way of representing the phase angle between voltage and current (as seen earlier on the graphs).

Once students get a good understanding of the behavior of the **single-element circuits** and the **phasor** representation, they will find the ***RLC* series circuit** easy to deal with. Emphasize that the **impedance** is merely the effective resistance of an ***RLC* circuit**. Work several examples of **single-element circuits** as well as ***RLC* circuits** so students learn to calculate the reactance/**impedance**, **phase** angles and voltage drop across each of the elements.

Equation 33-32 is the starting point for introducing the concept of **resonance** in an ***RLC* circuit**. Ask students when the current will be a maximum in the circuit. Once they recognize that the **impedance** has to be a minimum, point out that the **capacitive reactance** must equal the **inductive reactance** to realize this. This condition then leads to **resonance**.

Students are familiar with the formula ($P = I^2R$) for **power** in the case of a DC circuit. Since the current is positive for one half of a cycle and negative for the second half, they will conclude that the average power delivered over one cycle is zero. However, in an AC circuit the power depends on the rms value of the current. Define root mean square value and go through the derivation of Equation 33-39. Emphasize the difference between peak and rms values of current and voltage.

Section 33-5

While typical modern circuits are far more complicated and include many more elements, it is still useful to learn how **filters**, **diodes** and **rectifiers** work. Bring in a charger that is used for recharging a battery. Point out that this charging device is plugged into a household AC outlet; yet, it is used to charge a battery that requires a DC current. Use this to start a discussion on how an AC voltage can be "rectified" to a DC voltage using a **diode**. Explain how **rectification** is produced using the unusual behavior of a semiconductor. Be sure to point out the symbol for a **diode** (see Fig. 33-15). Discuss the difference between a half-wave and full-wave **rectifier**. Be sure to mention the use of **rectifiers** in an automobile.

Filters are used to allow either an AC or DC signal to get across to one part of a circuit from an input that is a mixture of both AC and DC signals. Use Fig. 33-17 to explain how this can be achieved by using either a capacitor or an inductor.

To introduce the concept of **impedance matching**, use the example (given in the textbook) of a stereo amplifier and a loudspeaker and the need to maximize the power delivered to the loudspeaker. Students are sure to relate to this with great interest.

Textbook Resource Information

Transparency Acetates

Fig. 33-1	Two methods for creating fully linked coils
Fig. 33-3b	Voltage and current vs. time for resistive circuit
Fig. 33-4b	Voltage and current vs. time for a capacitive circuit
Fig. 33-5b	Voltage and current vs. time for an inductive circuit
Fig. 33-7	Phasor diagrams
Table 33-1	Analogy between driven RLC circuit and driven spring-mass system
Fig. 33-12	Driving voltage and current vs. time for RLC circuit
Fig. 33-14	Rms current vs. frequency plots for different R values
Fig. 33-16	Half and full wave rectifiers
Fig. 33-17	AC and DC filters
Fig. 33-20	Effect of filters on a signal

Physlet Physics Illustrations

31.2 AC Voltage and Current
31.3 Transformers
31.4 Phase Shifts
31.5 Power and Reactance
31.6 Voltage and Current Phasors
31.8 Impedance and Resonance, RLC Circuits

Physlet Physics Explorations

Physlet Physics Problems

End of Chapter Problems with Solutions in the *Student Study Guide*

3, 7, 29, 35, 59, 61

Suggested Readings

Akridge, R., "AC Reactance without Calculus," *The Physics Teacher* (January 1997), p. 20 – 21.

Backman, P., Murley, C., and Williams, P.J., "The Driven RLC Circuit Experiment," *The Physics Teacher* (October 1999), p. 424 – 425.

Johns, R., "Apparatus for Teaching Physics: Simplifying AC-Current Measurements," *The Physics Teacher* (May 2001), p. 314 – 315.

Mak, S., "From Electromagnetic Induction to Electromagnetic Radiation," *The Physics Teacher* (October 2000), p. 428 – 429.

Oliver, J., "Observing Voltage Phases in RC, RL, and RLC Circuits," *The Physics Teacher* (January 1997), p. 30.

Pomarico, J.A., "Apparatus for Teaching Physics: Seeing Rectifiers at Work," *The Physics Teacher* (February 2002), p. 118 – 119.

Ruby, L., "Why DC for Long-Range Power Transmission," *The Physics Teacher* (May 2002), p. 272 – 274.

Silverman, M.P., "Power, Reaction, and Excitement ... in an AC Circuit," *The Physics Teacher* (May 2002), p. 302 – 307.

Wood, H.T., "The RC circuit---A Multipurpose Laboratory Experiment," *The Physics Teacher* (September 1993), p. 372 – 373.

Notes and Ideas

Preparation time: *Estimated:* _____   *Actual:* _____

Class time spent on material: *Estimated:* _____   *Actual:* _____

Related laboratory activities:

Demonstration materials:

Notes for next time:

Chapter 34: Maxwell's Equations and Electromagnetic Waves

Outline

Summary

The study of electricity and magnetism in the last six chapters now come together in the form of **Maxwell's equations**. These equations are considered a set of fundamental laws that describe electricity and magnetism. **Electromagnetic waves**, their properties, and **dipole radiation** are discussed. **Polarization** of light and a look at **electromagnetic radiation** as **particles** completes this chapter.

Major Concepts

- Maxwell's equations

- Electromagnetic waves
    - Electromagnetic waves
    - The propagation of electromagnetic waves
    - The propagation speed of electromagnetic waves
    - The relation between E and B in electromagnetic waves
    - The transversality of electromagnetic waves
    - Electromagnetic waves are real

- Energy and momentum flow
    - The energy of electromagnetic waves
    - The transport of energy
    - Momentum in electromagnetic waves

- Dipole radiation
    - Dipole radiation
    - How the intensity of radiation from an antenna decreases with distance
    - The angular pattern of dipole radiation

- Polarization
    - Polarization of light
    - Malus's law
    - How to produce polarized radiation

- Electromagnetic radiation as particles

Teaching Suggestions and Demonstrations

Most of the topics in this chapter are very theoretical. As such, the mathematical treatment is essential to the study of these topics. With this in mind, allow enough time for going through the derivations in detail in class. Compared to the first half of the chapter, the discussion of **polarization** will be relatively easier.

Section 34-1

Begin this chapter by going over **Gauss' law** for electric fields and magnetic fields, **Ampère's law** and **Faraday's law**. Enumerate the salient features of these four equations (as described in the textbook). Point out the symmetry between electric and magnetic fields that is to be found in these equations and briefly touch on the fact that the presence of matter will affect these equations, albeit slightly. The most significant aspect of **Maxwell's equations** is the prediction of **electromagnetic waves** that travel at the speed of light (as we know it today). Students may not grasp the full import of this.

Sections 34-2 – 34-4

In discussing **electromagnetic waves** and its properties, the following points need to be emphasized. First, all **electromagnetic waves** travel at the same speed through vacuum. Second, these waves have an electric and a magnetic component to them, and the two fields are perpendicular to each other. Third, the direction of propagation of the wave is perpendicular to both the electric and magnetic fields. In other words, **electromagnetic waves** are transverse waves. (You may have to remind students of the definition of transverse waves.) The last point is the relationship between the frequency (and hence the energy) and wavelength of the waves. Use a chart of the **electromagnetic spectrum** to show the different parts of the spectrum and point out the small portion of the spectrum that forms the visible region. Emphasize that gamma rays have the greatest energy and radio waves have the longest wavelength.

It will be hard for students to accept that **electromagnetic waves** have momentum and transfer radiation pressure when they are absorbed. Work through Examples 34-5, 34-6 and 34-7 to help them relate to these concepts.

Section 34-5

In comparison to the earlier sections of this chapter, **polarization** will be easy for most students, especially when accompanied by suitable demos. Use the following demos to introduce the topic and to discuss the concept of **crossed polaroids** and the variation of intensity of the **polarized light**.

- ⮑ **DEMO** Use two pairs of Polaroid sunglasses and show how the intensity of the transmitted light varies from maximum to zero as one glass is rotated over the other. This is a very simple but impressive demonstration of polarization. Point out that one could indeed verify if his/her "polaroid" sunglasses are truly Polaroid.

- ⮑ **DEMO** Instead of sunglasses, use two Polaroid sheets and perform the same demo. Place the sheets on an overhead projector. Keep the bottom sheet stationary, rotate the top sheet. The variation in the intensity of the transmitted light is easily noticeable (to the whole class) on the projection screen.

- ⮑ **DEMO** Join two dowels together (parallel to each other) to form a long, narrow opening. Make a similar setup with two other dowels. Orient the two pairs of dowels so the openings are aligned. Pass a string through the two polaroids. Use a drill to produce circular standing waves in the string. The first opening/slit ('polaroid) will polarize the string and produce polarized waves. If the second opening/slit (analyzer) is parallel to the first, the string will continue with the same intensity through the analyzer. If the polarizer and analyzer are crossed, the wave will not be able to pass through the second slit.

When discussing **Malus's law**, work out an example to show how the intensity is affected when light goes through successive **polarizers**. Each time the intensity decreases according to Equation 34-34. For example, if light goes through three sheets, $I_1 = I_0\cos^2\theta$; $I_2 = I_1\cos^2\theta = (I_0\cos^2\theta)(I_0\cos^2\theta) = I_0\cos^4\theta$ and so on.

⊃ **DEMO** Three Polaroid sheets can be used to show how the intensity of the transmitted polarized light is affected by each successive polarizing sheet.

Section 34-6

Although the last section is marked as optional, a brief discussion of **photons** and the **energy** associated with **photons** would set the stage for wave optics. The fact that a massless particle can have momentum will be hard to swallow for many students, so this will give them some time to get used to the idea before they come back to it later on in wave optics.

Textbook Resource Information

Transparency Acetates

Fig. 34-2	Surface bounded by a closed loop
Fig. 34-3	Coupling of electric and magnetic fields
Fig. 34-5	Magnetic field of a series of parallel currents
Fig. 34-6	View of transverse electric and magnetic fields
Fig. 34-7b	Schematic diagram of Hertz's apparatus
Fig. 34-8b	Spectrum of electromagnetic radiation
Fig. 34-11	Schematic form of optical tweezers
Fig. 34-13	Angular distribution of power emitted by oscillating charges
Fig. 34-17	Unpolarized light passing through two polarizers
Fig. 34-19	Polarization of radiation by scattering
Fig. 34-21	Brewster's angle

Physlet Physics Illustrations

32.1 Creation of Electromagnetic Waves
32.3 Electromagnetic Plane Waves
32.4 Electromagnetic Waves: E x B
39.1 Polarization
39.2 Polarized Electromagnetic Waves

Physlet Physics Explorations

32.1 Representation of plane waves
32.2 Plane waves and the electric field equation

Physlet Physics Problems

End of Chapter Problems with Solutions in the *Student Study Guide*

5, 17, 25, 41, 51, 57

Suggested Readings

Benenson, R.E., "Light Polarization Experiments with a Diode Laser Pointer," *The Physics Teacher* (January 2000), p. 44 – 46.

Cortel, A., "Demonstrating the Relationship Between the Energy and Frequency of Light," *The Physics Teacher* (March 2000), p. 152.

Easton, D., "Apparatus for Teaching Physics: Transmission through Crossed Polaroid Filters," *The Physics Teacher* (April 2001), p. 231 – 233.

Krieble, K., and Powlette, J.L., "A Simple Apparatus for Optical Polarization Experiments," *The Physics Teacher* (December 2003), p. 537 – 541.

Mak, S., "Speed of Electromagnetic Signal Along a Coaxial Cable," *The Physics Teacher* (January 2003), p. 46 – 49.

Middleton, A.A., and Sampere, S., "Apparatus for Teaching Physics: Color Mixing via Polarization," *The Physics Teacher* (February 2001), p. 123 – 124.

Ouseph, P.J., "Apparatus for Teaching Physics: Polarization of Reflected Light," *The Physics Teacher* (October 2002), p. 438 – 439.

Ouseph, P.J., Driver, K., and Conklin, J., "Polarization of Light by Reflection and the Brewster Angle," *Am.J.Phys.* (November 2001), p. 1166 – 1168.

Stevens, R.E., "A Simulation of Optical Polarization," *The Physics Teacher* (April 2000), p. 222 – 223.

Wardle, D.A., "Absorption of Microwaves in the Microwave Oven," *The Physics Teacher* (April 2001), p. 210 – 211.

Notes and Ideas

Preparation time: *Estimated:* _____   *Actual:* _____

Class time spent on material: *Estimated:* _____   *Actual:* _____

Related laboratory activities:

Demonstration materials:

Notes for next time:

Chapter 35: Light

Outline

Summary

With this chapter we start the study of optics. A historical perspective of the measurement of the **speed** of **light** is explored briefly. The **index of refraction** is defined, and **light** as **rays** is considered. The phenomena of **reflection** and **refraction** in **plane surfaces** and **total internal reflection** are treated. **Huygen's** and **Fermat's principles** are discussed, and the formation of **rainbows** and the **blue** of the **sky** are also studied.

Major Concepts

- The speed of light
    - o   Experimental measurement of the speed of light
    - o   The index of refraction

- When can light waves be treated as rays
    - o   Huygen's principle

- Reflection and refraction
    - o   Reflection
    - o   Refraction
    - o   Energy in reflection and refraction
    - o   Total internal reflection

- Fermat's principle

- Dispersion
    - o   Rainbows and the blue sky
    - o   The atomic theory of dispersion

Teaching Suggestions and Demonstrations

This marks the beginning of the study of optics. Inform students that the particle nature of **light** will be considered to discuss **reflection**, **refraction** and **dispersion**, but that **light** behaves as a **wave** as well. Use plenty of visual aids and **ray diagrams** to explain the passage of rays to form images due to reflection and refraction.

Sections 35-1 – 35-2

Briefly discuss the experimental measurement of the **speed** of **light** and the fact that **light** travels at different **speeds** in different materials (media). Point out that it has the highest speed in vacuum, and the speed in other media is related to the speed in vacuum according to Equation 35-1. Stress the fact that the **index of refraction** cannot be less than 1 by definition. Since the different regions of the **electromagnetic spectrum** have different wavelengths, the **index of refraction** in a material will be different for different wavelengths in the same media. This is a connection often not made by students.

Huygen's construction of wavefronts from wavelets emitted at each point on the wavefront is now a well-accepted way of representing the progress of waves as they move through a medium. A **ray** depicts the direction in which a wave moves. This relation between wavefronts and **rays** is an important connection that must be remembered, so at least for the first couple of diagrams, take the time to draw the wavefronts and then the **rays**. This will help students remember this connection between wavefronts and **rays** at all times. Emphasize that a plane wavefront is a spherical wavefront with infinite radius, then connect this to the idea that light from a distant source will essentially consist of plane wavefronts.

Sections 35-3 – 35-4

In discussing **reflection** and **refraction**, define terms such as the normal at the point of incidence, the angle of incidence and the angle of **reflection/refraction**.

- ⮑ **DEMO** Set a plane mirror standing up on a black sheet of construction paper. Shine a laser light onto the mirror and trace the path of the incident and reflected rays. (A laser beam will form a sharp "ray" that is useful in depicting ray diagrams). Remove the mirror and draw a perpendicular at the point of incidence. Measure the angles of incidence and refraction and show that these two angles are equal.

- ⮑ **DEMO** Set up plane mirrors as shown in Figs. 35-9 and 35-10. Use a laser beam to show reflection by multiple mirrors.

- ⮑ **DEMO** Half fill a glass with water. Insert a pencil into the water and point out the appearance of a bend in the pencil at the water – air boundary. Students will be familiar with this phenomenon.

- ⮑ **DEMO** Place a glass slab on a dark-colored sheet of paper. Shine a laser beam on one of the side surfaces of the slab and at an angle to the surface. The bending of the beam as it goes through the slab will be noticeable. Change the angle of the incoming beam, and the path of the ray inside the slab will change.

Use the above two demos to introduce the concept of refraction. State Snell's law and point out that the index of refraction is inversely proportional to the sine of the angle in that medium. Again draw ray diagrams for the situation when the object is in a rarer medium and the observer is in the denser medium. Show that the image will appear to be farther from the surface than it actually is. When the object is in the denser medium and the observer is in the rarer medium, the image will appear closer to the surface than it actually is.

You can now lead the discussion toward total internal reflection. Use Fig. 35-17 to show the effect of increasing the angle of incidence. Define critical angle and grazing refraction. Two points need to be emphasized here. First, the light rays must start from a denser medium and go into a rarer medium. Second, the angle of incidence must be greater than the critical angle.

⊃ **DEMO** Use a laser light and prism in the two orientations shown below to illustrate total internal reflection.

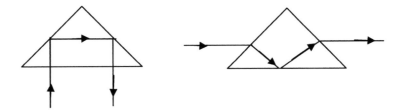

Point out that bicycle reflectors work in the manner shown in the first of the two diagrams above.

Section 35-3

Fermat's principle explains reflection as well as the bending of light rays at the surface of separation of two media of different indices of refraction. Use Fig. 35-21 and the analogy of a marching band changing direction to describe the behavior of light rays during refraction.

Section 35-5

⊃ **DEMO** Shine a well-defined narrow beam of white light on to the side of a prism or hold a prism in the path of sunlight to show the formation of a spectrum on the opposite wall.

Dispersion occurs because the index of refraction is different for different wavelengths of the electromagnetic spectrum. Use table 36-2 to show that near ultraviolet has the greatest index of refraction and hence it will undergo the largest deviation (Snell's law). Most students will remember the mnemonic ROYGBIV. Point out that a rainbow is formed due to dispersion of sunlight by water droplets that essentially behave like a prism. Use Fig. 35-27 to explain why we see a double rainbow at times.

The small section on why the sky is blue and the clouds are white will be edifying to most students. So take time to discuss this in class.

Textbook Resource Information

Transparency Acetates

Fig. 35-2   Fizeau's method for measuring speed of light
Fig. 35-5   Wave fronts passing through a slit
Fig. 35-20   Sequence of wave fronts approaching a mirror
Fig. 35-22   Geometry for proving Snell's law
Fig. 35-27a   How an observer sees a rainbow

Physlet Physics Illustrations

33.2 Flat Mirrors
34.1 Huygen's Principle and Refraction
34.2 Fiber Optics
34.3 Prisms and Dispersion

Physlet Physics Explorations

33.3 Image in a flat mirror
34.2 Snell's law and total internal reflection
34.4 Fermat's principle and Snell's law
34.5 Index of refraction and wavelength

Physlet Physics Problems

34.2 Unknown index of refraction
34.9 Total internal reflection

Ranking Task Exercises in Physics, Student Edition

Page 208   Person in plane mirror – fraction visible

End of Chapter Problems with Solutions in the *Student Study Guide*

3, 21, 33, 37, 49, 51

Suggested Readings

Beaver, J.E., "The Speed of Light with a Shortwave Radio," *The Physics Teacher* (March 2000), p. 172 – 174.

Brody, B., "The Speed of Light: Making an Easy Time of It," *The Physics Teacher* (May 2003), p. 276 – 277.

Cohen, A., and Galili, I., "Where is the Sky?," *The Physics Teacher* (February 2001), p. 92 – 96.

Cortel, A., "String & Sticky Tape Experiments: Apparent-Depth Demonstration Using a Plastic Box and Pins," *The Physics Teacher* (October 2002), p. 441.

Fakhruddin, H., "Specular Reflection from a Rough Surface," *The Physics Teacher* (April 2003), p. 206 – 207.

Hendry, A.W., "A Triple Rainbow?," *The Physics Teacher* (November 2003), p. 460 – 463.

Horst, K.E., "The Shape of Lamp Shade Shadows," *The Physics Teacher* (March 2001), p. 139 – 140.

Houser, B., "Demonstrating the Decreased Wavelength of Light in Water," *The Physics Teacher* (April 2001), p. 228 – 229.

Kokhanovsky, A.A., "Single Light Scattering: Bubbles versus Droplets," *Am. J. Phys.* (February 2004), p. 258 – 263.

Newburgh, R., Rueckner, W., Peidle, J., and Goodale, D., "Using the Small-Angle Approximation to Measure the Index of Refraction of Water," *The Physics Teacher* (December 2000), p. 478 – 479.

Niculescu, A., "Demonstration of Light-Wave Communication for High School Physics," *The Physics Teacher* (September 2002), p. 347 – 350.

Salinas, J., and Sandoval, J., "Geometrical Optics and Visual Perception," *The Physics Teacher* (October 2001), p. 420 – 423.

Sawicki, M., and Sawicki, P., "Supernumerary Rainbows," *The Physics Teacher* (January 2000), p. 19.

Thompson, G., and Mathieson, D., "Apparatus for Teaching Physics: The Mirror Box," *The Physics Teacher* (November 2001), p. 508 – 509.

Notes and Ideas

Preparation time: *Estimated:* _____   *Actual:* _____

Class time spent on material: *Estimated:* _____   *Actual:* _____

Related laboratory activities:

Demonstration materials:

Notes for next time:

Chapter 36: Mirrors and Lenses and Their Uses

Outline

Summary

The last chapter laid the foundation for geometric optics and use of ray diagrams. **Reflection** in **plane mirrors** and **spherical mirrors** and **refraction** at **spherical surfaces** are discussed here. **Mirror** and **lens equations** for object and image distances are derived and drawing of **ray diagrams** are illustrated. The **lens-maker's equation** for **thin lenses** is also derived. The working of the **human eye**, **simple magnifier**, **telescope** and the **camera** are looked at. The concept of **spherical aberration** is briefly discussed.

Major Concepts

- Images and mirrors
  - Plane mirrors
  - The image of an extended object

- Spherical mirrors
  - The concave mirror
  - The convex mirror
  - The relation between source distance and image distance
  - Magnification

- Refraction at spherical surfaces
  - Refraction at a single surface
  - The relation between source distance and image distance

- Thin lenses
  - The lens-maker's equation
  - Magnification

- Optical instruments
  - The eye
  - The camera
  - Angular magnification
  - The simple magnifier
  - The telescope

- Aberration

Teaching Suggestions and Demonstrations

Since we cannot see light travel in straight lines from the source to a **mirror** or a **lens**, it is difficult to visualize the formation of images in **mirrors** and **lenses** without visual aids, so use plenty of demos and follow up with ray diagrams to reinforce the concepts. Since light from a laser is like a ray, use a laser to show how rays are reflected or refracted.

Sections 36-1 – 36-2

In discussing reflection at a **plane mirror**, define terms like the normal at the point of incidence, the angle of incidence and the angle of reflection.

⮑ **DEMO** Set a plane mirror standing up on a black sheet of construction paper. Shine a laser light onto the mirror and trace the path of the incident and reflected rays. (A laser beam will form a sharp "ray" that is useful to depict ray diagrams.) Remove the mirror and draw a perpendicular at the point of incidence. Measure the angles of incidence and refraction and show that these two angles are equal.

⮑ **DEMO** Bring a fairly reasonably sized mirror to class. Hold it in front of the class and ask students to identify the images she/he notices. Point out that not all of the students can see images of all of the objects in a room. A person sees only those images from which the reflected rays meet the eye of the observer. Follow this with a ray diagram for image formation (see Fig. 36-1).

Draw the ray diagram for the formation of the image due to **reflection** by a **plane mirror**. Point out that the **reflected** rays diverge and hence appear (this is the key term here) to come from a point behind the mirror. This sets the stage for the definition of a virtual image.

⮑ **DEMO** Bring in concave and convex mirrors of different focal length. Direct the concave mirror toward an object (trees or buildings outside the window) and adjust the tilt and location of the mirror until you get a well-defined image on the wall. Point out that the image is inverted and the distance between the mirror and the image defines the focal length. Now repeat the process with a convex mirror, and you will see a blurred white spot instead of a well-defined image.

⮑ **DEMO** Use a laser light to show how a ray gets refracted by a lens and emphasize that the ray goes through to the other side.

⮑ **DEMO** Set up a concave mirror on an optic bench. A small candle or a bulb can act as the source. Locate the image for different object distances and have the students note the nature of the image (magnification and if it is inverted or upright). As the object is moved closer to the mirror, the image will become larger and larger. Place the object real close to the mirror and show that a real image is not possible. Repeat the process with a convex mirror and a real image cannot be located for any object distance.

Emphasize that the image formed by a **convex mirror** is virtual, and the focal point is behind the **mirror**. Discuss the difference between a **concave** and **convex mirror** and the kind of image that can be obtained with each. Give students plenty of practice with ray diagrams so they become familiar with converging and diverging reflected rays and formation of real and virtual images. Review Table 36-1 and discuss the sign convention used for **mirrors**. Again, have them work plenty of problems so they learn to apply the sign convention to different situations.

Summarize the image formation in **concave** and **convex mirrors** and point out that a **convex mirror** will always form a virtual, upright, and diminished image, while a **concave mirror** will form a virtual, upright image only when the object is too close to the **mirror,** and this virtual image will be enlarged. This is a good way to distinguish between the two **mirrors**. Ask students what kind of **spherical mirror** is used for surveillance in stores and as a makeup **mirror**.

⮑ **DEMO** Have students hold a concave mirror at arms length in front of them. They should then bring the mirror slowly forward and toward them. They will initially see an inverted image, and when the mirror is at the focal distance, students will see a blurred image. As they continue to bring the mirror closer, they will see an upright and magnified image.

Sections 36-3 – 36-4

The image formation and the sign conventions for **convex lenses** parallel those for **concave mirrors**, and similarly a **convex mirror** and a **concave lens** form similar kind of images. Because of this, students will invariably be confused and show the rays as reflecting in the case of a **lens** when drawing ray diagrams. Again, practice in drawing ray diagrams will lessen this kind of confusion.

⮑ **DEMO** Use a laser light to show how a ray is refracted by a lens and emphasize that the ray goes through to the other side.

⮑ **DEMO** Bring in concave and convex lenses of different focal lengths. Direct the convex lens toward an object (trees or buildings outside the window) and adjust the tilt and location of the lens until you get a well-defined image on the wall. Point out that the image is inverted and the distance between the lens and the image defines the focal length. Now repeat the process with a concave lens and you will see a blurred white spot instead of a well defined image.

⮑ **DEMO** Set up a convex lens on an optic bench. A small candle or a bulb can act as the source. Locate the image for different object distances and have the students note the nature of the image (magnification and if it is inverted or upright). As the object is moved closer to the lens, the image will become larger and larger. Place the object very close to the lens and show that a real image is not possible. Repeat the process with a concave lens, and a real image cannot be located for any object distance.

Ask students to recall that in a **concave mirror** the object and the real image are on the same side of the **mirror** while in a **convex lens**, the image is on the other side of the **lens** from the object. Continue to stress the difference between **reflection** and **refraction** and how this is indicated in a ray diagram.

Sections 36-5 – 36-6

The study of **optical instruments** will be of great interest to students. Use Fig. 36-29 to review the parts of the **human eye**. While students will be able to explain the concept of farsightedness and nearsightedness, they will have difficulty with the near and far points.

➲ **DEMO** Have students hold a book at arms' length in front of them. They should then bring the book slowly forward and toward their eye. When the words are no longer in focus, they have located their near point. If students work in pairs, they can actually measure this distance.

Discuss the fact that the **camera** is similar to the human eye. Bring in a **simple camera** and pass it around the class.

➲ **DEMO** A pin-hole camera can be constructed without much difficulty. Take a shoe box, seal the top and cover the sides, top and bottom with black poster paper. Cut a small square out of the front of the box and cover it with aluminum foil. Make a small pin-hole in the center of the aluminum foil. Remove the opposite end of the box and cover it with waxed paper to form a view screen. Seal the edges with black electrical tape so the box is light tight. In a darkened room direct the pin-hole toward a window, and the image will be seen on the waxed paper.

The simple **magnifying glass** works on the principle that a **convex lens** forms an enlarged virtual image when the object is very close to the lens.

➲ **DEMO** Place a transparent plastic sheet (plastic food wrap will work well) on the page of your book. Place a drop of water on the wrapper and you will see the printed words enlarged. Have students experiment with different clear liquids.

In the case of a **telescope** the magnification depends on the focal length of the objective and the eyepiece. The following demo illustrates how a **refracting telescope** works.

➲ **DEMO** Place two convex lenses on an optic bench and view the image of an object that is across the room or outside the window. The position of the lenses will have to be adjusted to get a magnified image.

Aberration is briefly introduced in this chapter.

Textbook Resource Information

Transparency Acetates

Physlet Physics Illustrations

Physlet Physics Explorations

Physlet Physics Problems

Ranking Task Exercises in Physics, Student Edition

End of Chapter Problems with Solutions in the *Student Study Guide*

3, 11, 33, 35, 45, 59

Suggested Readings

Andereck, B., and Secrest, S., "Apparatus for Teaching Physics: The Magic Magnifier," *The Physics Teacher* (May 2001), p. 301 – 302.

Chandler, D., "Understanding Parabolic Reflectors through Paper Folding," *The Physics Teacher* (January 2001), p. 24 – 25.

Chakravarti, S., and Siegel, P.B., "Visualizing the Thin-Lens Formula," *The Physics Teacher* (September 2001), p. 342 – 343.

Cox, A.J., and DeWeerd, A.J., "The Image between the Lenses: Activities with a Telescope and a Microscope," *The Physics Teacher* (March 2003), p. 176 – 177.

Gardner, M., "Physics Trick of the Month: A Pinhole Paradox," *The Physics Teacher* (September 2000), p. 372.

Graf, E.H., "How Do You Use a Magnifying Glass?," *The Physics Teacher* (May 2001), p. 298 – 300.

Greenslade, Jr., T.B., "A Quick Experiment on Reflection from Concave Mirrors," *The Physics Teacher* (April 2000), p. 206.

Lawrence, R.W., "Magnification Ratio and the Lens Equations," *The Physics Teacher* (March 2000), p. 170 – 171.

Layton, B., "Inverted Images and Noninverted Shadows," *The Physics Teacher* (December 2001), p. 530 – 532.

Libertun, A.R., "Warning! Objects in Mirror Are Closer Than They Appear," *The Physics Teacher* (January 2003), p. 20 – 21.

O'Connell, J., "Optics Experiments Using a Laser Pointer," *The Physics Teacher* (October 1999), p. 445 – 446.

Vollmer, M., Möllmann, K., Pinno, F., and Karstadt, D., "There is More to See Than Eyes Can Detect," *The Physics Teacher* (September 2001), p. 371 – 376.

Wagner, D.L., and Walkiewicz, T.A., "When the Eye Meets the Lens," *The Physics Teacher* (November 2000), p. 474 – 475.

Notes and Ideas

Preparation time: *Estimated:* _____   *Actual:* _____

Class time spent on material: *Estimated:* _____   *Actual:* _____

Related laboratory activities:

Demonstration materials:

Notes for next time:

Chapter 37: Interference

Outline

Summary

This and the next chapter consider phenomena that support the wave theory of light. **Young's double-slit** experiment is described, and the **interference** pattern formed is studied. **Interference from reflection**, **reflection** in **thin films**, and **Newton's rings** are also discussed. Two types of **interferometers**, the **Michelson interferometer** and the **Fabry – Perot interferometer** are studied.

Major Concepts

- Young's double-slit experiment
    - Double-slit experiment
    - The two-source interference pattern
    - Waves or particles

- Intensity in the double-slit experiment

- Interference from reflection
    - Interference fringes from the space between two glass plates
    - Newton's rings
    - Thin-film interference

- Interferometers
    - The Michelson interferometer
    - The Fabry – Perot interferometer

Teaching Suggestions and Demonstrations

The phenomena discussed in this chapter can be best understood through demonstrations. Several are listed in this chapter of the manual, so plan to include these in your classroom presentation. The material in the textbook also includes a fair amount of derivation, which is essential to the understanding of the concepts. Bear this in mind when preparing to teach this chapter.

Sections 37-1 – 37-2

There are three important points to remember when introducing the phenomenon of **interference** of light waves. First, the superposition of sound waves applies to light waves as well. Remind students that they studied this back in Chapter 15. Fig. 37-1 shows **constructive** and **destructive interference** of two waves using the superposition principle. The second point is the need for **coherent waves** for the formation of **interference** pattern. Define **coherent waves** and stress the fact that two waves must have the same wavelength and a constant phase difference in order to be coherent. Discuss why an incandescent light bulb is not a source of **coherent waves**. The final point is the condition for **constructive** and **destructive interference**.

The conditions for **constructive** and **destructive interference** can be defined in broad terms as shown in Fig. 37-1. However, Equations 37-3a and 37-3b are specific to **interference** from two **coherent sources**. Go through the derivation in detail. Students need to recognize that Equation 37-1 gives these conditions in terms of the path-length difference, while Equation 37-3 restates the same condition in terms of the geometry of the experimental setup. Equation 37-2 merely connects these two representations.

Figures 37-5 and 37-7 clearly show the **interference** patterns formed in the case of the **Young's double-slit** experiment. Some of the main features that need to be emphasized are: the central point on the screen will always be a maximum; the various orders of maxima and minima alternate on either side of the central maximum; for small values of θ, the maxima and minima will be evenly spaced on either side. Be sure to inform students that **Young's double-slit** experiment has more than just historical significance – it verified the wave nature of light.

> ⮑ **DEMO** Pasco Scientific has adjustable spacing slits that work well in this demo. Use a laser to get a good pattern on the wall. You will have to darken the room so all students can see this clearly.

The discussion on **intensity** of the maxima and minima in the **double-slit** experiment includes a fairly lengthy derivation. If you do not care to go through the derivation, be sure to discus the significance of Equation 37-14. The plot of **intensity** vs. distance from the central maximum shows that the **intensity** in the case of incoherent waves do not exhibit the peaks and valleys that can be found in the case of **coherent sources**.

Sections 37-3 – 37-4

A very thin space between two glass plates will form bright and dark bands that are due to **interference by reflection**. The path-length difference in this case is expressed in terms of the thickness of the wedge at any given distance from the point where the plates touch. Note that a phase change of one-half wavelength is introduced when the wave is reflected at a denser medium. This is similar to a pulse moving along a lighter string and undergoing a phase change at the boundary (see Fig. 37-12) where it meets a denser string. Because of this additional phase change the condition for **constructive interference** will be similar (in mathematical form) to that for **destructive interference** in the case of **Young's double-slit** experiment. This can be a source of confusion to some students.

Newton's rings and **thin-film interference** are two other examples of **interference by reflection.** Unlike **Young's double-slit interference**, in the case of **Newton's rings** the center will always be dark due to destructive interference. The interference phenomenon in thin films due to reflection has two important points that students need to bear in mind. First, since the path difference is in the material of the film, the equation $2t = m \lambda_n$ refers to the wavelength of light in the material and $\lambda_n = \lambda / n$ (n being the refractive index of the material of the film). Second, when the reflection is at a denser surface, this introduces an additional path difference of $\frac{1}{2} \lambda$.

The following two demos are simple and effective in illustrating the two phenomena.

> ⮑ **DEMO** Unused microscope slides come in handy to demonstrate Newton's rings. Tape a pair of slides along the short edges. This will trap a thin film of air between the slides. Now apply

pressure at the center and you will be able to observe Newton's rings around the area where the pressure is applied.

⮕ **DEMO** Cut off the end faces of a small, hollow, plastic cylinder. The length of the cylinder is about 4 – 6 cm long and the diameter is about 4 cm. Make a soap solution using dishwashing liquid and warm water. Add about a tablespoon of glycerine to the solution. Pour a little of the solution into a shallow dish. Mount the plastic cylinder on a stand using a clamp that can be rotated about a horizontal axis. With the cylinder vertical, dip it in the soap solution and slowly rotate the cylinder end off the soap solution to a horizontal position. You should have a nice film of soap on the end of the cylinder. A slide projector is used as a light source. Shine the light on to the soap film and adjust the angle of the cylinder until you get a nice interference pattern on the wall due to reflection from the soap film.

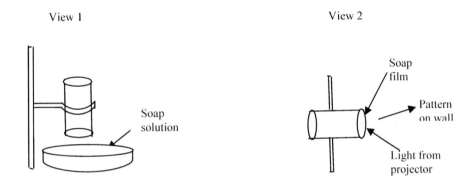

⮕ **DEMO** A variation to the above demo is one where you use a red filter slide in the projector. The interference patterns will appear as red and black lines.

Section 37-4

Two **interferometers** are described in this last section of the chapter. These instruments have the ability to measure (to a high degree of precision) quantities such as wavelength, wave speed, indices of refraction and even small path differences. For this reason, it is important to understand how they work. **Michelson's interferometer** produces two coherent sources by splitting the light from a single source. The schematic of the instrument is shown in Fig. 37-20a. A very small shift in the moveable mirror M will cause a shift in the fringe pattern. By counting the number of fringes that move across the cross wires of the eyepiece, the distance the mirror has shifted can be determined. Since a shift of one fringe corresponds to a distance of half a wavelength, this instrument can be used to make very precise distance measurements. Students will come across this instrument again in Chapter 39 when they study the ether controversy.

The **Fabry – Perot interferometer** is an improvement on the **Michelson interferometer** as far as the strength of the maxima is concerned. This facilitates counting of the fringes that shift as the mirror is moved. Figures 37-22a and 37-22b compare the fringe patterns formed by the two instruments. It is obvious that the **Fabry – Perot** forms more distinct and sharp maxima that can be easily counted as they shift across the eyepiece viewing area.

Textbook Resource Information

Transparency Acetates

Fig. 37-1   Superposition of two waves
Fig. 37-2   Example of two coherent waves
Fig. 37-5   Interference of two coherent waves
Fig. 37-7   Interference pattern due to double vertical slits
Fig. 37-8   Geometry for finding interference pattern conditions
Fig. 37-12   Phase change of light upon reflection
Fig. 37-14   Newton's rings
Fig. 37-17   Geometry for thin-film interference
Fig. 37-20a   Schematic of Michelson's interferometer
Fig. 37-21b   Schematic of a Fabry – Perot interferometer

Physlet Physics Illustrations

37.1   Ripple Tank

Physlet Physics Explorations

37.2   Changing the separation between sources

Physlet Physics Problems

37.2 Identifying constructive and destructive interference
37.6 Interference patterns from two source interference
37.7 Slit separation

End of Chapter Problems with Solutions in the *Student Study Guide*

7, 19, 25, 31, 37, 63

Suggested Readings

Ambrose, B., Shaffer, P., Steinberg, R., and McDermott, L., "An Investigation of Student Understanding of Single-Slit Diffraction and Double-Slit Interference," *Am.J.Phys.* (February 1999), p. 146 – 155.

Chandler, D., "Simulate Interference...While Supplies Last," *The Physics Teacher* (September 2001), p. 362 – 363.

Gallis, M.R., "Automating Microwave Optics Experiments," *The Physics Teacher* (April 2002), p. 217 – 219.

Kovacs, A., Varju, K., Osvay, K., and Bor, Z., "On the Formation of White-Light Interference Fringes," *Am.J.Phys.* (November 1998), p. 985 – 989.

Mahoney, J., "Laser Interference by a Convex Mirror," *The Physics Teacher* (October 1972), p. 406.

Mallette, V., "Brilliant Newton's Rings," *The Physics Teacher* (March 2003), p. 186.

Moloney, M.J., "Homemade Interference," *The Physics Teacher* (November 1999), p. 504 – 505.

Perkalskis, B.S., and Freeman, J.R., "Apparatus for Teaching Physics: Herschel's Interference Demonstration," *The Physics Teacher* (March 2000), p. 142.

Poon, D.C.H., "How Good Is the Approximation "*Path Difference* $\approx$ *d sin* θ"?," *The Physics Teacher* (November 2002), p. 460 – 462.

Sawicki, C.A., "Easy and Inexpensive Demonstration of Light Interference," *The Physics Teacher* (January 2001), p. 16 – 19.

Sharpe, J., "'Stellar' Interferometry with Streetlights," *The Physics Teacher* (October 2001), p. 428 – 430.

Sobel, M.I., "Algebraic Treatment of Two-Slit Interference," *The Physics Teacher* (October 2002), p. 402 – 404.

Wheeler, C.R., Henriksen, P.N., and Ramsier, R.D., "Visibility of Thin-Film Interference Fringes," *Am. J. Phys.* (February 2004), p. 279 – 281.

Notes and Ideas

Preparation time: *Estimated:* _____   *Actual:* _____

Class time spent on material: *Estimated:* _____   *Actual:* _____

Related laboratory activities:

Demonstration materials:

Notes for next time:

Chapter 38: Diffraction

Outline

38-1   The Diffraction of Light
38-2   Diffraction Gratings
38-3   Single-Slit Diffraction
38-4   Resolution of Optical Instruments
38-5   Slit width and Grating Patterns
38-6   X-Ray Diffraction
38-7   Holography

Summary

Diffraction, along with interference, illustrates the wave nature of light. In this chapter, **diffraction gratings**, and **single-slit diffraction,** along with slit width and **grating** patterns, are discussed. **Angular** and **spatial resolution** and **resolution** of **telescopes** are considered. **X-ray diffraction** and the physics of **holography** are also studied.

Major Concepts

- The diffraction of light

- Diffraction gratings
    - Diffraction gratings
    - Energy conservation and intensity
    - Intensity pattern
    - Resolution of diffraction gratings

- Single-slit diffraction
    - Single-slit diffraction
    - The intensity pattern of single-slit diffraction
    - Deriving single-slit intensity values

- Resolution of optical instruments
    - Angular and spatial resolution
    - The resolution of telescopes

- Slit width and grating patterns

- X-ray diffraction

- Holography

Teaching Suggestions and Demonstrations

The topics in this chapter are as difficult to visualize as those in the last chapter. Make use of the demos listed here to give students a better understanding of the phenomenon of **diffraction**. Many of the demos are fairly simple and can be carried out with just a laser.

Sections 38-1 – 38-3

To observe **diffraction** effects, the obstacle casting the shadow needs to be comparable in size to the wavelength of light. For this reason, the light and dark fringes at the edges of shadows are not easily observable. The following demos will give students the opportunity to observe **diffraction** patterns without having to use complicated equipment.

- ⟳ **DEMO** Hold your palm up to the light so the fingers are close together and directed upwards. Now create an extremely small "slit" between two adjacent fingers and squint at the light through this aperture. You will be able to observe bright and dark vertical fringes.

- ⟳ **DEMO** Mount a penny vertically on a stand. Shine a laser beam at the penny and adjust the distance of the penny from the wall till you get a good shadow of the penny. If you observe closely, you will see the diffraction pattern within the shadow of the penny.

- ⟳ **DEMO** Single slits with adjustable widths and circular apertures can be obtained from Pasco Scientific. Use a laser beam to examine the diffraction patterns formed when the slit width is altered.

- ⟳ **DEMO** Use a laser beam and diffraction grating to examine the pattern formed due to diffraction by multiple slits.

The condition for maximum is very similar to that of Young's double-slit experiment. This is where the similarity stops. In the case of interference by a double-slit, the intensity is the same as you go from the central maximum out on either side. In the case of **diffraction**, Equation 38-4a gives the dependence of the **intensity** on the number of slits and this is plotted in Fig. 38-8. Point out that the greater the number of slits, the higher and narrower the maxima are. The dramatic difference in the **intensity** of the maxima for 10, 4 and 2 slits can be seen in this plot.

Students do not have a good grasp of the concept of **resolution**. Define **angular** and **spatial resolution**. Again, use Fig. 38-8 to point out the poor **resolution** in the case of the two-slit pattern compared to the 10-slit pattern. The **intensity** pattern is quite different for **diffraction** at a single-slit. Note how the **intensity** falls off very quickly on either side of the central maxima. Also, the width of the central maxima is greater than the secondary maxima. It is important to remember that $m = 0$ is not an allowed value in Equation 38-8 because the central spot is always a maximum. These three points differentiate a **single-slit diffraction** pattern from a **multiple-slit pattern** or a double-slit pattern.

Sections 38-4 – 38-5

Circular apertures also produce **diffraction** patterns. This section looks at the limitations imposed on optical instruments because of this effect. Begin by discussing the meaning of **angular** separation. State the condition required for two point sources to be considered as resolved. Use Fig. 38-15 to show the effect of the **angular** separation on the **resolution** of two point sources.

Discuss the limitations of the world's largest **telescope** in Mt. Palomar due to the **diffraction** effects. Point out the advantage of using lots of small pieces for the mirror in a reflecting **telescope** and how this reduces the **diffraction** effects.

Sections 38-6 – 38-7

X-ray diffraction and **holography** are two very interesting topics that have practical applications. Even though these two sections are marked as optional, consider including them in your syllabus. Point out that **diffraction** does not happen only with light. **X-rays** (which are a part of the electromagnetic spectrum) also get **diffracted,** but by a crystalline solid because of the arrangement of atoms in a regular array. Bragg's condition provides a way of studying crystal structures using **diffraction** patterns produced by them. Students will find it interesting to learn that the double-helical structure of the DNA molecule was discovered through **X-ray diffraction.**

Students are familiar with the concept of **holograms** but perhaps not how they are produced. Discuss how **holograms** are produced. Go through the section Think About This...What Are The Uses Of **Holograms** to illustrate the multiple uses of **holograms** in our everyday lives.

Textbook Resource Information

Transparency Acetates

Fig. 38-5a	Formation of bright Poisson spot
Fig. 38-7	Geometry of a diffraction grating
Fig. 38-8	Plot of relative intensity vs. phases
Fig. 38-10	Phase differences of diffracted waves at varying angles
Fig. 38-11	Single-slit diffraction
Fig. 38-15	Resolution of two objects
Fig. 38-16	Minimum separation distance for resolution of images
Fig. 38-18	Intensity pattern as a function of observation angle
Fig. 38-23a	Schematic diagram of the von Laue experiment
Fig. 38-24	Bragg planes for a three-dimensional crystal
Fig. 38-25	X-ray diffraction from adjacent Bragg planes
Fig. 38-26	Schematic of an X-ray spectrometer
Fig. 38-28	Reconstruction of image using holographic film
Fig. 38-30	Schematic diagram of hologram formation

Physlet Physics Illustrations

38.1 Single-Slit Diffraction
38.2 Application of Diffraction Gratings

Physlet Physics Explorations

38.3 Diffraction grating

Physlet Physics Problems

38.1 Diffraction from a single-slit
38.4 Single-slit diffraction – changing the slit-width
38.6 Diffraction grating

End of Chapter Problems with Solutions in the *Student Study Guide*

9, 13, 21, 35, 37, 45

Suggested Readings

Ambrose, B., Shaffer, P., Steinberg, R., and McDermott, L., "An Investigation of Student Understanding of Single-Slit Diffraction and Double-Slit Interference," *Am.J.Phys.* (February 1999), p. 146 – 155.

Byrne, A., "Compact Disk Spectroscopes Revisited!," *The Physics Teacher* (March 2003), p. 144 – 145.

Chiaverina, C., "The Doctor Is In," *The Physics Teacher* (May 2003), p. 270 – 271.

DePino, Jr., A., "Diffraction Patterns Using a Constant-Velocity Cart," *The Physics Teacher* (October 2002), p. 418 – 419.

Gallis, M.R., "Automating Microwave Optics Experiments," *The Physics Teacher* (April 2002), p. 217 – 219.

Gluck, P., "Compact Disk Optics," *The Physics Teacher* (November 2002), p. 468 – 469.

Greenslade, Jr., T.B., "Diffraction by a Cat's Whisker," *The Physics Teacher* (October 2000), p. 422.

Higbie, J., "Depth of Field in Hologram Images," *The Physics Teacher* (October 1997), p. 418 – 419.

Isenberg, C., "Laser Diffraction Experiments with Pseudoliquids and Pseudosolids," *The Physics Teacher* (October 2000), p. 411 – 413.

Knauer, T., "A Compact Disk Transmission Spectroscope," *The Physics Teacher* (November 2002), p. 466 – 467.

Linthwaite, M., and Shimmens, C., "Simple Method of Producing Good-Quality Holograms without the Need for Expensive Equipment," *The Physics Teacher* (September 1987), p. 382 – 383.

Moloney, M.J., "Homemade Interference," *The Physics Teacher* (November 1999), p. 504 – 505.

Olson, D.W., "Real and Virtual Images Using a Classroom Hologram," *The Physics Teacher* (April 1992), p. 202 – 208.

Poon, D.C.H., "How Good Is the Approximation 'Path Difference $\approx d \sin \theta$'?," *The Physics Teacher* (November 2002), p. 460 – 462.

Rokoske, T.L., "A New Perspective for Viewing Holograms," *The Physics Teacher* (December 1992), p. 557.

Schubert, W.K., and Throckmorton, C.R., "Making a 360 degree hologram," *The Physics Teacher* (May 1975), p. 310 – 311.

Wein, R.G., "A Video Technique for the Quantitative Analysis of the Poisson Spot and other Diffraction Patterns," *Am.J.Phys.* (March 1999), p. 236 – 240.

Notes and Ideas

Preparation time: *Estimated:* _____   *Actual:* _____

Class time spent on material: *Estimated:* _____   *Actual:* _____

Related laboratory activities:

Demonstration materials:

Notes for next time:

Chapter 39: Special Relativity

Outline

Summary

In Chapter 39 you are given an overview of the **special theory of relativity** starting with the important question of whether a medium like **ether** was necessary for the propagation of light. The two **postulates** as stated by **Einstein** and the phenomena of **time dilation** and **length contraction** are discussed. The **relativistic Doppler shift** and the **Lorentz transformations** are studied. The well known $E = mc^2$ equation is derived, and the **equivalence principle** is discussed.

Major Concepts

- Is an ether necessary?
    - Ether
    - The Michelson – Morley experiment

- The Einstein postulates

- Space, time, and simultaneity
    - Simultaneity

- Time dilation and length contraction
    - Time dilation
    - The twin paradox
    - Length contraction

- The relativistic Doppler shift
    - Blue and red shift
    - The Doppler shift for light and cosmology
    - The relativistic addition of velocities
    - Energy conservation and intensity

- The Lorentz transformations
    - Lorentz transformation for space – time coordinates
    - Lorentz transformations of electric and magnetic fields

- Momentum and energy in special relativity
  - Momentum
  - Kinetic energy
  - Energy associated with mass
  - The relation between the momentum and energy of a particle

- Beyond special relativity
  - The equivalence principle

Teaching Suggestions and Demonstrations

Many curricula omit this chapter for lack of time. In actuality, you will find that the majority of students are intrigued and interested in **special relativity**. The topics in this chapter rely heavily on mathematical derivations, which in themselves are not difficult to follow. However, concepts such as **time dilation**, **length contraction**, and **simultaneity** of events do not appear to be credible to students. For this reason, do not skip over experimental evidences that can give credence to **special relativity**.

Sections 39-1 – 39-2

Start with the significance of the Michelson – Morley experiment, which conclusively showed that there was no evidence for the existence of an **ether** wind. Remind students that this apparatus is the same as the interferometer they studied in Chapter 37.

Einstein's two postulates stated in Section 39-2 form the basis for **special relativity**. Point out that **postulates** are statements made without proofs. Acceptance (or not, as the case may be) of a **postulate** comes from experiments. Plan to spend some time discussing the **postulates** and what they mean.

In discussing reference frames, remind students of the observer in a moving train that was discussed way back in Chapter 4. Emphasize that the essence of the **first postulate** is the fact that when you are in an inertial frame, there is no way you can tell whether you are moving or at rest. The **second postulate** states that nothing can travel faster than the speed of light.

Equations 39-3 and 39-4 form the Galilean transformations. One direct consequence of Equation 39-4 is that the time measurement is independent of the frame of reference. Discuss why these are in direct violation of the **second postulate** and point out that this was the reason Einstein sought to modify the **transformation equations**.

Sections 39-3 – 39-5

The concept that **simultaneity** is not absolute is very counterintuitive (as pointed out in the textbook) but is very essential to the understanding of the concepts of **time dilation** and **length contraction**. Carefully go through the setup leading to the discussion of **simultaneity** of events in the two reference frames. In the experiment described in the text book, both observers in frames F and F' are correct. This needs to be emphasized because students will conclude that one of them was wrong in their measurements. Be sure to discuss why we do not encounter this in our everyday lives.

Two important consequences of non-**simultaneity** of events are the **dilation** of **time** and the **contraction** of **length**. Use Fig. 39-8 to go through the derivation of Equation 39-9. While the math in itself is easy to follow, the concept is a hard one to accept. The statement "moving clocks run more slowly than clocks at rest do" invariably leads to the misconception that the moving clock is malfunctioning. Point out that the clock is working properly, but it is time that slows down in a moving frame. Be sure to discuss the experiments done to test **time dilation** (see the section Think About This…Are Experimental Tests Of **Time Dilation** Possible?) so students will recognize that acceptance of **time dilation** is now based on experimental proof. Work as many examples as you can to help students recognize which clock 'slows' down and which one does not. Be sure to discuss the twin paradox, which essentially points out that the **dilation** of **time** depends on the observer and the frame that he/she is in.

Now the stage is set for the discussion of **length contraction**. Again, the math will not be difficult to follow. This **contraction** occurs only in the direction of motion and not if the length measurement is done perpendicular to the direction of motion; a point that is often ignored or missed by students.

Remind students that in Chapter 14 we saw the shift in frequency of sound waves for situations involving relative motion between source and observer. By measuring this shift one could identify if the source or the observer is in motion. In the case of **Doppler shift** of electromagnetic radiation, depending on the relative motion of the source toward or away from the observer, we get a higher or lower shift in the frequency of light. Equations 39-15 and 39-16 give the observed frequencies and wavelengths for the two cases of the source moving toward the observer and away from the observer. Discuss why these shifts are referred to as the blueshift and the redshift.

Be sure to discuss the importance of the measurement in **Doppler shifts** to applications in the field of astronomy and cosmology. Another consequence of the **Doppler shift** can be seen in how the law of **addition** of **velocities** is different. Equation 39-18 gives the **addition law** for **velocities**. Point out that this will reduce to the more familiar addition law $V = v_1 + v_2$ when v_1 and v_2 are $<< c$.

Section 39-6

The **Lorentz transformations** and its inverse (as given by Equations 39-19, 39-20, 39-25, and 39-26) show that the space and time coordinates in one reference frame depend on the space and time coordinates in a frame that is in relative motion to the first frame and vice versa. Note that the constant reduces to 1 when the velocities under consideration are much smaller than the speed of light, and the set of **Lorentz transformations** are now none other than those of the Galilean transformations seen earlier.

The **length contraction** discussed in Section 39-4 can now be expressed in terms of the **Lorentz transformation** coefficient (see Equation 39-27). In defining "proper" length, be sure to explain that "proper" here by no means refers to a "correct" length. Rather, it is the length as measured in the frame in which the object is at rest. Go through the many worked examples so students get a better understanding of the consequences of relative motion between frames of references.

Sections 39-7 – 39-8

The expressions for **relativistic momentum** and **relativistic energy** are derived in Section 39-7. It is quite common for students to think of these equations as different from the classical equations for momentum and energy they learned earlier in this book. Emphasize that the relativistic equations are true at all speeds and that these equations reduce to the nonrelativistic expressions for situations where $v << c$. Again, they will not be able to distinguish between what is considered as low speeds. Have students calculate the value of γ for $v = 0.01c$, $0.1c$, $0.5c$, $0.9c$, $0.99c$, and $0.999c$ so they can see when it would be okay to use the nonrelativistic **momentum** and **energy** and when they would have to consider the relativistic effects.

While almost all of your students will have heard of the famous $E = mc^2$ expression, go through the derivation carefully so they understand the full import of this relation. Discuss the significance of this in relation to matter – antimatter and point out that they will learn more about this in Chapters 44 and 45. Define the term *rest energy* and emphasize that for a particle in motion, the total energy consists of its rest energy plus its kinetic energy of motion. Equation 39-36 is another way of expressing the energy of a particle in terms of its momentum and its rest energy. This will reduce to $E = p^2c^2$ for a photon which has no mass. It is not unusual for students to disregard the momentum of a photon because of its having no mass.

The last section has to do with the noninertial or accelerating frames, which is the basis for general relativity. Begin by stating the **equivalence principle** and discuss the two examples listed in the textbook. Remind students that they had studied the **equivalence** between gravitational and inertial mass back in Chapter 12. Be sure to point out that this **equivalence** has been experimentally proved to a great degree of accuracy.

The second of the two consequences of the **equivalence principle** is the gravitational deflection of light. Go through the discussion given in the book, and point out the significance of the frequency shift when the gravitational potential is very large. In this case the frequency shift is zero and refers to the formation of a black hole. When this was first proposed, the concept of a black hole was merely considered to be possible in theory alone!

Textbook Resource Information

Transparency Acetates

Fig. 39-1   Measurement of the speed of light
Fig. 39-2   Michelson – Morley experiment – schematic diagram
Fig. 39-4   Two reference frames in relative motion
Fig. 39-5   Observation of an event from two reference frames in relative motion
Fig. 39-7   Simultaneity experiment
Fig. 39-8   Time dilation
Fig. 39-10   Length contraction
Fig. 39-11   Absence of transverse length contraction
Fig. 39-12   Doppler shift of spectral lines
Fig. 39-14   Frequency of light source as measured by moving observers
Fig. 39-15   Space – time coordinates of an event in two reference frames
Fig. 39-20   Electromagnetic pulse emitted inside a railroad car
Fig. 39-22   Gravitational deflection of light
Fig. 39-23a   Image formation by a gravitational lens

End of Chapter Problems with Solutions in the *Student Study Guide*

5, 7, 21, 29, 49, 59

Suggested Readings

Akridge, R., "A Simple Cosmology: General Relativity Not Required," *Am.J.Phys.* (February 2001), p. 195 – 200.

Bedran, M.L., "A Comparison between the Doppler and Cosmological Redshifts," *Am.J.Phys.* (April 2002), p. 406 – 408.

Blackman, E.G., "Astrophysical Perspective in Teaching Special Relativity," *The Physics Teacher* (March 1998), p. 176 – 177.

Brown, H.R., "The Origins of Length Contraction: I. The FitzGerald – Lorentz Deformation Hypothesis," *Am.J.Phys.* (October 2001), p. 1044 – 1054.

Coisson, R., and Guidi, G., "Electromagnetic Interaction Momentum and Simultaneity," *Am.J.Phys.* (April 2001), p. 462 – 463.

Cranor, M.B., Heider, E.M., and Price, R.H., "A Circular Twin Paradox," *Am.J.Phys.* (November 2000), p.1016 – 1020.

Dibble, W.E., Hart, G.W., and Stokes, H.T., "A Pedagogical Note on the Relativistic Velocity Addition Formula," *The Physics Teacher* (September 1999), p. 369.

Dolby, C.E., and Gull. S.F., "On Radar Time and the Twin ``Paradox''," *Am.J.Phys.* (December 2001), p. 1257 – 1261.

Ehrlich, R., "Faster-Than-Light Speeds, Tachyons, and the Possibility of Tachyonic Neutrinos," *Am.J.Phys.* (November 2003), p. 1109 – 1114.

Greenslade, T.B., "Relativistic Metersticks," *The Physics Teacher* (May 2000), p. 315.

Hartman, H.I., and Nissim-Sabat, C., "On Mach's Critique of Newton and Copernicus," *Am.J.Phys.* (November 2003), p. 1163 – 1169.

Hecht, E., "From the Postulates of Relativity to the Law of Inertia," *The Physics Teacher* (November 2000), p. 497 – 498.

Hecht, E., "On Morphing Neutrinos and Why They Must Have Mass," *The Physics Teacher* (March 2003), p. 164 – 1 68.

Henry, R.C., "Special Relativity Made Transparent," *The Physics Teacher* (December 1985), p. 536 – 539.

Hestenes, D., "Spacetime Physics with Geometric Algebra," *Am.J.Phys.* (July 2003), p. 691 – 714.

Hill, C.T., and Lederman, L.M., "Teaching Symmetry in the Introductory Physics Curriculum," *The Physics Teacher* (September 2000), p. 348 – 353.

Hobson, A., "Enlivening Introductory Physics with SETI," *The Physics Teacher* (October 2001), p. 436 – 441.

Luetzelschwab, J.W., "Apparatus to Measure Relativistic Mass Increase," *Am.J.Phys.* (September 2003), p. 878 – 884.

Muller, R., "The Ether Wind and the Global Positioning System," *The Physics Teacher* (April 2000), p. 243 – 246.

Murphy, G.L., "Einstein + Newton + Bohr = Quantum Cosmology," *The Physics Teacher* (November 1997), p. 480 – 481.

Naddy, C.J., Dudley, S.C., and Haaland, R.K., "Projectile Motion in Special Relativity," *The Physics Teacher* (January 2000), p. 27 – 29.

Peterson, R.S. and Walkiewicz, T.A., "An Apparatus Evaluation," *The Physics Teacher* (May 2000), p. 266 – 268.

Rich, J., "Experimental Consequences of Time Variations of the Fundamental Constants," *Am.J.Phys.* (October 2003), p. 1043 – 1047.

Scherr, R.E., Shaffer, P.S., and Vokos, S., "Student Understanding of Time in Special Relativity: Simultaneity and Reference Frames," *Am.J.Phys.* (July 2001), p. S24 – S35.

Scherr, R.E., Shaffer, P.S., and Vokos, S., "The Challenge of Changing Deeply Held Student Beliefs About the Relativity of Simultaneity," *Am.J.Phys.* (December 2002), p. 1238 – 1248.

Strnad, J., "A Stepwise Approach to Special Relativity," *The Physics Teacher* (November 1979), p. 522 – 524.

Western, A.B., "Star Colors for Relativistic Space Travelers," *The Physics Teacher* (March 1997), p. 160 – 162.

Notes and Ideas

Preparation time: *Estimated:* _____   *Actual:* _____

Class time spent on material: *Estimated:* _____   *Actual:* _____

Related laboratory activities:

Demonstration materials:

Notes for next time:

Chapter 40: Quantum Physics

Outline

Summary

This chapter begins the study of modern physics. The behavior of **particles** as **waves** and the behavior of **radiation** as **particles** are discussed in detail by considering phenomena like **blackbody radiation**, **photoelectric effect**, the **Compton effect** and **double-slit interference**. **Heisenberg's uncertainty principle** is introduced, and the connection between **quantum mechanics** and **probabilities** is considered.

Major Concepts

- The particle nature of radiation
  - Blackbody radiation
  - The photoelectric effect
  - The Compton effect

- The wave nature of matter
  - The de Broglie wavelength
  - Experimental evidence for the wavelike behavior of matter

- The Heisenberg uncertainty relations
  - The Heisenberg uncertainty principle
  - The double-slit dilemma and its resolution
  - The ground state energy

- Quantum mechanics and probability

Teaching Suggestions and Demonstrations

At first glance this chapter seems to consist of descriptions of different experiments that have no connection to each other. Each of these experiments, however, clearly demonstrates the **particle-wave** behavior of matter and is essential to the understanding of this dual nature. The ideas presented here are abstract and not easy to understand, so go over the experiments and in each case stress the connection between the predictions and the experimental verification. Be sure to work as many examples as possible.

Sections 40-1 – 40-2

To understand the particle nature of **radiation**, begin with a discussion of **blackbody radiation**. Remind students that **blackbody radiation** was discussed in Chapter 17. The significance of **Planck's** formula is that it agrees with the data for the energy density of radiation of a **blackbody,** not just for the lower frequencies (which the Rayleigh-Jeans formula did) but for a wide range of frequencies. Define terms such as photon and quanta. Point out that a photon has a momentum even though it has zero rest mass and it travels at the speed of light.

The **photoelectric effect** is of great significance from a historical perspective as explained in the second paragraph of page 1115 of the textbook. Go over the characteristics of the **photoelectric effect** that do not agree with the classical picture and can only be explained using the idea of **quantization** of energy. Students will be surprised to learn that Einstein received the Nobel prize for his work on **photoelectric effect** and not relativity.

Explain the concept of threshold frequency and work function. Emphasize that for the ejected electrons to have any kinetic energy of motion, the energy of the incident photons must be greater than the work function for that metal. This is a connection that students often fail to make.

> ➲ **DEMO** You can get a complete package from Pasco to perform photoelectric experiments. You can measure the current for different light intensity. You can also determine the threshold frequency and the work function. This demo is very useful in showing students the dependence of the photoelectric current on the intensity of the incident light.

The **Compton effect** uses the conservation of momentum and energy to study the scattering of X-rays and provides a further contradiction to the classical radiation theory.

While Section 40-1 considered experimental evidence that showed the particle behavior of radiation, in Section 40-2 we learn about the wave nature of matter. Point out that the wave property of matter can be evident only on a microscopic scale. This is due to the small value of **Planck's** constant and the definition of the **de Broglie** wavelength as given in Equation 40-6. Have students calculate the wavelength of a baseball traveling at 90 mph. Then discuss why the wave nature of a baseball is not observable.

This is the first time that students are introduced to the concept of a potential barrier and **tunneling**. Take time to go over this because students will have a hard time accepting it. Start by stating the classical picture in which an object in the region $r_1 < r < r_2$ cannot go into the region $r_2 < r < r_4$ (see Fig. 40-10) as it will have a negative kinetic energy, and this is disallowed. Then discuss how **tunneling** through the barrier can only be explained using quantum mechanics and the wave properties of matter.

Sections 40-3 – 40-4

The **Heisenberg uncertainty relation** is another abstract concept that will be difficult for many students to visualize and accept. Discuss the fact that the principle has to do with the limitations in the measurement of two complementary quantities such as position and momentum or energy and time. It is important that you introduce this concept and discuss its implications, especially at the microscopic level. Take the example (given in the textbook) of determining the location of an electron (inside an atom) to within 10 % of the size of the atom. This will lead to an uncertainty in the momentum that is 10 times the radius of the classical atom. This large uncertainty implies that we cannot say with any certainty that the electron will stay within the atom. If time permits, you may want to go over the **double-slit** dilemma and how it was resolved.

Energy levels and the concept of ground state energy are discussed in the next chapter. But here the **uncertainty principle** is used to estimate this energy for a particle subjected to a force. The derivation is straightforward and is important to the understanding of the stability of atoms. It will also set the stage for the discussion of energy states of the hydrogen atom in the next chapter.

The concept of **probability** is very important in **quantum mechanics**. The last section of this chapter takes a quick look at this. Introduce the concept of wave function and explain that the square of the wave function gives the probability distribution function for finding the particle at a given location. Go through conceptual Examples 40-9 and 40-10. Students will find it difficult to accept these explanations as they seem to go against their common sense and intuition. Point out that **quantum mechanics** can only make predictions about the **probability** of the outcome and not the outcome of any event.

Textbook Resource Information

Transparency Acetates

Fig. 40-2	Experimental setup for measuring photoelectric effect
Fig. 40-5	Experimental data for Compton's experiment
Fig.40-7	An image-intensifier tube
Fig. 40-8	Electron tube used in the Davisson – Germer experiment
Fig. 40-9	Double-slit diffraction pattern produced by neutrons
Fig. 40-11	Tunneling of an electromagnetic field
Fig. 40-15	Double-slit experiment using electrons
Fig. 40-16	Monitor for a double-slit experiment
Fig. 40-17	Path length difference for a double-slit experiment

End of Chapter Problems with Solutions in the *Student Study Guide*

5, 11, 29, 41, 51, 61

Suggested Readings

Barnett, J.D., and Stokes, H.T., "Improved Student Laboratory on the Measurement of Planck's Constant Using the Photoelectric Effect," *Am.J.Phys.* (January 1988), p. 86 – 87.

Battimelli, G., "When Did the Indeterminacy Principle Become the Uncertainty Principle?," *Am.J.Phys.* (April 1998), p. 280. See related articles in the same issue.

Chen, C., and Zhang, C., "New Demonstration of Photoelectric Effect," *The Physics Teacher* (October 1999), p. 442.

Fisher, H., "Planck's Constant Experiment," *The Physics Teacher* (September 1985), p. 334.

Gavenda, J.D., "On 'Sunscreens and the Photoelectric Effect'," *The Physics Teacher* (March 1998), p. 132.

Geballe, R., "A Comment on Waves and Particles," *The Physics Teacher* (December 1993), p. 525.

Grote, M., and Heinmiller, W., "Sunscreens and the Photoelectric Effect," *The Physics Teacher* (December 1996), p. 549.

Hiatt, T., "In My Opinion: Another Uncertainty Principle," *The Physics Teacher* (January 1996), p. 46 – 47.

Hilgevoord, J., "The Uncertainty Principle for Energy and Time. II," *Am.J.Phys.* (May 1998), p. 396 – 402.

Hobson, A., "Teaching Quantum Theory in the Introductory Course," *The Physics Teacher* (April 1996), p. 202 – 209.

Holcomb, D.F., "Apparatus for LED Measurement of Planck's Constant," *The Physics Teacher* (May 1997), p. 261.

Kinderman, J.V., "Investigating the Compton Effect with a Spreadsheet," *The Physics Teacher* (October 1992), p. 426 – 428.

Ludlow, J.C., "A Chlorophyll Solar Cell," *The Physics Teacher* (April 1982), p. 230 – 232.

Milonni, P.W., "What (if Anything) Does the Photoelectric Effect Teach Us?," *Am.J.Phys.* (January 1997), p. 11 – 12.

Nieves, L., Spavieri, G., Fernandez, B., and Guevara, R.A., "Measuring the Planck Constant with LED's," *The Physics Teacher* (February 1997), p. 108 – 109.

Sawicki, C.A., "Simple Uncertainty-Principle Experiment," *The Physics Teacher* (February 2003), p. 84 – 87.

Spradley, J., "Hertz and the Discovery of Radio Waves and the Photoelectric Effect," *The Physics Teacher* (November 1988), p. 492 – 497.

Steinberg, R.N., Oberem, G.E., and McDermott, L.C., "Development of a Computer-Based Tutorial on the Photoelectric Effect," *Am.J.Phys.* (November 1996), p. 1370 – 1379.

Vokos, S., Shaffer, P.S., Ambrose, B.S., and McDermott, L.C., "Student Understanding of the Wave Nature of Matter: Diffraction and Interference of Particles," *Am.J.Phys.* (July 2000), p. S42 – S51.

Wadlinger, R.L., and Hunter, G., "Max Planck's Natural Units," *The Physics Teacher* (November 1988), p. 528 – 529.

Zangara, R. and Lanzara, E., "Photoemission Energy Distribution Measurements in a Simple Metal: A Modern Physics Undergraduate Laboratory," *Am.J.Phys.* (September 1994), p. 855. Also see the December 1993 issue.

Notes and Ideas

Preparation time: *Estimated:* _____   *Actual:* _____

Class time spent on material: *Estimated:* _____   *Actual:* _____

Related laboratory activities:

Demonstration materials:

Notes for next time:

Chapter 41: Atomic and Molecular Structure

Outline

Summary

In Chapter 40 we saw that particles exhibit wave behavior, and radiation had a particle nature to it. In this chapter we learn more about the properties of microscopic systems like atoms and molecules using concepts such as **energy** and **angular momentum quantization**. The **Bohr model** of the **hydrogen atom** is described, and the **hydrogen spectrum** is discussed. The **exclusion principle** is used to look into the **atomic** and **molecular structure.**

Major Concepts

- The quantization of energy
  - o The wave nature of matter and energy quantization
  - o The Bohr model of hydrogen
  - o Emission and absorption of photons from atoms

- The true spectrum of hydrogen
  - o The wave function
  - o Angular momentum
  - o The spectrum of hydrogen

- The exclusion principle and atomic structure
  - o The spin of the electron
  - o Multi-electron atoms and the exclusion principle
  - o Do all particles obey the exclusion principle?

- Molecular structure
  - o The formation of molecules
  - o Van der Waals forces
  - o Molecular spectra

Teaching Suggestions and Demonstrations

Students may already be familiar with several of the topics discussed in this chapter, if they have had at least one introductory chemistry course. Still, **energy quantization**, the **hydrogen spectrum** and the **exclusion principle** are important to the understanding of the structure of atoms and molecules, so make time to discuss these topics in class.

Sections 41-1 – 41-2

Begin a discussion of this chapter by emphasizing that "quantum systems can have only certain quantized values of energy". Explain the concept of **energy levels** and define ground state and excited states.

State and explain the three assumptions of **Bohr** and go over the derivation for the **Bohr** radius (Equation 41-8), the allowed energies for a hydrogen atom (Equation 41-10) and the wavelength of **spectral lines** (Equation 41-12). Point out that the allowed radii in a **Bohr** atom are discrete as are the energy levels.

It is important that students understand the **energy level diagram** for the hydrogen atom based on **Bohr's** assumption of circular orbits. The following points need to be emphasized: first, the energy increases as the value of n increases. Students are apt to look at the numerical values and conclude that the energy is decreasing. Point out that the energy is becoming less negative. Second, the levels are closer as it goes higher up, and this is indicated by the spacing of the horizontal lines. Thirdly, $E = 0$ corresponds to the ionization point, and beyond this the electron is not in a bound state anymore.

Discuss the concept of the angular momentum being quantized and define the different quantum numbers. The selection rules based on the conservation of the angular momentum is important. Have students calculate the energy values for the ground state and the first few excited states of the hydrogen atom. Have them then calculate the wavelengths of the **spectral lines** in the Balmer series. Show them how to sketch the **emission lines** on the energy level diagrams. Point out the difference between an **emission** and an **absorption spectrum**.

> ⟳ **DEMO** To show emission spectra, set up a hydrogen spectral tube and pass out gratings to the students. (Inexpensive student gratings can be purchased from Edmund Scientific). Have students view the spectral lines and note the different colors and positions of the lines. Use other spectral tubes (mercury and neon are the most common ones used by many instructors) to show the difference in the distribution of the spectral lines and the colors.

Sections 41-3 – 41-4

The **Pauli exclusion principle** is important to the study of the **structure** of **atoms** and **molecules**. Define and explain the principle. Point out that an electron has an intrinsic angular momentum or spin that can have only a plus or minus ½. This explains the splitting of the energy level into $2l + 1$ levels with slightly different energies in the presence of a magnetic field. Remind students that the $2l + 1$ comes from the magnetic dipole moment orientations of the atom. Review Fig. 41-16 and explain how energy levels are filled up using the exclusion principle. Most students would have learned this in their chemistry courses. Briefly discuss the concept of fermions.

The last section of this chapter considers the formation of **molecules**. Begin by taking the example of the H_2 molecule given in the textbook. Point out the different forces that need to be considered based on the separation between the two atoms. When the separation is small, the two nuclei can be considered as a helium nucleus. Go over the contributions to the energy from these various factors, and then discuss the three conditions listed for the formation of **molecules**. Again, you will find that most students are familiar with valence and ionic bonding.

Students may be familiar with the **Van der Waals** force as well. Point out that the **Van der Waals** force is a weak force and is the electromagnetic force that exists between neutral atoms. Remind students that it is this weak force that can explain properties like adhesion of a liquid to the sides of a container and why a gas deviates from the ideal gas picture.

The **molecular spectra** are more complicated than the **atomic spectra** due to the vibrational and rotational motion. Emphasize that the energy associated with these two motions are quantized as well. The vibrational energy levels are given by the equation $E_{vib} = n\hbar\omega$. Remind students of the harmonic oscillator potential that they encountered in Chapter 7 and that ω is related to the spring constant. While the vibrational energy levels are obtained by considering a spring and ball model of the atom, the molecule is considered as a rotating dumbbell to get the energy due to rotation. Go over the derivation for the vibrational and rotational energies (Equations 41-19 and 41-21). Figure 41-19 shows the energy levels due to the electronic, vibrational and rotational motion. Point out that corresponding to each electronic energy level there are vibrational energy levels. In turn, these vibrational levels have rotational energy levels associated with them. Notice that the wavelengths of these spectral lines are in the infrared region, which shows that these lines have wavelengths that are about 10^4 times the wavelengths of **atomic spectra**.

Textbook Resource Information

Transparency Acetates

Fig. 41-2	Wavelength of standing waves on a string
Fig. 41-4	Energy levels in a hydrogen atom
Fig. 41-5	Emission of a photon to produce spectral lines
Fig. 41-7	Direction of angular momentum vectors
Fig. 41-8	Bar magnet in nonuniform magnetic field
Fig. 41-9	The Stern – Gerlach experiment
Fig. 41-10	Possible transitions in a hydrogen atom
Fig. 41-14	Energy levels for an atom – schematic
Fig. 41-16	Pattern of electron energy level occupation
Fig. 41-19	Molecular energy levels

End of Chapter Problems with Solutions in the *Student Study Guide*

3, 13, 27, 37, 41, 49

Suggested Readings

Bloom, D., and Bloom, D.W., "Vibrating Wire Loop and the Bohr Model," *The Physics Teacher* (May 2003), p. 292 – 294.

Collins, D.F., "Video Spectroscopy — Emission, Absorption, and Flash," *The Physics Teacher* (December 2000), p. 561 – 562.

Golab-Meyer, Z., "'Piekara's Chair': Mechanical Model for Atomic Energy Levels," *The Physics Teacher* (April 1991), p. 215 – 220.

Laloe, F., "Do We Really Understand Quantum Mechanics? Strange Correlations, Paradoxes, and Theorems," *Am.J.Phys.* (June 2001), p. 655 – 701.

Lo Presto, M.C., "A Closer Look at the Spectrum of Helium," *The Physics Teacher* (March 1998), p. 172 – 173.

Mohrhoff, U., "What Quantum Mechanics Is Trying to Tell Us," *Am.J.Phys.* (August 2000), p. 728 – 745.

Morgan, M.J., and Jakovidis, G., "Characteristic Energy Scales of Quantum Systems, *The Physics Teacher* (September 1994), p. 354 – 358.

Palmquist , B.C., "Interactive Spectra Demonstration," *The Physics Teacher* (March 2002), p. 140 – 142.

Pasachoff, J.M., "The Bohr Staircase," *The Physics Teacher* (January 2004), p. 38 – 39.

Shadmi, Y., "Teaching the Exclusion Principle with Philosophical Flavor," *Am.J.Phys.* (August 1978), p. 844 – 848.

Notes and Ideas

Preparation time: *Estimated:* _____   *Actual:* _____

Class time spent on material: *Estimated:* _____   *Actual:* _____

Related laboratory activities:

Demonstration materials:

Notes for next time:

Chapter 42: Quantum Effects in Large Systems of Fermions and Bosons

Outline

Summary

The behavior of multiparticle systems of **fermions** and **bosons** is the main topic of this chapter. The exclusion principle is extended to the study of **bulk matter**. The working of the **laser** is discussed, and topics such as **superconductivity** and **superfluidity** are considered from a quantum mechanical perspective.

Major Concepts

- The exclusion principle in bulk matter
  - Electrons in metals and the Fermi energy
  - The incompressibility of matter
  - White dwarfs and neutron stars

- Lasers and the behavior of bosons
  - Transitions between energy levels
  - Lasers
  - Some uses of lasers
  - Bose – Einstein condensation

- Superconductivity
  - Cooper pairs and the BCS theory
  - The BCS theory and the electromagnetic properties of superconductors
  - Flux quantization
  - Tunneling of pairs and the Josephson effects

- Superfluidity and liquid helium

Teaching Suggestions and Demonstrations

This chapter consists of concepts that will be new to many students. These topics are also typically omitted from many curricula for lack of time. However, the concepts discussed here are very current and students will find them very interesting.

Section 42-1

Conductivity and **superconductivity** were introduced in Chapter 26 from a classical point of view. Here **superconductivity** is explained using quantum physics. Both theories consider the idea of free electrons in metals. However, quantum mechanics considers the motion of the free electrons quite differently from the classical picture. Begin with the energy level expression for a particle in a box and extend it to a three-dimensional box. Point out that a "state" is now identified by the values given to n_1, n_2 and n_3. Have students go through the exercise of identifying some of these states so they can understand the concept of an energy level having more than one state. Now define *degeneracy*.

Go over the points that need to be emphasized when discussing the application of the **exclusion principle** to **bulk matter**. First, the energy levels will have to be filled from the bottom up with two electrons in each level. Second, let students compute some typical values for $(n_1^2+n_2^2+n_3^2)$ and then point out that, because of the closeness of the energy levels they are almost a continuum. Further more, the degree of degeneracy increases with the value of n. Third, only the electrons in the top of the filled levels are capable of moving to higher energy levels. Define *Fermi energy* and go over the estimation of the **Fermi energy** starting from Equation 42-2. Fourth, the degeneracy pressure, which is a repulsive force between electrons, helps to explain why matter is incompressible. The final point to note is that the **exclusion principle** also explains the evolution of a star and particularly why a star does not collapse despite the mutual gravitational attraction of its mass. The electron degeneracy pressure must balance the gravitational pressure to reach equilibrium. Go over Example 42-2 to give students an idea of the order of magnitude for the degeneracy pressure. Example 42-3 shows how the radius of a neutron star can be determined using the equilibrium condition.

Section 42-2

Students are always intrigued by **lasers**. To understand how **laser** beams are produced, discuss the mechanics of spontaneous **transitions**. Point out that when an electron gets the right amount of energy, it will jump from the $l = 0$ state to a higher state, say $l = 2$. It can then jump back to the $l = 0$ state back again by first going down to the $l = 1$ state. If the $l = 1$ state is not present, then the probability of the electron jumping to the ground state is greatly reduced. This probability is even more reduced if the electron has to jump down from the $l = 3$ state, since now the change in l it must undergo has increased. With this basic concept explained, discuss metastable energy levels using the analogy (given in the text book) of a tub, filled with water, having one large and two small drain holes. Point out that the same results can be achieved through **stimulated transitions**. Emphasize that it is important to have a coherent, monochromatic plane wave to produce a **laser** beam.

Go over the requirements for the construction of a **laser**. Figure 42-8a is a schematic diagram of a **laser**. Use this to explain how the four requirements (as listed in the textbook) are met. Discuss the uses of **lasers** and point out that **laser** beams are essential in holography. It is also used in isotope separation and in controlled thermonuclear fusion reactions, to name a few. Students will be familiar with **laser** surgery to correct defects in vision as well as the use of lasers in other fields of medicine.

Bose – Einstein condensate is a very current field in physics research, and as such it is important that students are introduced to it. Discuss how it is produced. Make sure that students understand the significance of the single quantum state that can be formed when the temperature of a very dilute gas is lowered to a critical value. The process of **laser** cooling and evaporative cooling leaves the coldest atoms to form the **condensate**. Point out the tremendous potential for this "new state of matter" to current-day technology.

Section 42-3

Superconductivity was discussed in Chapter 26 and in Chapter 31. Here it is once again considered, but using quantum mechanics. **Superconductivity** is possible when **fermions** pair up to form **bosons** in the same quantum state. Explain what **Copper pairs** are and why they cannot be considered as two electrons or as a localized bound system.

The **Josephson effect** is another example of quantum mechanical **tunneling**. Start with an explanation of **tunneling** across two normal metals and then discuss how **tunneling** is achieved across two superconductors separated by a thin insulating strip. Because of the **tunneling** property (known as the **Josephson effect**) of electron pairs, it is now possible to study and measure very small magnetic fields.

Section 42-4

Another consequence of the **bosons'** ability to **condensate** at low temperatures (into the same quantum state) is the **superfluidity** of **helium**. Emphasize that the liquid has no internal friction at all and this is what makes it **superfluid**. Use Fig. 42-16 to show how liquid helium in the **superfluid** state can defy gravity and flow out of the container like a fountain. Point out that helium in a **superfluid** state has a coefficient of thermal conductivity that is many times (hundreds of thousands) greater than that of copper. Liquid helium is hence a very effective coolant that can maintain very large magnets (like those used in magnetic resonance imaging) below a crucial temperature. The discussion Think About This…Of What Use Is **Superfluid Helium** will give students a feel for the importance of the study of this field.

Textbook Resource Information

Transparency Acetates

Fig. 42-5	Spontaneous emission of a photon
Fig. 42-7	Stimulated emission
Fig. 42-8a	Schematic of a laser
Fig. 42-11	Magnetic field lines expelled by a ring of material
Fig. 42-12	Two metals with different Fermi energy levels
Fig. 42-15	Current through a pair of Josephson junction

End of Chapter Problems with Solutions in the *Student Study Guide*

3, 15, 29, 31, 37, 41

Suggested Readings

Austen, D., and Brouwer, W., "A Superconductivity Workshop," *The Physics Teacher* (April 1990), p. 232 – 233.

Bransky, J., "Superconductivity — a New Demonstration," *The Physics Teacher* (September 1990), p. 392 – 394.

Hall, D., "Resource Letter: BEC-1: Bose — Einstein Condensates in Trapped Dilute Gases," *Am.J.Phys.* (July 2003), p. 649 – 660.

Ihas, G.G., and Meisel, M.W., "Teaching Superconductivity via Analogy," *The Physics Teacher* (November 1990), p. 554 – 555.

Notes and Ideas

Preparation time: *Estimated:* _____   *Actual:* _____

Class time spent on material: *Estimated:* _____   *Actual:* _____

Related laboratory activities:

Demonstration materials:

Notes for next time:

Chapter 43: Quantum Engineering

Outline

Summary

Continuing with the concept of quantum physics, Chapter 43 looks at how materials are engineered (or fabricated) using quantum mechanics. Formation of **band energies** and how these bands are filled are discussed. **Semiconductors** and **semiconductor** structures are studied. How concepts such as **quantum wells**, **quantum wires**, **quantum dots** and **semiconductor lasers** have been made possible through **band-gap engineering** is considered. To complete the chapter, **scanning microscopy** is discussed.

Major Concepts

- Energy bands

- Semiconductors
    - The effects of temperature
    - Semiconductors, electrons, and holes
    - Doping
    - Optical effects in semiconductors

- Semiconductor structures
    - The *p-n* junction
    - Biasing
    - LEDs

- Band-gap engineering
    - Quantum wells, quantum wires, and quantum dots
    - Semiconductor lasers

- Scanning microscopy
    - Scanning tunneling microscopy
    - Atomic force microscopy
    - The ultimate in quantum engineering

Teaching Suggestions and Demonstrations

The concepts in this chapter rely on the Fermi – Dirac probability distribution that will most certainly be unfamiliar to students. However, this probability distribution can be used to consider the topics in a very qualitative way without getting into the mathematics to any depth.

Sections 43-1 – 43-2

The **band structures** with gaps and the Pauli exclusion principle help to explain the electrical conduction properties of solids, so begin this chapter with a discussion of how **band structures** are formed. Students learned about energy levels in Chapter 41. But now they will learn how these energy levels can split under certain conditions. Emphasize the following points regarding how **energy bands** are formed: In the case of atoms that are far apart, there is no interaction between the atoms. Hence, there are $2N$ degenerate states available for N atoms. The $2N$ comes from the fact that an **electron** can have a spin orientation of up or down. However, when these N atoms are in a closely spaced lattice arrangement, there now is an interaction between the atoms. As a consequence, the $2N$ levels split. N levels move up and N levels move down, creating a gap between them and the **electrons** fill up the lowest energy levels.

Now that students know how **energy bands** are formed, explain the difference between conductors, **semiconductors** and insulators based on which energy levels get filled up and how the **electrons** are affected in the presence of an external electric field. Use the example given in the book comparing magnesium to sodium. Illustrate why magnesium is a good conductor when influenced by an electric field.

The effect of temperature on the **electrons** and the levels they occupy are very basic to the understanding of the electrical conductivity of materials. Emphasize that Pauli's exclusion principle dictates that the energy distribution follows the Fermi – Dirac model and not the Maxwell – Boltzman distribution. As mentioned earlier in this chapter of the manual, students will not be familiar with the Fermi – Dirac distribution, but this should not hinder them from understanding how the temperature of the material will affect the probability distribution of the **electron** energies. Discuss the significance of Equation 43-2 in a qualitative manner. Go through worked Example 43-1 to show how this equation is used to evaluate $f(E)$.

In the case of **semiconductors**, there can be some confusion regarding the use of μ in the place of the Fermi-energy in Equation 43-4, and yet the authors revert back to E_F in Equation 43-5. Be sure to explain the reasoning behind this before you go any further. Use the analogy of the air bubble in a tank of water to explain the creation of holes or p-carriers and n-carriers. Point out that for each **electron** that jumps the gap to the conduction band you get an n-carrier (which is the electron itself) and a p-carrier or hole in the valence band created by the absence of the **electron**. Explain intrinsic **semiconductors** and discuss how extrinsic **semiconductors** are obtained through the process of **doping**. Use Fig. 43-9 to present the concepts qualitatively.

Photoluminescence is the process by which radiation is produced in a **semiconductor** when an **electron** jumps back into a valence hole from the conduction band. Explain the condition under which this can occur and point out when this process is considered to be fluorescence or phosphorescence. Point out that such **semiconductors** (also described as photoconductive) are used in cameras to measure light intensity and in lighting fixtures that need to operate based on light intensity.

Sections 43-3 – 43-4

LEDs and transistors are based on **semiconductor structures**. Discuss how such **structures** can be created using two similar **semiconductors** with different **dopings**, or two dissimilar intrinsic **semiconductors,** or a combination of a **semiconductor** with a metal. Use the energy diagrams shown in Figs. 43-14 and 43-16 to explain *p-n* **junctions** and how they are affected when they are **biased**. Briefly discuss how **LEDs** and transistors are formed and mention their uses. Review the section Think About This…How Does A Solar Cell Operate and observe that **LEDs** are merely solar cells operating in reverse.

Band-gap engineering has allowed for great many advances in the electronic and computer fields. Many of your students are aspiring engineers and are sure to find these topics very interesting. So take time to discuss concepts such as **quantum wells, quantum wires**, and **quantum dots**, as well as **semiconductor lasers**.

Section 43-5

Scanning tunneling microscopes were briefly introduced in Chapter 24. Here, it is considered in greater detail. **STM** (as it is known) is based on the quantum mechanical **tunneling** property of electrons. Remind students that only the availability of empty energy levels can enable **electrons** to move from one sample to another. If an electric field is applied, this can lower the Fermi energy on one side, create the necessary empty energy levels and thus produce a condition that is conducive to **electron tunneling**. Take time to discuss (even if briefly) the concept of a single-atom tip because it is sure to fascinate students. Compare the **STM** to the **atomic force microscope** and discuss the uses of both kinds of imaging devices.

Textbook Resource Information

Transparency Acetates

Fig. 43-1	Band structure formation
Fig. 43-2	Band structure in magnesium
Fig. 43-6	Electrons jump the gap in a semiconductor
Fig. 43-9	Energy band structure for doped semiconductors
Fig. 43-11	Electron excited to the conduction band
Fig. 43-15	Depletion region in a *p-n* junction
Fig. 43-16	Biasing of *p-n* junction
Fig. 43-18	Schematic diagram of a solar cell
Fig. 43-24	A quantum well subjected to an external potential
Fig. 43-25	Energy diagram for a semiconductor laser
Fig. 43-29	Schematic of a scanning tunneling microscope
Fig. 43-31	Schematic of an atomic force microscope

End of Chapter Problems with Solutions in the *Student Study Guide*

9, 17, 23, 39, 49, 51

Suggested Readings

Austen, D., and Brouwer, W., "A Superconductivity Workshop," *The Physics Teacher* (April 1990), p. 232 – 233.

Bransky, J., "Superconductivity — a New Demonstration," *The Physics Teacher* (September 1990), p. 392 – 394.

Fisher, H.D., "A History of the Ubiquitous Semiconductor," *The Physics Teacher* (January 1979), p. 68 – 69.

Ihas, G.G., and Meisel, M.W., "Teaching Superconductivity via Analogy," *The Physics Teacher* (November 1990), p. 554 – 555.

Lindenfeld, P., "Size Effects in Conductivity and Superconductivity," *The Physics Teacher* (April 1980), p. 260 – 267.

O'Connell, J., "Decoding the TV Remote Control," *The Physics Teacher* (January 2000), p. 6.

Rehberger, P.J., "Semiconductors: Characteristics and Design," *The Physics Teacher* (September 1980), p. 474.

Notes and Ideas

Preparation time: *Estimated:* _____   *Actual:* _____

Class time spent on material: *Estimated:* _____   *Actual:* _____

Related laboratory activities:

Demonstration materials:

Notes for next time:

Chapter 44: Nuclear Physics

Outline

Summary

To study the **nucleus**, this chapter begins by looking at the **nuclear constituents** and their properties. The fundamental **nuclear forces** and **nuclear models** such as the shell model and the liquid drop model are presented. **Radioactivity** and **nuclear reactions** are discussed. How carbon-12 is used to date biological matter and the use of radioisotopes in medicine are explained. Generation of nuclear power using **fission** and **fusion** processes are considered.

Major Concepts

- Static properties of nuclei
    - Nuclear constituents
    - Scattering distributions
    - Some terminology
    - Nuclear masses and binding energies
    - Other properties

- Nuclear forces and nuclear models
    - The shell model
    - The liquid-drop model

- Energetics of nuclear reactions

- Radioactivity
    - Radioactivity
    - Alpha decay
    - Beta decay
    - Gamma decay
    - Radioactivity and life

- Fission and fusion
    - Fission
    - Fusion

- Applications of nuclear physics
    - Radiometric dating
    - Radioisotopes
    - Nuclear power generation

Teaching Suggestions and Demonstrations

Quite often the last few chapters are not covered for lack of time. The study of the **nucleus**, **radioactivity** and **fission/fusion** processes are important. Students will find the concepts presented here very interesting and relevant in today's world, so try to allocate a class period or two to discuss these concepts qualitatively, at least.

Section 44-1

To give students a historical perspective, discuss the famous Rutherford's **alpha-particle** scattering experiment. The discovery that the atom has all of its positive charges inside a **nucleus** was arrived at based on the results of this experiment. Go over the basic constituents of the **nucleus**. Define atomic number and atomic weight and point out the symbols used to represent them. Point out that the standard notation for a **nucleus** is $_Z^A X$.

Go over the properties of the **nucleus**, like nuclear mass, nuclear radius, charge and the **binding energy.** Define atomic mass unit and go over the new terminologies introduced in this chapter. It is best to not assume that students will be familiar with these new terms.

The concept of **binding energy** can be confusing. Equation 44-6 shows how the **binding energy** can be evaluated. Have students calculate the **binding energies** of some nuclei. Use Fig. 44-6 to explain why iron is the most stable element in the periodic table. Emphasize that when a heavy nucleus like ^{235}U breaks up the resulting nuclei have greater **binding energies** and are hence more stable than the ^{235}U. By the same argument, when two light nuclei (like two hydrogen nuclei) are fused, the resulting nucleus has a greater **binding energy**. The concept of **nuclear stability** is important for the understanding of spontaneous **radioactivity**. So discuss the significance of Fig. 44-8 which is a plot of the number of protons versus the number of neutrons in a nucleus. Point out the $N{:}Z$ ratio of the isotopes that lie along the line of stability.

Section 44-2

What holds a **nucleus** together when you would expect the protons to repel each other? Define the fermi and discuss the concept of the short-range attractive force. Point out that there are forces of interaction between protons, between a neutron and a proton and between two neutrons. The basic difference in the interaction between these nucleons is the proton-proton interaction which is electromagnetic nature. Define the Yukawa potential and use the graphs shown in Fig. 44-9 to discuss the difference between the Yukawa and Coulomb potential. Point out that the two are pretty similar when r is small, but differ quite a bit for greater separation distances.

There are three points that need to be emphasized with regard to **nuclear forces**. First, the nucleons repel each other if the distance is greater than 1 fermi. Second, the spin orientation of the nucleus affects the **nuclear forces**. Third, these **nuclear forces** are due to the interaction between more than two particles.

The **shell model** and the **liquid-drop model**, are two models that are considered in this chapter. The **shell model** is based on the premise that the nucleus has energy levels that are well defined and similar to the electron energy levels (remind students that they learned this in Chapter 41). Discuss the concept of magic numbers and the spin-orbit coupling. The spin-orbit coupling is important because it explains the splitting of energy levels and gives a better prediction of the magic numbers.

The **liquid-drop model** is based on the energy of a **liquid drop**. Go over the six steps outlined in the textbook to show how Equation 44-16 is arrived at. Be sure to point out that the mass formula is a semiempirical one. Discuss the significance of each term. Go through worked Example 44-7.

Section 44-3

In discussing **nuclear reactions,** remind students that more than one conservation law is applicable here. The charge, energy and momentum are all conserved in any **nuclear reaction**. While they will not use the momentum conservation here, they will certainly be using the other two conservation laws. Emphasize that we are now dealing with speeds close to the speed of light, and hence they must remember to use the relativistic form of the energy equation. Students will more than likely assume that the mc^2 terms on either side of the energy equation will cancel. Point out that, when there is an identity change of the particle, the rest mass (mc^2) will be different. Show how the Q-value is determined using energy considerations. Work several numerical examples and remind students of the danger of rounding off the values too soon.

Sections 44-4 – 44-5

Now that students have some concept of nuclear stability, **binding energies** and **nuclear forces**, they will be in a good situation to understand the phenomenon of **radioactivity**. Introduce the topic by giving them a little background about Henri Becquerel and Marie Curie. Point out that she got the Nobel prize for her work in this area.

Define decay constant, decay rate, half-life, and activity. Discuss the three types of decay processes and give examples in each case. Point out that in these reactions both charge (Z) and nucleon number (A) are conserved. Discuss **radioactive** series. Figure 44-6 shows a specific series. After explaining this graph, use another series for which only the starting nucleus and the kind of decay are indicated. Have them use the periodic table and figure out the intermediate nuclei in the series. With practice they will recognize that an **alpha decay** will move the series to the left while **beta decay** will correspond to a shift to the right in the graph.

⊃ **DEMO** The exponential nature of radioactivity can be illustrated with a very simple experiment. Bring about 1000 to 1500 pennies to class and distribute them equally among the students. The students then flip the pennies and discard those that fell tail side up. The process is repeated until there are very few pennies left. The number left each time (the ones that fell heads up) is recorded. Taking the initial number of pennies as N_o, have them plot the data. Use this to discuss the concept of half-life.

Fission and **fusion** are discussed qualitatively in the text book. Go back to Fig. 44-6 and ensure that students see the connection between the **binding energy/nucleon** and **fission/fusion** process. Work through examples to show how much energy is released in a **fission/fusion** process.

Section 44-6

There are several applications of **nuclear physics** discussed in the book. **Radiometric dating** is used in the field of biology and geology while **radioisotopes** have important uses in medicine. Every student should know how **nuclear power** plants work. Take time to discuss these topics in class.

Textbook Resource Information

Transparency Acetates

Fig. 44-4   Scattering of alpha particles from gold atoms
Fig. 44-5   Schematic of Chadwick's experiment
Table 44-2   Some nuclear binding energies
Fig. 44-6   The binding energy per nucleon vs. mass number
Fig. 44-8   Plot of neutron number vs. number of protons
Fig. 44-10   Total cross section for neutron absorption by ^{23}Na
Fig. 44-14   Some gamma ray transitions
Fig. 44-16   The decay series for ^{238}U
Fig. 44-17   The fission process
Fig. 44-19   Chain reaction
Fig. 44-20b   Fusion by inertial confinement
Fig. 44-21   Fusion by magnetic confinement

End of Chapter Problems with Solutions in the *Student Study Guide*

5, 17, 23, 39, 49, 51

Suggested Readings

Bouffard, K., "Rutherford Meets Einstein," *The Physics Teacher* (February 1999), p. 125 – 126.

Deacon, C.G., "A Background to Background Radiation," *The Physics Teacher* (February 2003), p. 78 – 80.

Hanson, R., "More on Alphas," *The Physics Teacher* (March 1998), p. 131 – 132.

Hartt, K., "Beta Decay," *The Physics Teacher* (October 1988), p. 471 – 472.

Jesse, K.E., "Computer Simulation of Radioactive Decay," *The Physics Teacher* (December 2003), p. 542 – 543.

Lederman, L., "Unraveling the Mysteries of the Atom," *The Physics Teacher* (January 1982) p. 15 – 20.

Mak, S., "Radioactivity Experiments for Project Investigation," *The Physics Teacher* (December 1999), p. 536 – 539.

Neff, R., "Tabletop Fusion?," *The Physics Teacher* (May 1999), p. 320.

Phillips, D.W., "Physics on Graphing Calculators," *The Physics Teacher* (April 1999), p. 230 – 231.

Silverman, M.P., Strange, W., Silverman, C.R., and Lipscombe, T.C., "On the Run: Unexpected Outcomes of Random Events," *The Physics Teacher* (April 1999), p. 218 – 225.

Smith, F.A., "The Cross-Sectional Area of Objects in a Hat Box," *The Physics Teacher* (May 2004), p. 310 – 311.

Steiger, W.R., "A Radioactive Tracer in Medicine," *The Physics Teacher* (October 1999), p. 408 – 409.

Walkiewicz, T.A., "Alpha Problems," *The Physics Teacher* (March 1998), p. 131.

Weinberg, R., "The Half-Lives of Silver," *The Physics Teacher* (November 1997), p. 456 – 460.

Notes and Ideas

Preparation time: *Estimated:* _____   *Actual:* _____

Class time spent on material: *Estimated:* _____   *Actual:* _____

Related laboratory activities:

Demonstration materials:

Notes for next time:

Chapter 45: Particles and Cosmology

Outline

Summary

A brief study of elementary **particles** and **cosmology** brings us to the end of this textbook. **Baryons, leptons** and **quarks** are introduced. The **fundamental forces** are discussed, and the tools used to probe the structure of matter are considered. On a macro scale, concepts such as **expanding universe, Hubble's law** and the **Big-Bang** model are discussed.

Major Concepts

- Probing the structure of matter
  - Seeing subatomic systems
  - Elastic and inelastic scattering

- New quantum numbers
  - The discovery of antimatter
  - Baryon number
  - Leptons and their quantum numbers

- The fundamental constituents of matter: leptons and quarks
  - The quark model

- The fundamental forces and their carriers
  - The carriers of forces: the Yukawa theory
  - The electroweak force
  - The strong force
  - The standard model

- The tools of particle physics
  - Accelerators
  - Detectors

- Cosmology and the expanding universe
  - Cosmological principles
  - Hubble's law
  - The Big Bang model
  - The uniformity of the universe

Teaching Suggestions and Demonstrations

The topics in this last chapter introduce students to ideas that are powerful and fascinating. It makes for fairly easy reading, and the concepts can be discussed qualitatively. We encourage you to make time to cover the topics in this chapter.

Section 45-1

Much of the study of the structure of matter is done through scattering experiments. Begin by reminding students that they had studied about the limitations on the target size placed by the momentum of the projectile. Now discuss the significance of Equation 45-1 and explain how the small size of the nucleus requires that the projectile has very large energies. Briefly discuss the importance of elastic and inelastic scattering in the quest for **fundamental particles** that form matter. You may have to review the concept of cross-section (see Chapter 19, Section 7).

Sections 45-2 – 45-3

Students are introduced to an array of new **particles**. Define each one and review its properties. Review the several reactions given in the text. Discuss how antimatter was discovered. Make sure that students understand the concept of **baryon** and **lepton number** conservation and its significance.

Discuss the **quark** model. Use Table 45-1 to introduce the quantum numbers of the **quarks** and their rest energies. Give examples of **quark** combinations resulting in different kinds of **baryons**. For instance, the proton is made up of 3 **quarks**, 2 up **quarks** and a down **quark**. Use this to explain the angular momentum (spin) such particles can have.

Sections 45-4 – 45-5

To understand the structure of matter at the micro level, we need to study the **fundamental forces** that act between particles. Table 45-2 lists these **forces**. We have seen three of these **forces** in earlier chapters. Introduce each one and discuss the salient features. Go over the concept of "virtual photons" that are used to discuss the **electromagnetic forces**.

Introduce the idea of a meson field. Point out that in order for a meson to be absorbed or emitted by a nucleon and not violate angular momentum conservation principles, it must be a boson. Students must also recognize that the meson needs to exist in the three charge states in order to obey charge conservation.

To understand the **electroweak force**, first discuss the salient features of the weak interaction **forces**. Give some examples of reactions that are governed by the weak interaction. Point out that the **electroweak force** is a unification of the **weak force** and the **electromagnetic force**. It can be compared to the unification of the electric and magnetic forces to form the **electromagnetic forces** that students are already familiar with.

A discussion of the **fundamental forces** will not be complete without looking at the **strong force**. Introduce the concept of gluons and color charge of the quarks. Emphasize that the color charge of a **quark** does not refer to the colors of the visible spectrum, but that it is used to merely describe the charge of a **quark**. Also point out, that the color charge obeys charge conservation principles, as well. Make sure students understand the basic difference between photons (that are an integral part of the **electromagnetic** force) and gluons. While photons do not carry any electric charge at all, the gluons are described by the color quantum number.

Discuss the **standard model** that helps to describe **fundamental** particles and interactions. Use Fig. 45-8 to go over the features of the model and point out that there are still pieces of knowledge missing. Emphasize that the **standard model** is not a single theory. On the contrary, it helps to understand **electroweak** and **strong forces** from a common angle.

Section 45-5 gives an insight into the experimental setup needed to probe the structure of matter at the nuclear level. Table 45-3 gives an idea of the capabilities of the different **colliders** in terms of maximum beam energy.

The depth to which you discuss these topics will be dictated by the time you have left in the semester.

Section 45-6

Cosmology will be of interest to the majority of your students. Start with a discussion of the **Cosmological Principle**. Explain the significance of **Hubble's Law** and introduce the idea of the **expanding universe**. Discuss the concept of open, closed and critical universes using Fig. 45-18. Explain how the age of the universe is gauged in terms of Planck's time, as given by Equation 45-15. Conclude the study of **cosmology** with a brief look at the **Big-Bang** theory.

Textbook Resource Information

Transparency Acetates

Fig. 45-2	Elastic scattering of positive pions from protons
Fig. 45-3	Schematic of the hierarchical structure of matter
Table 45-1	Properties of quarks
Fig. 45-6	Electromagnetic and gluon field lines
Fig. 45-7	Creation of two mesons from one
Fig. 45-9	Schematic diagram of a fixed-target machine
Table 45-3	Characteristics of some colliders
Fig. 45-17	One-dimensional version of Hubble's law
Fig. 45-18	Evolution of open, closed, and critical universe
Fig. 45-19	A view of many galaxies

End of Chapter Problems with Solutions in the *Student Study Guide*

3, 13, 19, 25, 39, 41

Suggested Readings

Haxton, W.C., and Holstein, B.R., "Neutrino Physics," *Am.J.Phys.* (January 2000), p. 15 – 32.

Haxton, W.C., and Holstein, B.R., "Neutrino Physics: An Update," *Am.J.Phys.* (January 2004), p. 18 – 24.

Johansson, K.E., Nilsson, C., Engstedt, J., and Sandqvist, A., "Astronomy and Particle Physics Research Classes for Secondary School Students," *Am.J.Phys.* (May 2001), p. 576 – 581.

Krauss, L.M., "The History and Fate of the Universe," *The Physics Teacher* (March 2003), p. 146 – 155.

Muhry, H., and Ritter, P., "Muons in the Classroom," *The Physics Teacher* (May 2002), p. 294 – 300.

O'Connell, J., "Comparison of the Four Fundamental Interactions of Physics," *The Physics Teacher* (January 1998), p. 27.

Pasachoff, J.M., "What Should Students Learn?," *The Physics Teacher* (September 2001), p. 381 – 382.

Silverman, C., "The Turbulent World of Physics Explained," *The Physics Teacher* (December 1998), p. 528.

Spradley, J.L., "Yukawa and the Birth of Meson Theory Fiftieth Anniversary for Nuclear Forces," *The Physics Teacher* (May 1985), p. 283 – 289.

Notes and Ideas

Preparation time: *Estimated:* _____   *Actual:* _____

Class time spent on material: *Estimated:* _____   *Actual:* _____

Related laboratory activities:

Demonstration materials:

Notes for next time:

Instructor Notes on ConcepTest Questions

CORNELIUS BENNHOLD
The George Washington University

—

GERALD FELDMAN
The George Washington University

PHYSICS

for Scientists and Engineers

THIRD EDITION

FISHBANE | GASIOROWICZ | THORNTON

Instructor Notes on ConcepTests
Table of Contents

Instructor Notes on ConcepTests
Table of Contents (continued)

Introduction

A. Facilitating the paradigm shift: From knowledge delivery to skill training

Teaching by telling is an ineffective mode of instruction for most students.
L.C. McDermott

In most science and engineering courses, a primary goal of the course is to help the students develop their competencies in critical thinking, problem solving and analytical reasoning. However, many instructors have come to recognize that, in spite of their best intentions, many students emerge from their study of these technical fields with serious shortcomings regarding their level of ability in these cognitive skills and thus with significant gaps in their understanding of important topics. As a consequence, there is a discernible shift from "content-driven" learning toward a more "skill-centered" type of instruction. In particular, there is consensus that "doing science" does not just mean acquiring a body of knowledge of scientific facts and formulas — it also involves a specific set of skills to mediate the application of this knowledge. In order to achieve a reasonable level of competence, as with most physical and mental activities, this enhancement of thinking skills cannot be achieved without extensive exercise and many hours of practice.

In the last two decades, physicists have begun to approach this problem from a scientific perspective by conducting detailed systematic studies on the learning and teaching of physics [McD99]. Research in Physics Education, which focuses on empirical evidence of student understanding of science content, complements traditional education research that has a stronger emphasis on educational theory and methodology. From the perspective of science departments, discipline-based education research conducted by science faculty has proven to be an effective approach for improving student learning in science [McD01].

Guided by such recent results in Physics Education research, many physics departments have set out to reinvent their introductory physics courses to create a forum in which students can significantly improve their conceptual understanding of physical principles and better develop their skills in critical thinking, analytical reasoning and problem solving. However, reallocating classroom time from lecturing to interactive student engagement requires a fundamental shift in teaching philosophy. It changes the focus from the subject content to the intellectual activity of the students; thus, to some degree, knowledge transfer is being replaced by the development and practice of such cognitive skills.

B. Practicing Physics: The Socratic Method and Peer Instruction

Research in the field of Physics Education has revealed a basic ineffectiveness in the conventional lecture course [Cr01]. This refers to a "typical" classroom course, in which the students attempt to absorb information that is presented by the lecturer. In fact, it is the passivity of the student audience that is at the heart of the problem. The notion that the "traditional" lecture communicates little to students is a conclusion not readily accepted in the physics community. Indeed, the idea that a very clear explanation suffices for complete student comprehension may appear sensible. However, numerous empirical studies have shown this not to be the case [Me96]. On the other hand, Physics Education research has uncovered convincing evidence that an "interactive engagement" (IE) approach, in which the students are active participants in the classroom environment, is considerably more effective in the learning process [Ha98]. The main point is that the students spend more of the classroom time practicing the material, thereby exercising their minds and developing their skills, which allows them to assimilate the basic concepts in a more natural manner. Further studies in general higher education have shown that students develop complex reasoning skills most effectively when actively engaged with the material and have found that cooperative activities are an excellent way to engage students [Jo91].

As a first step toward engaging the students in the classroom, it is recommended that the entire philosophy of the classroom period be altered. Rather than repeat the same material that is already covered in the textbook, we begin practicing the material as soon as possible and as often as possible. Thus, we require the students to read the class material in advance, and they are expected to have some familiarity with the concepts to be covered that day. The material presentation can be limited to the highlights in order to get to the major classroom activity, which is the implementation of a technique known as Peer Instruction.

Peer Instruction is a Socratic teaching style pioneered by Eric Mazur at Harvard University in which students actively participate in the learning process through an interactive sequence of questions and answers, called *ConcepTests* [Ma97]. Largely abandoning the principles of behavioral learning theory, Peer Instruction is based on Piagetian learning principles that promote student constructing their understanding of concepts rather than rote memorization.

Peer Instruction replaces the traditional lecture format by partitioning the class period into 10 – 15 minute "mini-lectures," each of which is terminated by a series of short multiple-choice conceptual questions (*ConcepTests*) designed to challenge the students to immediately apply the material. The students think for 1 – 2 minutes about the questions and then commit to individual answers. They then spend 2 – 3 minutes attempting to convince their neighbors about the accuracy of their answer. After this period, students are asked to reconsider their original answer and record it again. Another quick poll is taken, after which the instructor indicates the correct answer. The immediate feedback reveals to the students their level of understanding, leading them to ask more questions, while the instructor, based on the student answers, can decide whether to move on to the next subject or to supplement the current one with additional practice.

The objective of Peer Instruction is to foster active student learning, even (or especially) in a large lecture environment. By encouraging student participation and interaction during the lecture, Peer Instruction encourages students to think critically about the arguments being developed and to discuss their ideas and insights with other students. Engaging students in the learning process has been shown to improve student learning of and attitude toward the subject, increase classroom attendance and reduce attrition. It is important to point out that the *ConcepTests* are not numerical questions that require a calculator or other manipulation. Mazur found that students understood concepts better and performed more successfully on conventional problems in this environment, as reflected in scores on the Force Concept Inventory [He92] (a nationally distributed assessment instrument) and final exams in the course.

It is helpful (but not essential) to supplement Peer Instruction with an electronic student response system that records the student responses to the *ConcepTests*. Most such systems display the composite class responses for each question as a histogram and records all of the responses for each individual student during the class period. Depending on the system, students may login to the system at the beginning of each class with a valid ID number, so the keypad responses are unambiguously linked to each student in a unique fashion. Student authentication permits complete tracking of each student's activity throughout the class period; such systems allow giving credit for participation and permit far more analysis possibilities than the simple display of a response histogram during class.

It is during the discussion with neighbors that the primary learning can take place. Students sometimes have their own way of thinking or explaining that can often differ from the approach taken by the instructor. The "student way" of thinking may be different in such a way as to be more attuned to the other students. The instructor is still a primary resource, but generally during the discussion time, the instructor is surveying the discussion and listening to the arguments of the students. In that sense, the role of the instructor is more akin to that of a "coach" who facilitates and advises while the student "players" work at the desired activity. Following the second round of responses, the correct answer and a full explanation are provided, and possible reasons why students might have selected a particular wrong answer are offered. Often a particular misconception can be uncovered in this manner. Those students who have not changed to the correct answer after discussion are forced to confront their own deeply seated beliefs, and the "shock" of getting the wrong answer can be an effective means of dislodging this misconception, or at least, getting them to reconsider what they had previously believed.

In our five years of experience of using such a system, certain aspects of the system and its use as an interactive engagement tool have become apparent, such as:

- Students enjoy using the system and readily engage in the in-class activities.
- Attendance in class is typically at the 90% level or higher for *every* class.
- Answering questions in class and discussion with neighbors breaks up the monotony of a traditional lecture.
- Anonymity during class responses permits students to answer honestly.
- Discussion among the students often reveals hidden misconceptions or elicits interesting questions that pertain to the entire class.
- Students reach a higher level of motivation with active in-class participation.

Even relatively simple concepts that are "covered" in a few minutes of conventional lecture time turn out to be profoundly confusing to students (*e.g.,* "The only force [neglecting air resistance] acting on a projectile in flight is gravity"). Furthermore, ideas which instructors may consider too trivial to warrant more than a passing reference have been found to stump many students when they are asked to make use of them in problems (*e.g.,* "The total momentum of a pair of objects sitting at rest is zero"). The improvement in student comprehension and retention from the interactive engagement methods is a measurable effect, obtained from experimental data subjected to a rigorous statistical analysis. A landmark study by Richard Hake [Ha98] with a data set of over 6000 students in 62 independent introductory physics courses identified an increase in the normalized gain (defined as the ratio of the average gain to the maximum possible gain) on the Force Concept Inventory [He92] by a factor of two for courses employing IE techniques, compared to traditional lecture courses.

C. From *ConcepTests* to *ConcepModules*

As discussed above, the term *ConcepTest* refers to a single conceptual multiple-choice question that challenges the student to immediately apply certain material and thereby develop critical thinking and analytical reasoning skills. Since Mazur's publication [Ma97], many new such questions have been developed and tested within the physics education community. With extensive implementation of Peer Instruction, some disadvantages of an isolated *ConcepTest* have become apparent, among them [Fe99]:

- The question may be too difficult, thus students have little chance to arrive at the correct answer, even after extensive discussion.
- The question may be too easy and thus appear gratuitous to the students.
- The students may not see the connection between the question and the material being discussed, thus it "comes out of nowhere."
- The students may not realize how discussing a particular conceptual question helps them solve numerical homework problems, thus students may question the purpose of engaging in the activity.
- The students may be left with the feeling that, after answering a particular question, they have exhausted all open questions pursuant to this line of inquiry.

We therefore advocate using a refinement of the *ConcepTest* in class, the **Conceptual Module**, or *ConcepModule*. This instrument contains the following features:

1. A sequence of 2 – 4 *ConcepTests*, usually ordered by level of difficulty or ranked according to some other pedagogical reason. This allows students to "climb the mountain slowly" when a difficult concept is being practiced.
2. A follow-up numerical problem to be solved by the instructor in class after or in between several *ConcepTests*. This relates the conceptual question(s) to the numerical problems the students will need to solve for homework and in exams and thus establishes a linkage between different knowledge representations.
3. An accompanying demo (or movie of a demo) that further elucidates the concept and accommodates different student learning styles.
4. Open-ended follow-up questions for the last *ConcepTest* in the sequence that emphasize that each answer to a *ConcepTest* invites another question.

The use of *ConcepModules* in class, rather than isolated *ConcepTests*, integrates the exploration of certain material, especially for the average or below-average student who may otherwise perceive each class activity in isolation. Clearly, not all *ConcepModules* contain all the above features, and many instructors may wish to continue using individual *ConcepTests* without the accompanying features of a Module. As an example, we show below a conceptual module from chapter 3 (the assignment of the difficulty level is discussed in the next section):

Conceptual Module 3.10 (three parts)

ConcepTest 3.10a: Shoot the Monkey I
Difficulty Level: 3

This series deals with variations of the "monkey hunter" problem. The first question deals with the relatively simple case of the shooter and the monkey on the same level.

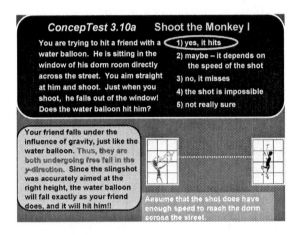

ConcepTest 3.10b: Shoot the Monkey II
Difficulty Level: 4
Suggested follow-up numerical problem: Problem 3.10

This is the standard formulation of the "monkey hunter" problem, in which the shooter is on the ground and the monkey is located at some elevation. It is hoped that the students will be able to extrapolate their experience from the first question to this one.

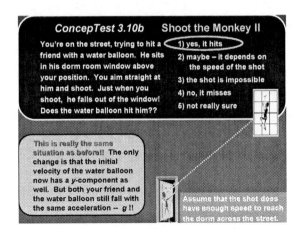

ConcepTest 3.10c: Shoot the Monkey III
Difficulty Level: 4
Suggested follow-up conceptual questions:
- **When would they *not* hit each other?**

In this case, two projectiles initially aimed at each other are fired. The fact that both projectiles are only under the influence of gravity means that they will indeed hit. This can be more easily seen for the case of projectiles that are launched at the same level.

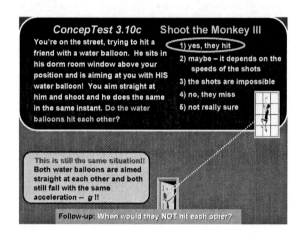

D. Classification of question difficulty according to *Bloom's Taxonomy of Thinking Skills*

As an introductory science course moves from the mere delivery of knowledge to the acquisition and training of thinking skills, the question arises, what performance indicators instructors are to use to determine if the learning objectives of the course have been achieved. As a prerequisite, problems the student uses to train with must be classified according to some scale. Usually, for numerical end-of-chapter problems, most standard textbooks tend to use an "easy – medium – hard" distinction that is based on the experience of the textbook author, rather than any rigorous analysis of the level of thinking skills needed to solve a particular problem. Conceptual questions are usually not rated at all.

To clarify our educational objectives, we have found it helpful to work with a classification scheme referred to as Bloom's Taxonomy [An94], which establishes a hierarchy of cognitive skills, listed below:

Level 1: Knowledge

Knowledge in this context refers to the ability to recall previously learned material. This may cover a wide range, from specific facts to complete theories, but all that is required is remembering the appropriate information. Knowledge represents the lowest level of thinking skills in the cognitive domain.

Examples of general learning objectives at this level are: know common terms, know specific facts, know methods and procedures, know basic concepts and principles.

Physics questions at this level would simply require familiarity with specific facts. Reading quizzes that test students having read the book before class would use this level.

Level 2: Comprehension

Comprehension is defined as the ability to grasp the meaning of material. This may be shown by translating material from one form to another (words to numbers) or by interpreting material (explaining or summarizing). These learning outcomes go one step beyond the simple remembering of material and represent the lowest level of understanding.

Examples of general learning objectives at this level are: understand facts and principles, interpret verbal material, interpret charts and graphs, translate verbal material to mathematical formulae, and estimate the future consequences implied in data.

Physics questions at this level would test the lowest level of understanding of a concept beyond the mere remembering of a fact, but without expecting the student to apply it in a given problem or situation.

Level 3: Application

Application refers to the ability to use learned material in concrete situations. This may include the application of such things as rules, methods, concepts, principles, laws, and theories. Learning outcomes in this area require a higher level of understanding than those under comprehension.

Examples of general learning objectives at this level are: apply concepts and principles to new situations, apply laws and theories to practical situations, solve simple mathematical problems, construct graphs and charts, and demonstrate the correct usage of a method or procedure.

Physics problems at this level could require simple numerical calculations. It is thus an important step, since it constitutes the first link between theory (concepts) and practice (applications). Conceptual questions would require applying a concept to a specific new situation or problem. Simple laboratory procedures would fall into this category.

Level 4 (higher order): Analysis

Analysis refers to the ability to break down material into its component parts so that its organizational structure may be understood. This may include the identification of parts, analysis of the relationship between parts, and recognition of the organizational principles involved. Learning outcomes here represent a higher intellectual level than comprehension and application because they require an understanding of both the content and the structural form of the material.

Examples of general learning objectives at this level are: recognize unstated assumptions, recognize logical fallacies in reasoning, distinguish between facts and inferences, evaluate the relevancy of data, and analyze the organizational structure of a work.

Physics problems at this level involve taking apart the elements of a more complex exercise and independently manipulating the components. Usually, multi-step numerical problems (end-of-chapter exercises) fall into this category. Another aspect of the analysis level would include processing of data in lab exercises with the objective of drawing conclusions from those data.

Level 5 (higher order): Synthesis

Synthesis refers to the ability to put parts together to form a new whole. This may involve items like a plan of operations (research proposal) or a set of abstract relations (scheme for classifying information). Learning outcomes in this area stress creative behaviors, with major emphasis on the formulation of new patterns or structure.

Examples of general learning objectives at this level are: write a well-organized funding proposal, propose a plan for an experiment, integrate learning from different areas into a plan for solving a problem, formulate a new scheme for classifying objects (or events, or ideas).

The physics problems at this level normally involve analyses between categories or topics that are not alike, requiring the students to reassemble component parts of these categories in new ways. Problems at this level are seldom found in standard textbooks.

Level 6 (higher order): Evaluation

Evaluation is concerned with the ability to judge the value of material (statement, novel, poem, research report) for a given purpose. The judgments are to be based on definite criteria. These may be internal criteria (organization) or external criteria (relevance to the purpose), and the student may determine the criteria or have them be given. Learning outcomes in this area are highest in the cognitive hierarchy because they contain elements of all the other categories, in addition to performing value judgments based on clearly defined criteria.

Examples of general learning objectives at this level are: judge the logical consistency of written material, judge the adequacy with which conclusions are supported by data, judge the value of a work by the use of internal criteria or of external standards of excellence.

The physics problems in this level should require students to make judgment calls as to the validity of the information provided and place material in a larger context of other knowledge. Problems at this level are very rarely found in standard textbooks.

E. Student response histograms

Many conceptual questions will be presented with a *student response histogram (SRH)* [Gu01] that displays student responses when the question was asked in class. It allows an instructor to anticipate the potential student response and may influence the decision to use this question in class. Clearly, student responses to individual questions depend on many factors, some of which will be discussed in the context of each question. Normalizing the student response to the overall quality of the student body is a difficult issue, which is addressed below.

The complete SRH consists of two graphs, the *response histogram* and the *change graph*. The *response histogram* displays five entry columns, where each entry reports the percentage of students giving one possible answer in the ConcepTest. The number of students giving a particular answer in round 1 is shown as red (light gray) bars. The blue (dark gray) bars display the number of students who have chosen this answer in round 2, after discussion with peers. The correct answer is displayed in the PowerPoint slide and is shown as a circle below the correct column.

To further evaluate and anticipate the effectiveness of a given *ConcepTest*, the change graph displays five separate groups of students:

- C-C (Correct → correct): This group of students ("sustainers") chose the correct answer both before and after discussion. This group constitutes the best students who are confident about having chosen the correct answer and stick to it.
- I-C (Incorrect → correct): This group of students ("improvers") chose an incorrect answer before discussion but the correct answer after discussion. This group has

obviously benefited from the discussion process and either was persuaded by a line of reasoning or just followed a group consensus.

- I-S (Incorrect → same incorrect): This group of students ("insisters") chose the same incorrect answer both before and after discussion. This group clearly felt confident about their wrong answer, and the group discussion could not change their conviction.

- I-D (Incorrect → different incorrect): This group of students ("switchers") chose an incorrect answer before discussion and then switched to a different incorrect answer after discussion. This group may have randomly selected an answer the first time and may follow an incorrect line of argument during discussion.

- C-I (Correct → incorrect): This group of students ("doubters") chose the correct answer before discussion and then switched to an incorrect answer after discussion. This group may either have chosen the correct answer accidentally before discussion or had a low level of confidence in their answer.

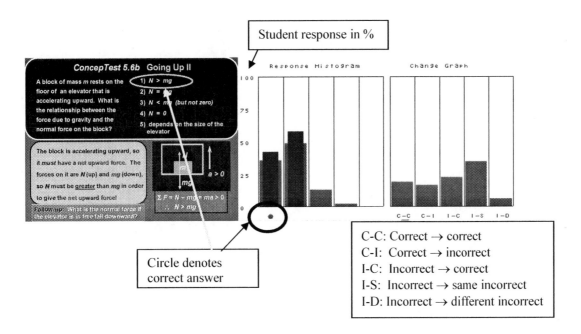

Student response in %

Circle denotes correct answer

C-C: Correct → correct
C-I: Correct → incorrect
I-C: Incorrect → correct
I-S: Incorrect → same incorrect
I-D: Incorrect → different incorrect

F. Examples of common histogram types

- <u>The "softball" question:</u>
  Such questions are usually easy for students, indicating the large number of correct responses before discussion. The purpose of asking these questions is to either perform a quick reality check for the instructor – that the students have indeed acquired this level of competency – or as a warm-up exercise with harder questions to follow.

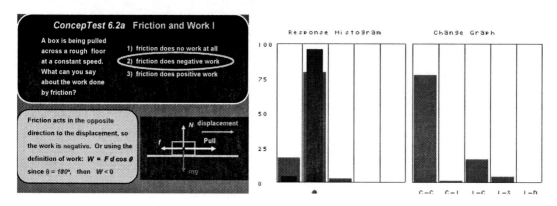

- <u>The "perfect" question:</u>
  Questions with such histograms display an ideal *ConcepTest*. Around half the students answered the question correctly by themselves. After discussion, enough students convinced others of the correct answer that most of the class ends up with the right answer.

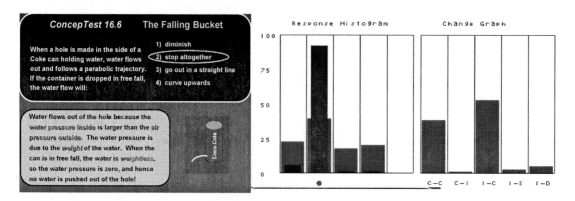

- The "corrected misconception" question:
  Questions of this type indicate that initially most students follow their instincts when answering. Upon further deliberation within groups, most students recognize that the correct answer may be counterintuitive and change their initial choice, with a significant percentage moving toward the correct answer.

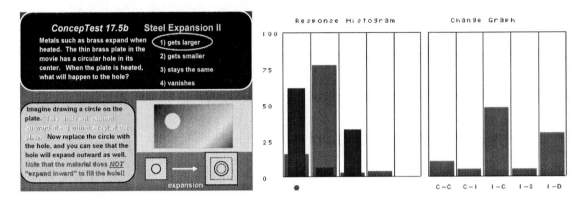

- The "stubborn misconception" question:
  Questions of this type reveal misconceptions held by students that are not easily resolved, even after group discussion with peers. Most students hold on to their initial choices, even though they realize that there is a fairly significant spread. Such responses definitely require further intervention by the instructor.

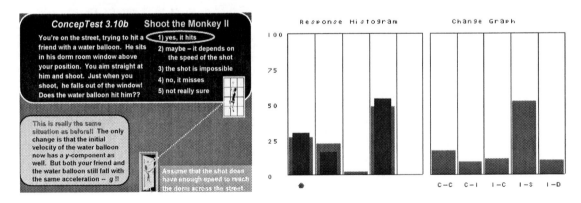

- The "killer" question:

  Every once in a while a very tough question comes along that will throw the entire class for a loop. When histograms of this nature are displayed in class after discussion with peers, they can incite a riot-like atmosphere. This can be useful for certain purposes (such as dampening overflowing student self-confidence), but the instructor needs to be prepared for it! Aim to spend about 20-30 minutes of class time to discuss the solution to such questions.

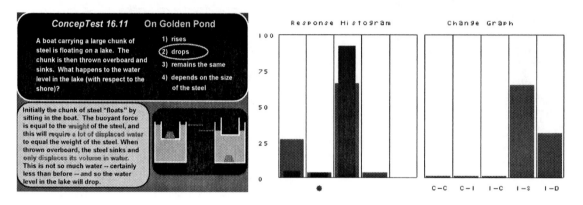

G. Normalizing student responses through FCI scores

The student response histograms have to be used with caution since there can be many factors that lead to a particular student response, besides the nature of the question. One important overall factor is clearly the level of student preparation. Students attending Harvard University can on the whole be expected to have higher correct scores (a higher number of "sustainers" and "improvers") than students in two-year community colleges. To provide a benchmark for instructors we recommend giving the class the FCI as a pretest at the beginning of the semester. The SRHs displayed in this manual were obtained at The George Washington University, where the pretest FCI score has been about **33 ± 3 %** (10 ± 1 correct questions out of the 30 FCI questions) over a number of years. Thus, our SRH should be understood based on that background of student preparation. A lower pretest FCI score would lead to a smaller student group of "sustainers" and "improvers." To provide a different reference point, Mazur reported a pretest FCI score of Harvard students of around 66% [Ma97]. Ideally, one would like to see SRHs analyzed as a function of their pretest FCI scores, a project far beyond the scope of this manual.

We hope that you find this manual a useful teaching resource as you implement *ConcepTests* and *ConcepModules* in the classroom, and we welcome all questions, comments, and corrections.

August, 2004

Cornelius Bennhold
bennhold@gwu.edu

Gerald Feldman
feldman@gwu.edu

References

[An94]   Lorin W. Anderson, Lauren A. Sosniak (Editors), *Bloom's Taxonomy: A forty-year retrospective* (University of Chicago Press, 1994).

[Cr01]   C.H. Crouch and E. Mazur, Am. J. Phys. **69**, 970 (2001).

[Fe99]   G. Feldman and C. Bennhold, AAPT Announcer **29**, 114 (1999).

[Gu01]   N. Guttenberg, G. Feldman and C. Bennhold, AAPT Announcer **31**, 137 (2001).

[Ha98]   R.R. Hake, Am. J. Phys. **66**, 64 (1998).

[He92]   D. Hestenes, M. Wells and G. Swackhammer, Physics Teacher **30**, 141 (1992).

[Jo91]   D.W. Johnson, R.T. Johnson and K.A. Smith, *Active Learning: Cooperation in the College Classroom* (Interaction Book Co., Edina, MN, 1991).

[Ma97]   E. Mazur, *Peer Instruction: A User's Manual* (Prentice-Hall, Upper Saddle River, NJ, 1998).

[McD99]   L.C. McDermott and E.F. Redish, Am. J. Phys. **67**, 755 (1999).

[McD01]   L.C. McDermott, Am. J. Phys. **69**, 1127 (2001).

[Me96]   D.E. Meltzer and K. Manivannan, Physics Teacher **34**, 72 (1996).

Conceptual Module 2.1
ConcepTest 2.1:   **Walking the Dog**
Difficulty Level: **2**
Suggested follow-up numerical problem: **Problem 2.3**
Suggested follow-up conceptual questions:
- **Have you and your dog traveled the same distance?**

This question examines the difference between displacement and distance. These concepts are often confused by students, and this ConcepTest is intended to help emphasize the main distinction between these two quantities.

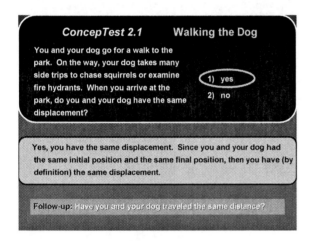

Conceptual Module 2.2
ConcepTest 2.2:   **Displacement**
Difficulty Level: **2**

The displacement of an object does *not* depend on the origin, because the displacement is the difference between two positions. The *absolute position* of an object *will* depend on the origin, but when you take the difference between two positions, the origin drops out.

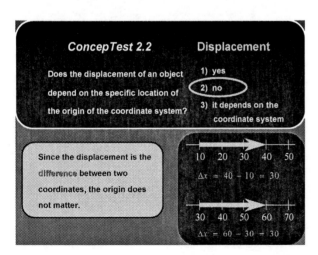

Conceptual Module 2.3
ConcepTest 2.3:   **Position and Speed**
Difficulty Level: 2
Suggested follow-up numerical problem: Problem 2.5

The position of an object and its speed have no relation. An object can have any speed, in principle, at any position.

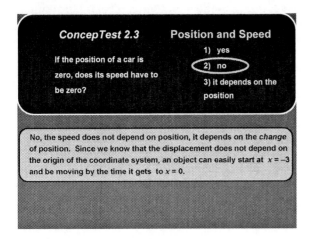

Conceptual Module 2.4
ConcepTest 2.4:   **Odometer**
Difficulty Level: 1
Suggested follow-up conceptual questions:
* **How would you measure displacement in your car?**
*

This question again addresses the distinction between distance and displacement.

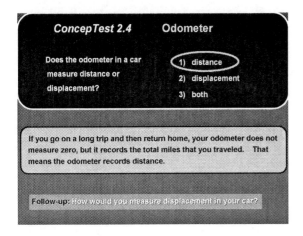

Conceptual Module 2.5
ConcepTest 2.5:   Speedometer
Difficulty Level: 1
Suggested follow-up conceptual questions:
- **How would you measure velocity in your car?**

This question examines the difference between speed and velocity. One is a vector while the other is a scalar. These concepts are often confused by students, and this ConcepTest is intended to help emphasize the main distinction between these two quantities.

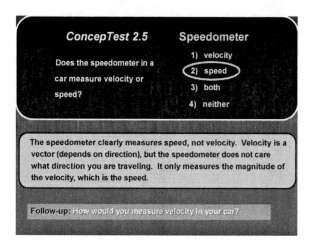

Conceptual Module 2.6 (two parts)
ConcepTest 2.6a: Cruising Along I
Difficulty Level: 3
Suggested follow-up numerical problem: Problem 2.8

The definition of average speed is the ratio of total distance over total time. In this ConcepTest, different speeds apply to two identical time intervals, so the average speed is straightforward to determine.

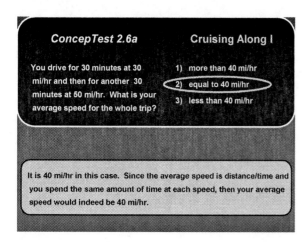

ConcepTest 2.6b: **Cruising Along II**
Difficulty Level: **4**
Suggested follow-up numerical problem: Problem 2.9
Suggested follow-up conceptual questions:

- **How much further would you have to drive at 50 mi/hr in order to get back your average speed of 40 mi/hr?**

This ConcepTest is different from the previous one in the sense that different speeds now apply to two identical distances. In this case, determining the average speed is not quite as straightforward as in the previous ConcepTest.

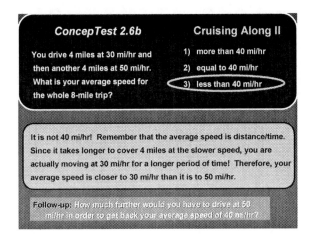

ConcepTest 2.6b   **Cruising Along II**

You drive 4 miles at 30 mi/hr and then another 4 miles at 50 mi/hr. What is your average speed for the whole 8-mile trip?

1) more than 40 mi/hr
2) equal to 40 mi/hr
3) less than 40 mi/hr

It is not 40 mi/hr! Remember that the average speed is distance/time. Since it takes longer to cover 4 miles at the slower speed, you are actually moving at 30 mi/hr for a longer period of time! Therefore, your average speed is closer to 30 mi/hr than it is to 50 mi/hr.

Follow-up: How much further would you have to drive at 50 mi/hr in order to get back your average speed of 40 mi/hr?

Conceptual Module 2.7
ConcepTest 2.7:   **Velocity in One Dimension**
Difficulty Level: **2**
Suggested follow-up numerical problem: Problems 2.8 or 2.9

This ConcepTest addresses the concepts of average velocity and instantaneous velocity.

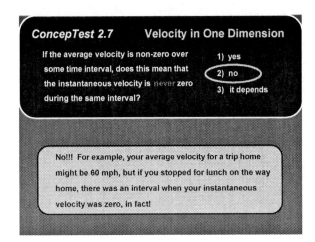

ConcepTest 2.7   **Velocity in One Dimension**

If the average velocity is non-zero over some time interval, does this mean that the instantaneous velocity is never zero during the same interval?

1) yes
2) no
3) it depends

No!!! For example, your average velocity for a trip home might be 60 mph, but if you stopped for lunch on the way home, there was an interval when your instantaneous velocity was zero, in fact!

Conceptual Module 2.8 (two parts)
ConcepTest 2.8a: **Acceleration I**
Difficulty Level: **2**
Suggested follow-up numerical problem: Problem 2.38

Acceleration is an especially difficult concept for students. This question is intended to give a feeling that "acceleration is not the same as velocity," which is a notion that many students seem to hold.

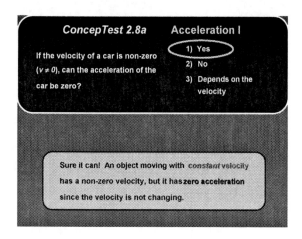

ConcepTest 2.8b: **Acceleration II**
Difficulty Level: **3**
Suggested follow-up conceptual questions:
  • **…and the value of *a* is?**

This illustrates an example that is the opposite of the previous question. That is, in this case, the velocity is zero but the acceleration is not. The idea that an object that is not moving can actually have a non-zero acceleration is very tricky for students.

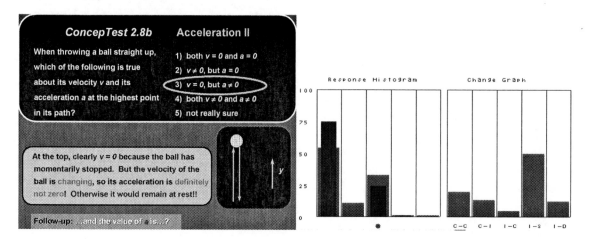

Conceptual Module 2.9 (two parts)
ConcepTest 2.9a: Free Fall I
Difficulty Level: 2

This question is intended to make students realize that the acceleration of a freely falling object is always –g, independent of the initial velocity of the object.

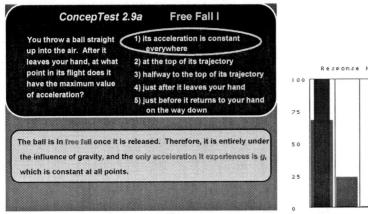
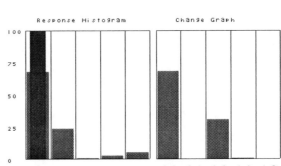

ConcepTest 2.9b: Free Fall II
Difficulty Level: 3
Suggested follow-up numerical problem: Problem 2.59
Suggested follow-up conceptual questions:
*   **Which one has the greater velocity when they hit the ground?**

This question is intended to make students realize that the acceleration of a freely falling object is always –g, independent of the initial velocity of the object.

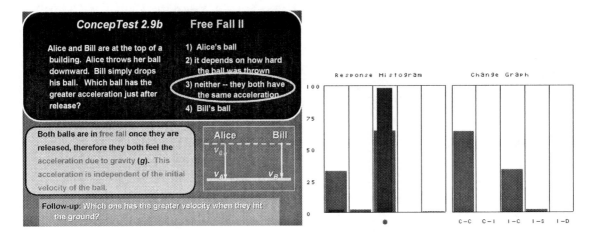

Conceptual Module 2.10 (two parts)
ConcepTest 2.10a: Up in the Air I
Difficulty Level: 3
Suggested follow-up numerical problem: Problem 2.60

The symmetry of the rising and falling ball is illustrated in this ConcepTest. Since the acceleration of the freely falling ball is –g, on the way up and on the way down, its downward trajectory is just the reverse of its upward trajectory.

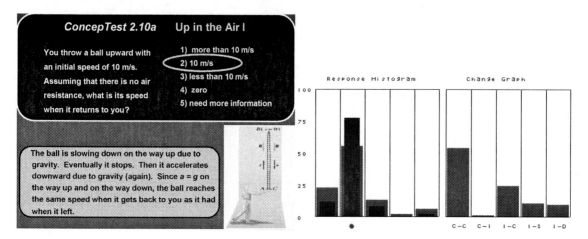

ConcepTest 2.10b: Up in the Air II
Difficulty Level: 4
Suggested follow-up numerical problem: Problem 2.61
Suggested follow-up conceptual questions:
- **What happens if there is air resistance?**

This ConcepTest continues to build on the idea addressed in the previous question. By recalling the previous answer, students should realize that the two cases depicted in this question are identical, in terms of the behavior of the ball *below* the thrower's position.

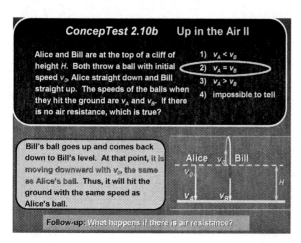

Conceptual Module 2.11
ConcepTest 2.11:   Two Balls in the Air
Difficulty Level: 5
Suggested follow-up numerical problem: Problem 2.42
Suggested follow-up conceptual questions:
- **How could you calculate where they meet?**

Students will have a tendency to say that the balls will meet in the middle. This is not true, however, due to the different initial velocities of the balls.   Realizing that the balls will meet after traveling for similar time periods (not similar distances) requires a bit of sophisticated thinking on the part of the students.

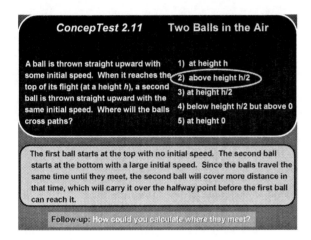

Conceptual Module 2.12
ConcepTest 2.12a: Throwing Rocks I
Difficulty Level: 4

Students will recognize that both rocks have the same acceleration, but the rocks obviously have different velocities. While the velocity difference will remain the same (see next question), the position difference will always increase.

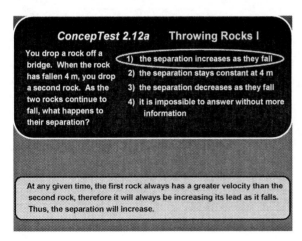

ConcepTest 2.12b: Throwing Rocks II
Difficulty Level: 4
Suggested follow-up conceptual questions:
- **What happens when air resistance is present?**

This question moves to the next step, which is asking about the velocities. Here the notion of constant acceleration (and what it means) is emphasized.

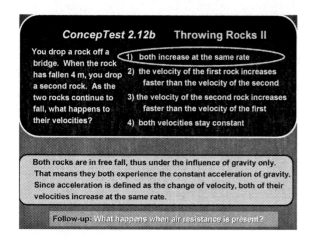

Conceptual Module 2.13 (two parts)
ConcepTest 2.13a: Graphing Velocity I
Difficulty Level: 2
Suggested follow-up numerical problem: Problem 2.5

Understanding graphical representations is the theme of this question and the questions that immediately follow. Here the slope of the *x* vs. *t* plot is constant.

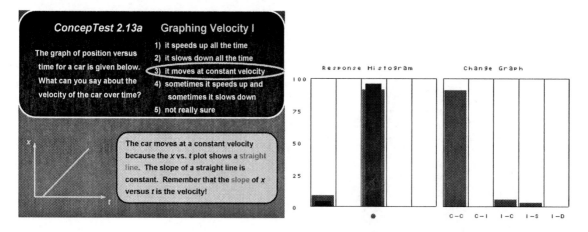

ConcepTest 2.13b: Graphing Velocity II
Difficulty Level: 2

In this question, the *x* vs. *t* plot has a changing slope, which requires students to explain the connection of the slope to the concept of velocity.

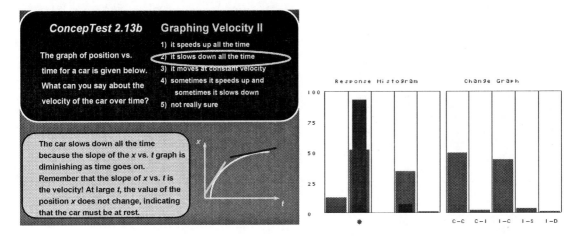

Conceptual Module 2.14 (two parts)
ConcepTest 2.14a: *v* versus *t* graphs I
Difficulty Level: 2

This question moves on to the understanding of the *v* vs. *t* graph. This question has nothing to do with the slope of the graph, but rather the actual velocity values that can be read off the *y*-axis (i.e., the velocity axis).

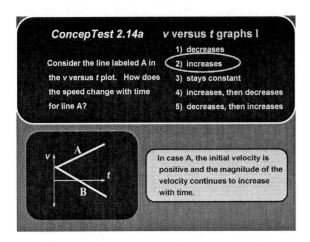

ConcepTest 2.14b: *v* versus *t* graphs II
Difficulty Level: 3

This question continues to examine the *v* vs. *t* graph. In this case, the velocity values decrease, pass through zero, and then become negative (but increasing in magnitude). Thus, the plot of line B actually describes a complicated motion, despite the simplicity of the actual plot.

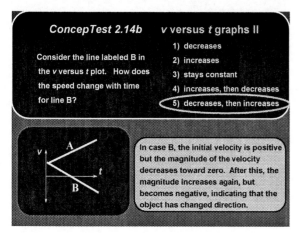

Conceptual Module 2.15 (three parts)
ConcepTest 2.15a: Rubber Balls I
Difficulty Level: 2

In this set of questions, the students must formulate their own view of the motion graphs, based on a description of the physical motion. In this case, the ball is simply dropped and falls down. The correct *v* vs. *t* plot has a negative slope that begins at *v* = 0.

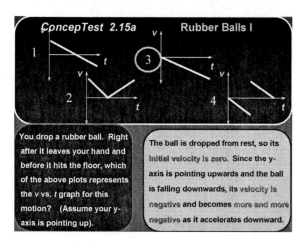

ConcepTest 2.15b: Rubber Balls II
Difficulty Level: 3

In this set of questions, the students must formulate their own view of the motion graphs, based on a description of the physical motion. In this case, the ball is tossed up in the air. The correct v vs. t plot has a negative slope which begins at $v > 0$ and then crosses $v = 0$ and goes to negative values of v.

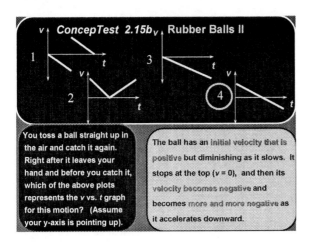

ConcepTest 2.15c: Rubber Balls III
Difficulty Level: 4

In this set of questions, the students must formulate their own view of the motion graphs, based on a description of the physical motion. In this case, the ball is dropped from rest, but bounces off the floor and rebounds up in the air. The bounce leads to a discontinuity in the v vs. t graph, but the acceleration is everywhere the same (except for the period during which the ball is in contact with the floor).

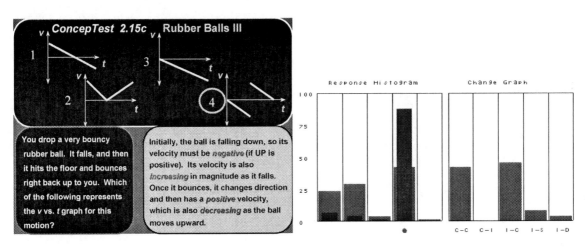

Conceptual Module 3.1 (three parts)
ConcepTest 3.1a: Vectors I
Difficulty Level: 2

This is a series of questions about basic characteristics of vectors. The questions are intended to give the students a feel for combining vectors. This first ConcepTest deals with two vectors that add up to zero.

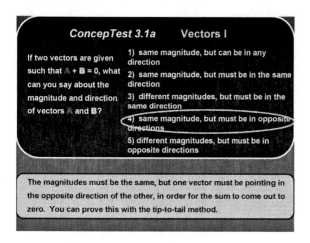

ConcepTest 3.1b: Vectors II
Difficulty Level: 3

In this case, students must recognize that when two vectors satisfy the Pythagorean theorem, then they must be perpendicular.

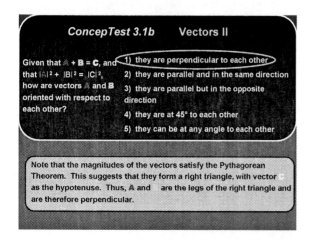

ConcepTest 3.1c: **Vectors III**
Difficulty Level: **3**

In this case, students must recognize that when two vectors add to their maximum resultant, then they must be parallel.

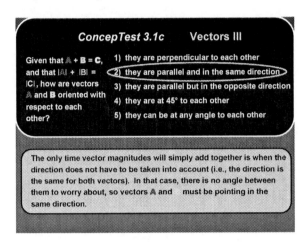

Conceptual Module 3.2 (two parts)
ConcepTest 3.2a: **Vector Components I**
Difficulty Level: **2**
Suggested follow-up numerical problem: Problems 1.50 and 1.56
Suggested follow-up conceptual questions:
- **If you double one component and not the other, how would the angle change?**

This series of questions deals with the components of a vector and how they relate to the angle of the vector. In this case, the components are multiplied by a factor, and the effect on the angle is sought.

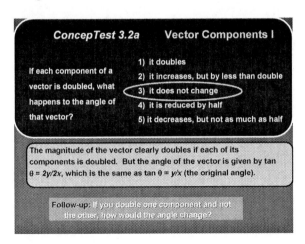

ConcepTest 3.2b: Vector Components II
Difficulty Level: 2
Suggested follow-up numerical problem: Problem 1.61

In this case, the angle of a vector with equal components is examined.

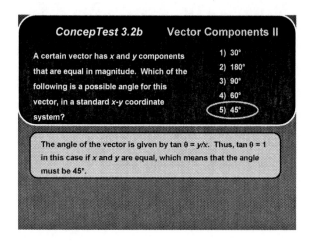

Conceptual Module 3.3
ConcepTest 3.3:   Vector Addition
Difficulty Level: 3
Suggested follow-up numerical problem: Problem 1.60

Two vectors being added can have a range of resultants, but this range is well defined. This ConcepTest asks the students to identify the range of validity for the resultant of two vectors.

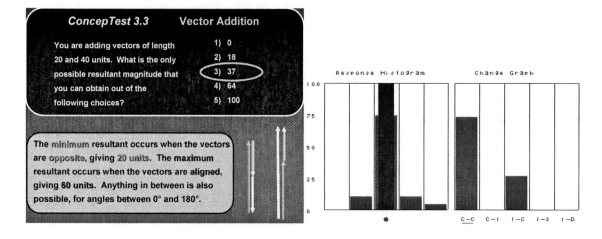

Conceptual Module 3.4 (three parts)
ConcepTest 3.4a: **Firing Balls I**
Difficulty Level: 3

Treating the *x* and *y* motions independently tends to be a problem for students. This series of ConcepTests explores this independence of the two motions. In this case, the cart is moving with a constant speed.

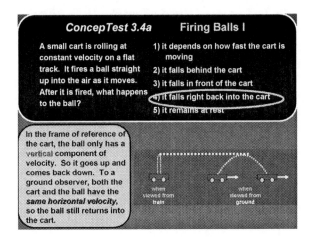

ConcepTest 3.4b: **Firing Balls II**
Difficulty Level: 4

In this variation of the preceding question, the cart is now being accelerated by an external force as it moves along the track.

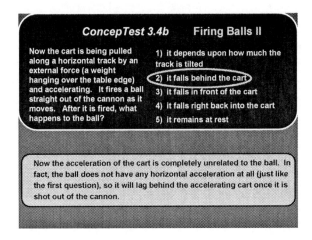

ConcepTest 3.4c: Firing Balls III
Difficulty Level: 5

In this final variation of the series, the cart is now accelerating down an inclined track, under the influence of gravity.

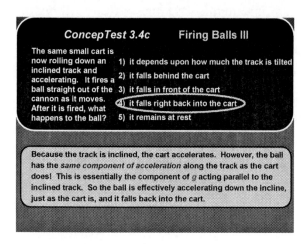

Conceptual Module 3.5
ConcepTest 3.5:   Dropping a Package
Difficulty Level: 2
Suggested follow-up numerical problem: Problem 3.30
Suggested follow-up conceptual questions:

- **What would happen if air resistance is present?**

This question again addresses the independence of the *x* and *y* motions. Since the horizontal motions of the package and the plane remain the same after the drop, the package will "pace" the plane and therefore remain directly under the plane as it falls.

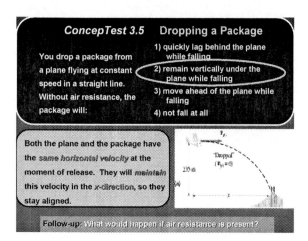

Conceptual Module 3.6 (three parts)
ConcepTest 3.6a: Dropping the Ball I
Difficulty Level: 3
Suggested follow-up conceptual questions:
- **Is that also true if there is air resistance?**

This series of ConcepTests continues to examine the *x* and *y* motions. While they are independent, some quantities (such as the range) depend on both motions, while others (such as flight time) only depend on one. This question addresses the flight time.

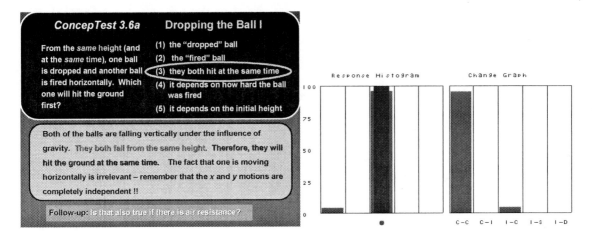

ConcepTest 3.6b: Dropping the Ball II
Difficulty Level: 3
Suggested follow-up numerical problem: Problem 3.32
Suggested follow-up conceptual questions:
- **What would you have to do to have them both reach the same final velocity at the ground level?**

The second question in this series deals with the final velocity, which involves the combination of both the x and y motions (velocities).

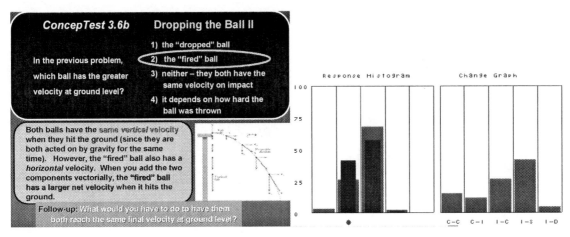

ConcepTest 3.6c: **Dropping the Ball III**
Difficulty Level: **3**
Suggested follow-up numerical problem: Problems 3.33 and 3.34

The total speed of a projectile is changing because the *y* velocity is changing (while the *x* velocity remains constant). The total speed is the resultant of *x* and *y* velocities at any given moment.

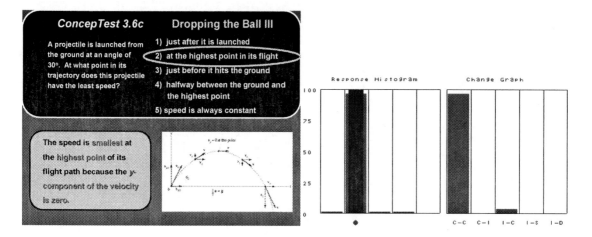

Conceptual Module 3.7 (two parts)
ConcepTest 3.7a: **Punts I**
Difficulty Level: **3**
Suggested follow-up numerical problem: Problem 3.44
Suggested follow-up conceptual questions:
- **Which one had the greater initial velocity?**

The time in the air is determined by the *y* motion, not the *x* motion. The students must recognize that these punts all have the same initial *y* velocity, and so they all spend the same time in the air.

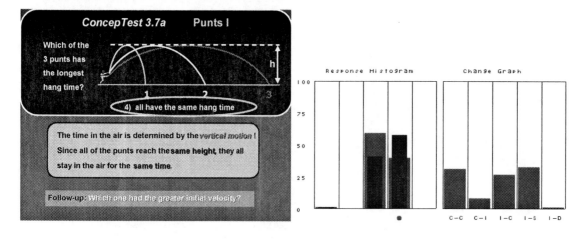

ConcepTest 3.7b: **Punts II**
Difficulty Level: **4**
Suggested follow-up numerical problem: **Problem 3.45**
Suggested follow-up conceptual questions:
- **Which one traveled the greater distance?**

Here again, the students must recognize that the flight time is determined by the *y* motion, which is independent of the *x* motion.

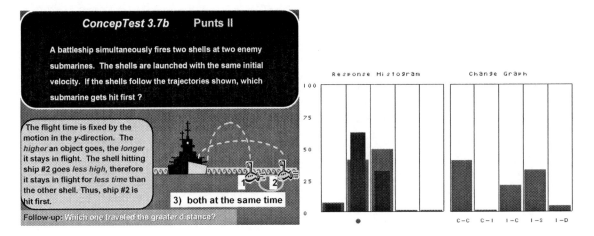

Conceptual Module 3.8
ConcepTest 3.8:   **Cannon on the Moon**
Difficulty Level: **3**
Suggested follow-up numerical problem: **Problem 3.46**
Suggested follow-up conceptual questions:
- **Which path would it take in outer space?**

In this case, the acceleration due to gravity has changed, and the students must realize what effect that will have on the subsequent motion. This variation cannot be related directly to an earthbound experience, so it requires a certain level of understanding.

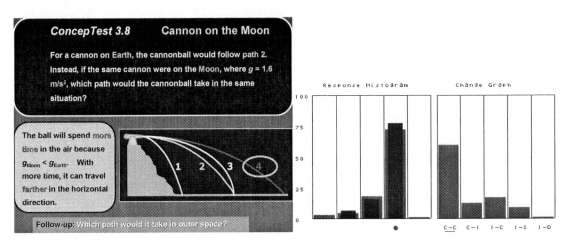

Conceptual Module 3.9
ConcepTest 3.9:   **Spring-loaded Gun**
Difficulty Level: 1
Suggested follow-up numerical problem: **Problems 3.36, 3.37, 3.39 and 3.41**

The question of maximum range is fairly standard. In this case, however, the students may wish to derive the range formula to prove that 45° is the optimal angle.

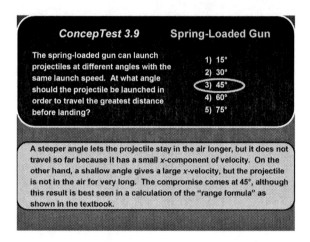

Conceptual Module 10 (three parts)
ConcepTest 3.10a: **Shoot the Monkey I**
Difficulty Level: 3

This series deals with variations of the "monkey hunter" problem. The first question deals with the relatively simple case of the shooter and the monkey on the same level.

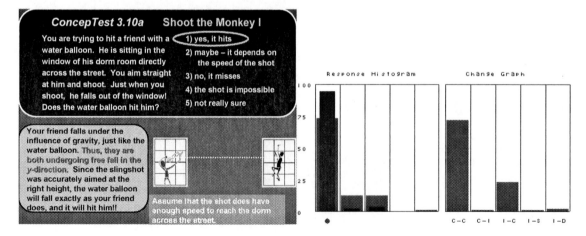

ConcepTest 3.10b: Shoot the Monkey II
Difficulty Level: 4
Suggested follow-up numerical problem: Problem 3.10

This is the standard formulation of the "monkey hunter" problem, in which the shooter is on the ground and the monkey is located at some elevation. It is hoped that the students will be able to extrapolate their experience from the first question to this one.

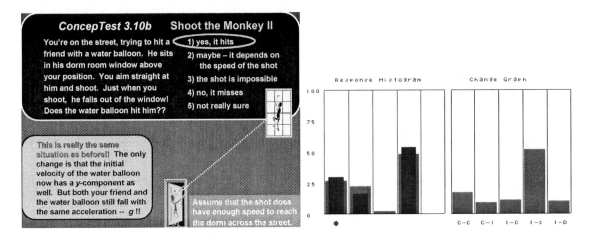

ConcepTest 3.10c: Shoot the Monkey III
Difficulty Level: 4
Suggested follow-up conceptual questions:
- **When would they not hit each other?**

In this case, two projectiles initially aimed at each other are fired. The fact that both projectiles are only under the influence of gravity means that they will indeed hit. This can be more easily seen for the case of projectiles that are launched at the same level.

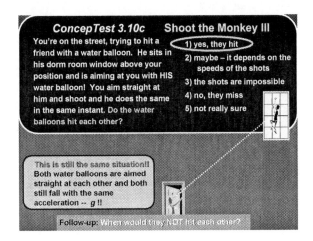

Conceptual Module 4.1 (four parts)
ConcepTest 4.1a: **Newton's First Law I**
Difficulty Level: **2**
Suggested follow-up numerical problem: Problem 4.1

This series of questions examines Newton's First Law. In the first question, students must realize that just because an object is at rest, it does not mean that there are no forces acting on it at all (*i.e.* no net force does not necessarily mean no force at all).

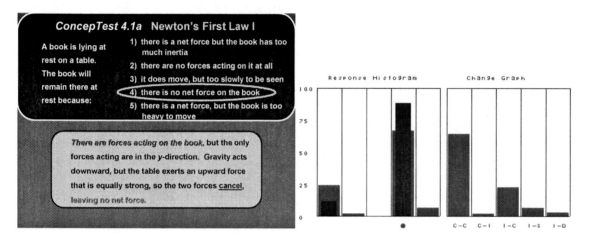

ConcepTest 4.1b: **Newton's First Law II**
Difficulty Level: **2**
Suggested follow-up numerical problem: Problem 4.2
Suggested follow-up conceptual questions:
   • **Are there any forces acting on the puck? What are they?**

A moving object does not need a force to keep it in motion. This misconception is addressed in this case, where an object moves at constant velocity.

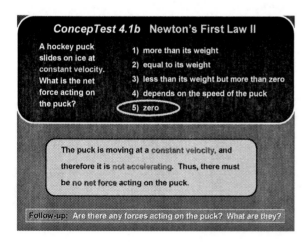

ConcepTest 4.1c: Newton's First Law III
Difficulty Level: 3
Suggested follow-up conceptual questions:
   • **What is the force that usually keeps the book on the seat?**

This question probes the students' ability to recognize that the book is simply following its natural tendency to remain in motion (unless acted upon by an outside force, which in this case, it is not). There can be some confusion possible due to different reference frames, since the students are actually in a non-inertial frame.

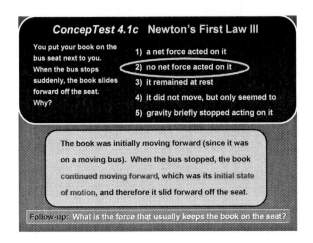

ConcepTest 4.1d: Newton's First Law IV
Difficulty Level: 3
Suggested follow-up numerical problem: Problem 4.9
Suggested follow-up conceptual questions:
   • **What would you have to do to keep the stone moving?**

Concluding with Newton's First Law, a common situation is presented in which an object slows and eventually comes to rest. This apparent contradiction to the First Law arises due to the presence of an external force acting on the object (in this case, friction).

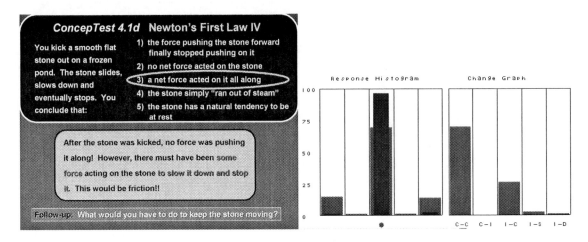

Conceptual Module 4.2 (two parts)
ConcepTest 4.2a: Cart on Track I
Difficulty Level: 2

This question serves as a reminder of Newton's First Law. It is important for students to recognize that the question is dealing with the motion *after* the push, not during the push. This distinction becomes important in the next question.

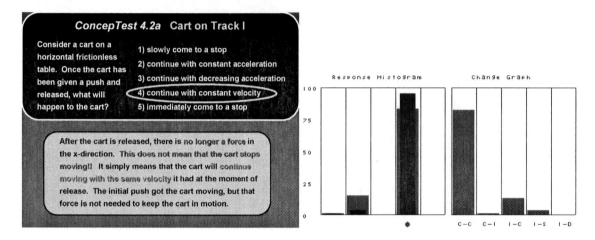

ConcepTest 4.2b: Cart on Track II
Difficulty Level: 2
Suggested follow-up numerical problem: Problem 4.12

Getting into Newton's Second Law now, the students should realize that in order to have a constant acceleration, a constant force must be *continuously* applied during the motion.

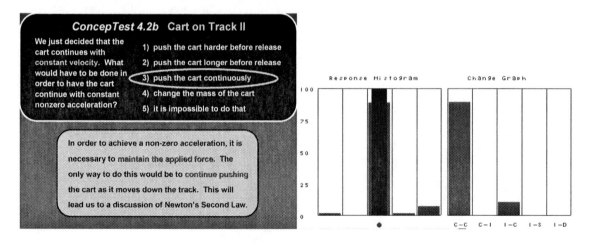

Conceptual Module 4.3
ConcepTest 4.3:   **Truck on Frozen Lake**
Difficulty Level: **3**
Suggested follow-up conceptual questions:
  • **What is the truck doing 5 minutes after the fly hit it?**

In this case, an impulsive force gives the truck a small but finite velocity, which it will maintain until something else happens. After the collision, the truck will continue moving with that same velocity, even though the fly is no longer in the picture.

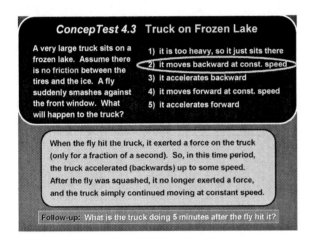

Conceptual Module 4.4 (four parts)
ConcepTest 4.4a: **Off to the Races I**
Difficulty Level: **3**
Suggested follow-up numerical problem: Problems 4.18 and 4.19

Kinematics plays a role in the following series of ConcepTests. In this first case, students must determine the acceleration (from the force) and then use it to obtain the time required to achieve the same final speed as before.

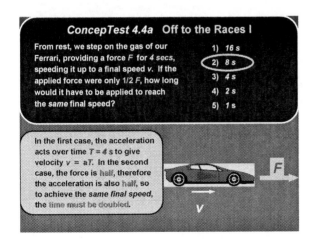

ConcepTest 4.4b: Off to the Races II
Difficulty Level: 3

In this case, students must determine the distance traveled when the same force is applied over a different time interval than before.

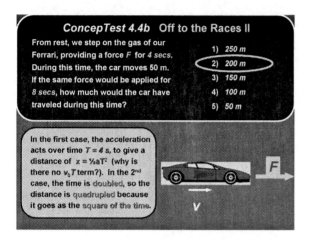

ConcepTest 4.4c: Off to the Races III
Difficulty Level: 4

This question is the "reverse" of the previous one, in the sense that in this case, the car is slowing down due to the applied force (rather than speeding up). The answer to this question is not nearly as intuitive as the previous one.

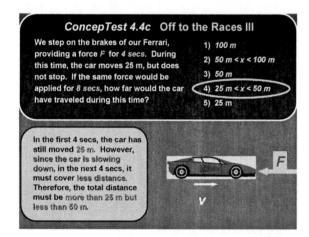

ConcepTest 4.4d: Off to the Races IV
Difficulty Level: 4

Here the students examine a different relationship. In this case, the same force is applied over a different distance and the question asks for the new final speed. In all of these questions, the students must be aware of the kinematics relations that govern the motion.

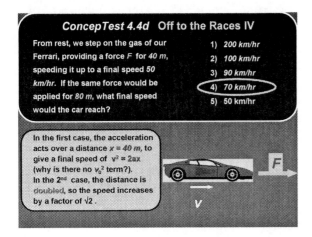

Conceptual Module 4.5
ConcepTest 4.5:   Force and Mass
Difficulty Level: 3
Suggested follow-up conceptual questions:
- **What would you have to do to get 2M to reach speed v?**

This is another exercise in linking the concepts of force and acceleration (from Newton's Second Law) with the kinematics equations that are used to calculate the motion of an object.

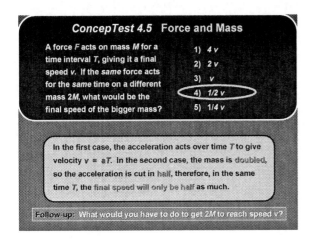

Conceptual Module 4.6
ConcepTest 4.6:   **Force and Masses**
Difficulty Level: 4
Suggested follow-up numerical problem: **Problem 4.28**

This is an applied example of Newton's Second Law. Students must learn to break the problem down into steps, using what they are given to determine what they need for a subsequent part of the problem.

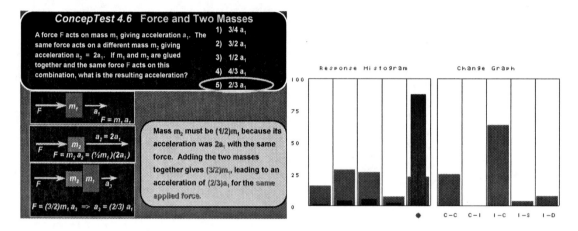

Conceptual Module 4.7
ConcepTest 4.7:   **Climbing the Rope**
Difficulty Level: 2
Suggested follow-up numerical problem: **Problem 4.23**

This is an introduction to Newton's Third Law. The notion that your pulling down on the rope somehow helps you ascend may seem a bit strange when students first think about it in those terms, but this is the essence of Newton's Third Law.

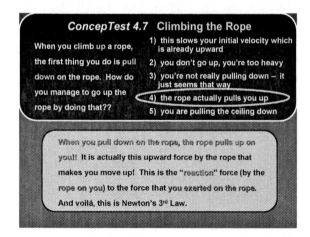

Conceptual Module 4.8 (two parts)
ConcepTest 4.8a: Bowling vs. Ping-Pong I
Difficulty Level: 2
Suggested follow-up numerical problem: Problem 4.62

This is a quick check of the level of understanding of Newton's Third Law. When the two objects in question are so different in size and mass, the students often have trouble convincing themselves that the forces are indeed still equal and opposite.

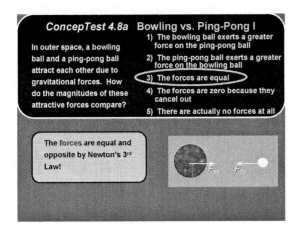

ConcepTest 4.8b: Bowling vs. Ping-Pong II
Difficulty Level: 3
Suggested follow-up numerical problem: Problem 4.25
Suggested follow-up conceptual questions:
  • **Where will the balls meet if they are released from this position?**

Following up on the previous question, now the impact of the different masses is revealed. While the forces are equal and opposite by Newton's Third Law, the accelerations are not equal, and are inversely proportional to the masses. This is a more intuitive result that the students are likely to be more comfortable with, and it emphasizes where the effect of the different masses comes in.

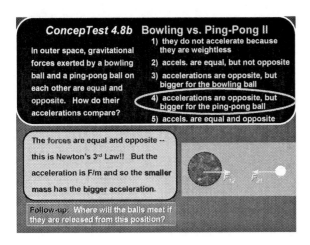

Conceptual Module 4.9 (two parts)
ConcepTest 4.9a: **Collision Course I**
Difficulty Level: **2**

This question is similar to ConcepTest 4.8a, where two rather different objects are seen to exert the same force on each other, due to Newton's Third Law.

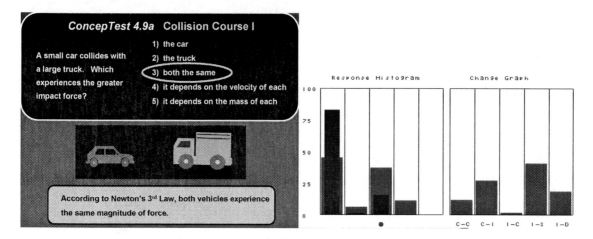

ConcepTest 4.9b: **Collision Course II**
Difficulty Level: **3**

This question is similar to ConcepTest 4.8b, where the accelerations between the two different objects are shown to be different, but the forces were the same. It is here (acceleration) that the mass enters.

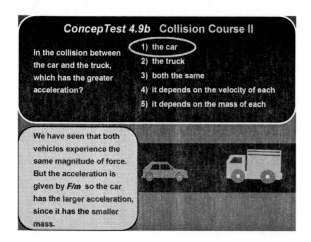

Conceptual Module 4.10 (two parts)
ConcepTest 4.10a: Contact Force I
Difficulty Level: 4
Suggested follow-up numerical problem: Problem 4.21

In this case, the problem must be broken down into parts in order to be able to address the question of the contact force acting on one of the blocks. Using the acceleration obtained by treating the combined system, the contact force can be determined from the individual masses and the acceleration.

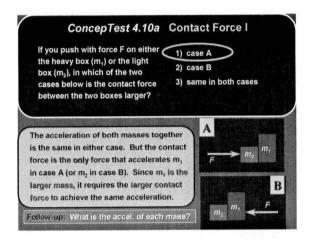

ConcepTest 4.10b: Contact Force II
Difficulty Level: 5
Suggested follow-up conceptual questions:
  - **What is the acceleration of each mass?**
  -

This is another question about contact forces.

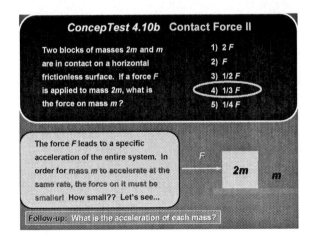

Conceptual Module 5.1 (two parts)
ConcepTest 5.1a: Gravity and Weight I
Difficulty Level: 1

Issues relating to gravity can often confuse students. While heavy and light objects do indeed have different forces of gravity on them (weight), the acceleration of these objects is in fact the same! This first question establishes that the students recognize the force (weight) difference between two objects.

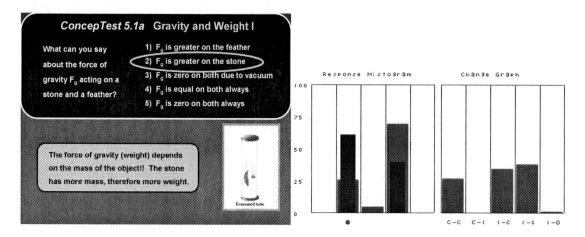

ConcepTest 5.1a   Gravity and Weight I

What can you say about the force of gravity F_g acting on a stone and a feather?

1) F_g is greater on the feather
2) F_g is greater on the stone
3) F_g is zero on both due to vacuum
4) F_g is equal on both always
5) F_g is zero on both always

The force of gravity (weight) depends on the mass of the object!! The stone has more mass, therefore more weight.

Evacuated tube

Response Histogram   Change Graph

c-c   c-i   i-c   i-s   i-d

ConcepTest 5.1b: Gravity and Weight II
Difficulty Level: 2
Suggested follow-up numerical problem: Problem 5.9
Suggested follow-up conceptual questions:
- ### Which one hits the bottom first?

In this second question, however, the acceleration is asked for. The students must realize that they must divide out the mass ($F=ma$) to obtain the acceleration, and that leaves them with the same value (g) for each of the objects.

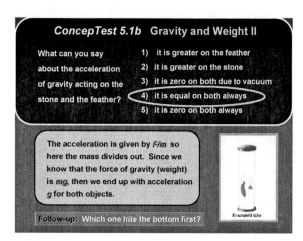

ConcepTest 5.1b   Gravity and Weight II

What can you say about the acceleration of gravity acting on the stone and the feather?

1) it is greater on the feather
2) it is greater on the stone
3) it is zero on both due to vacuum
4) it is equal on both always
5) it is zero on both always

The acceleration is given by *F/m* so here the mass divides out. Since we know that the force of gravity (weight) is *mg*, then we end up with acceleration *g* for both objects.

Follow-up: Which one hits the bottom first?

Evacuated tube

Conceptual Module 5.2
ConcepTest 5.2: **On the Moon**
Difficulty Level: **2**
Suggested follow-up conceptual questions:
 • **What is different about the bowling ball on the Moon?**

This is a classic question that is often misunderstood. The extent to which a body resists acceleration is characterized by the *mass*, not the weight. It is this issue that is relevant in this question, and so the fact that the bowling ball is lighter (weighs less) on the Moon does not alter the answer.

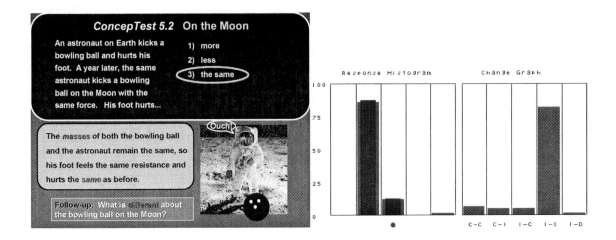

Conceptual Module 5.3 (three parts)
ConcepTest 5.3a: **Tension I**
Difficulty Level: **2**

The tension in the rope is the force that any segment of the rope experiences on it at each end. The force applied at one end of the entire rope is "transmitted" down the length of the rope, segment by segment (by Newton's Third Law), so this is the force that each segment feels.

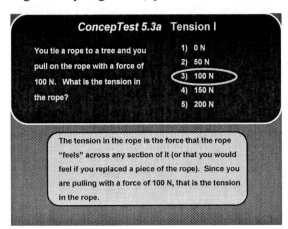

ConcepTest 5.3b: Tension II
Difficulty Level: 2
Suggested follow-up numerical problem: Problem 5.8

There is a tendency for students to believe that the tension is twice the force applied by each team. However, this is not the case at all. This situation is exactly the same as the previous question!

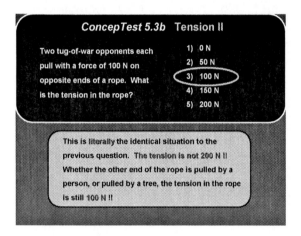

ConcepTest 5.3c: Tension III
Difficulty Level: 3
Suggested follow-up numerical problem: Problem 5.16

Using the experience gained by the previous two questions, the students should now be able to recognize that if they use a tree to provide a "passive" force to balance their own applied force, then they can achieve better results by pulling on the same end.

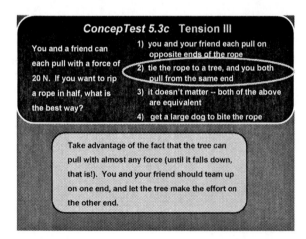

Conceptual Module 5.4
ConcepTest 5.4:   **Three Blocks**
Difficulty Level: 4
Suggested follow-up numerical problem: Problem 5.75
Suggested follow-up conceptual questions:
   • **What is T_1 in terms of m and a?**

This problem involves a basic knowledge of Newton's Second Law. The acceleration of each block is the same, since the combination of blocks moves together. Each string effectively is pulling all of the blocks to its left, so the largest tension would be for the case of string #1, and so on.

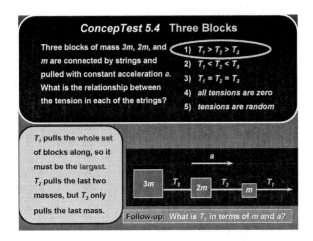

Conceptual Module 5.5
ConcepTest 5.5:   **Over the Edge**
Difficulty Level: 4
Suggested follow-up numerical problem: Problems 5.13 and 5.14

This question requires the students to determine the tension in the rope. In case #2, it is simply the applied force, but in case #1, it is not *mg* of the falling block! Since the block is accelerating downward, the tension must be *less* than *mg* in order to have a net downward force. This distinction is not so subtle, but the students must pay careful attention to realize this.

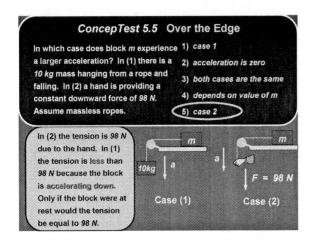

Conceptual Module 5.6 (two parts)
ConcepTest 5.6a: Going Up I
Difficulty Level: 2

If the elevator were at rest, this would be a trivial question (N = *mg*). But in this case, the elevator is moving at constant speed. Students must recognize that this changes nothing from the "at rest" case, so the normal force will still simply be the weight of the block.

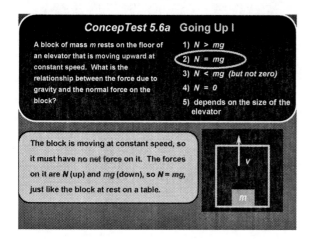

ConcepTest 5.6b: Going Up II
Difficulty Level: 3
Suggested follow-up conceptual questions:
* **What is the normal force if the elevator is in free fall downward?**

In this follow-up, the elevator is accelerating upward, so there must be a net upward force. So in this case, the normal force must exceed the weight, for a net upward force to be exerted on the block.

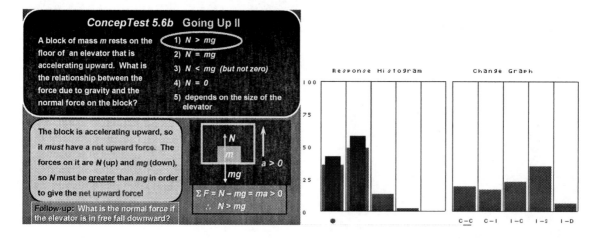

306

Conceptual Module 5.7
ConcepTest 5.7:   **Normal Force**
Difficulty Level: **2**

The normal force is often confused with the weight of the object. But the normal force must be determined by considering all forces applied to the object. In this case, the person pushing on the sled is providing an additional vertical component that will affect the normal force on the sled. This will later be revisited in the case of friction.

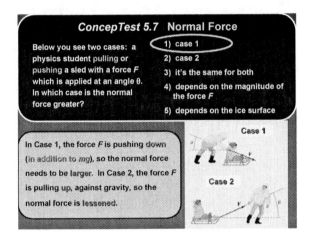

Conceptual Module 5.8
ConcepTest 5.8:   **On an Incline**
Difficulty Level: **4**
Suggested follow-up numerical problem: Problem 5.27

It is important for the students to get used to the fact that the normal force is perpendicular to a surface, and is not necessarily in a vertical direction. Here the normal force in case B is equal to the component of the weight perpendicular to the plane (which is not the same as the weight itself!).

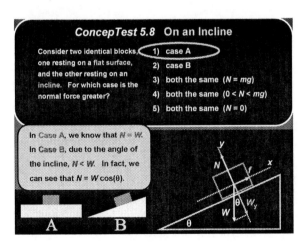

Conceptual Module 5.9
ConcepTest 5.9:   **Friction**
Difficulty Level: **2**
Suggested follow-up numerical problem: Problems 5.28, 5.32 and 5.36

This question revisits Newton's First Law. The box is not "pushed" off the back of the truck, it has simply stayed in one place while the truck moved away. If the box were to move with the truck, then a net force would be needed, and that would most likely be supplied by friction.

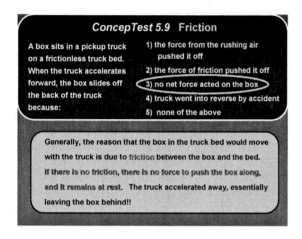

Conceptual Module 5.10
ConcepTest 5.10:   **Antilock Brakes**
Difficulty Level: **2**

Static friction can in principle exert larger forces than kinetic friction, due to the larger value of the coefficient of static friction. When the tires are making good contact with the road (not skidding), they are experiencing static friction. Students must appreciate that this is therefore better for braking, which is the logic behind antilock brakes (as well as maintaining control of the car).

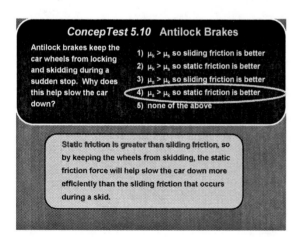

Conceptual Module 5.11
ConcepTest 5.11:   Going Sledding
Difficulty Level: 3
Suggested follow-up numerical problem: Problem 5.33

This question relates to the same issue as ConcepTest 5.7, which dealt with the normal force. Since the frictional force is proportional to the normal force, the situation below that is easiest is the one with the smallest normal force.

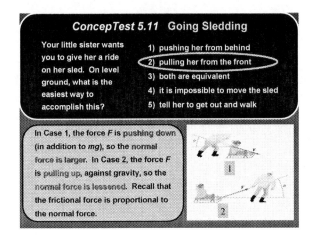

Conceptual Module 5.12
ConcepTest 5.12:   Will It Budge?
Difficulty Level: 3
Suggested follow-up numerical problem: Problem 5.25
Suggested follow-up conceptual questions:
        • **What happens if the tension is 35 N? What about 45 N?**

This is an exercise in determining the force of static friction and realizing that such a force can vary up to a maximum value (beyond which the object will slip). In this case, the maximum static friction force is 40 N, and so any force less than or equal to that value will not move the block.

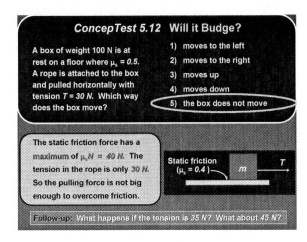

Conceptual Module 5.13 (two parts)
ConcepTest 5.13a: Sliding Down I
Difficulty Level: 4
Suggested follow-up numerical problem: Problem 5.26

This question addresses the concept of friction and, more generally, of the forces acting on a body. The motion of the box is determined by the forces acting parallel to the plane, which include a friction force and a component of gravity. Both of these change when the angle varies. For the friction force, it is the changing normal force that causes the variation.

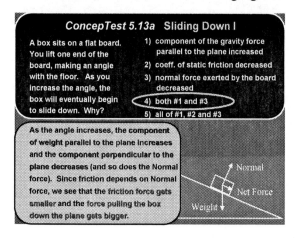

ConcepTest 5.13b: Sliding Down II
Difficulty Level: 5
Suggested follow-up numerical problem: Problem 5.31

In this case, the angle is not changed, but the mass on the plane is changed. By considering the same forces parallel to the plane as were examined in the previous question, students must come to the conclusion that both parallel forces change by the same amount in this case, so nothing is different.

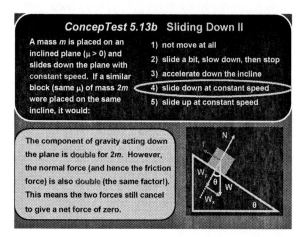

Conceptual Module 5.14
ConcepTest 5.14:   Tetherball
Difficulty Level: 3
Suggested follow-up numerical problem: Problems 5.61, 5.63 and 5.83

For uniform circular motion, there must be an inward force (centripetal force) that keeps the ball in motion. In this case, that inward force is supplied by the horizontal component of the tension. The other forces (vertical component of tension and the weight) are balanced.

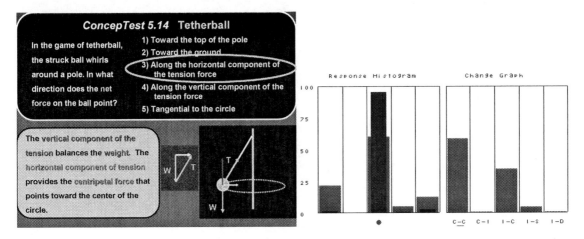

Conceptual Module 5.15 (three parts)
ConcepTest 5.15a: Around the Curve I
Difficulty Level: 2

This is an experience that most students will have had – that of being "thrown" into the car door when a car executes a sharp turn. Students must realize that they are not actually being thrown, but rather they are simply trying to continue moving in a straight-line path.

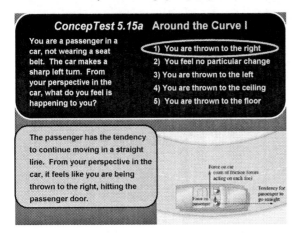

ConcepTest 5.15b: Around the Curve II
Difficulty Level: 2

This follow-up asks the students to interpret what is actually happening to them during the sharp turn in the car. They must realize that without the leftward force exerted by the door, they would continue moving in a straight line and therefore fall out of the car when it turns.

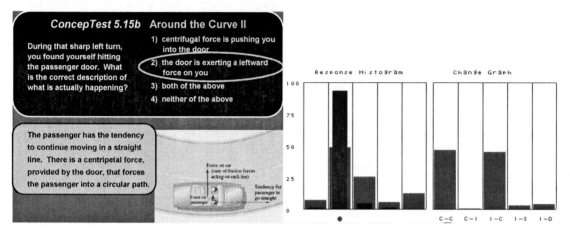

ConcepTest 5.15c: Around the Curve III
Difficulty Level: 3
Suggested follow-up numerical problem: Problems 5.74, 5.85 and 5.51
Suggested follow-up conceptual questions:
* **What could be done to the road or car to prevent skidding?**

This question emphasizes the tendency of a moving object to continue in a straight line (by Newton's First Law) by describing a skid. It is in fact the friction between the road and the tires that provides the centripetal force to make the car move in a circle. The lack of sufficient friction leads to the skid.

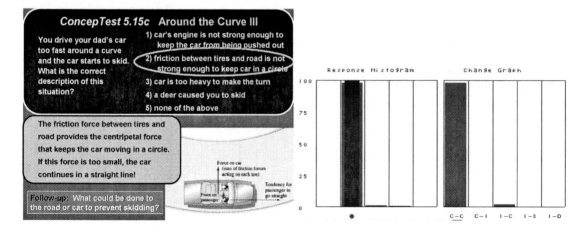

Conceptual Module 5.16
ConcepTest 5.16:   **Missing Link**
Difficulty Level: 3
Suggested follow-up conceptual questions:
- **What physical force provides the centripetal force?**

This question again addresses Newton's First Law and circular motion. In this case, the normal force of the tube wall is what provides the centripetal force to keep the ball moving in a circle. Once that force is removed, the ball will then continue in a straight line, as shown by path #2. Students might tend to think that the ball will "remember" its curved path and therefore choose path #1.

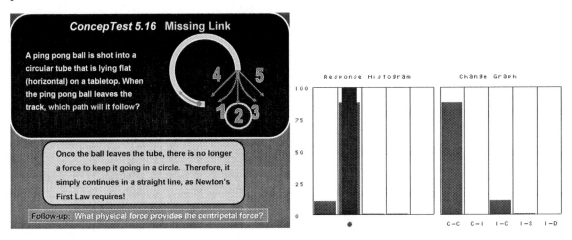

Conceptual Module 5.17
ConcepTest 5.17:   **Ball and String**
Difficulty Level: 5
Suggested follow-up numerical problem: **Problems 5.48, 5.59 and 5.60**

This is a multiple-step problem, demanding that the students use their knowledge of the relationship between mass, velocity and radius in the centripetal force and in the period. Relating these quantities will lead the students to the appropriate relationship between the tensions in the two cases.

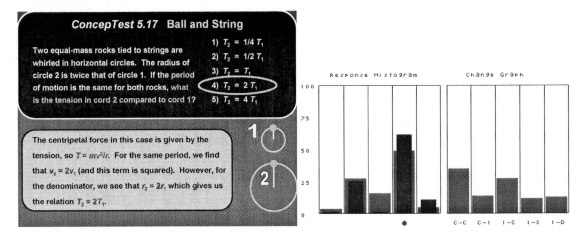

Conceptual Module 5.18
ConcepTest 5.18: **Barrel of Fun**
Difficulty Level: 3
Suggested follow-up numerical problem: Problems 5.81 and 5.82
Suggested follow-up conceptual questions:
- **What happens if the rotation of the ride slows down?**

This is an exercise in visualizing the free-body diagram for a case of circular motion. The example relates to a familiar amusement park ride, in which case the centripetal force is provided by the normal force of the wall. In the figures, the students must realize that the net force must point inward only, and that condition is satisfied by picture #1 and no other picture.

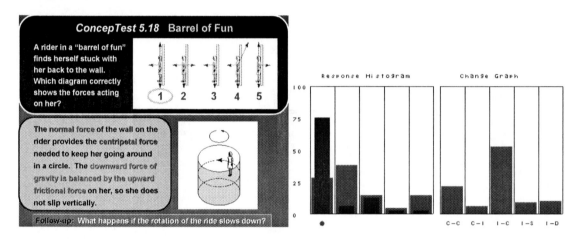

Conceptual Module 5.19 (three parts)
ConcepTest 5.19a: **Going in Circles I**
Difficulty Level: 4
Suggested follow-up numerical problem: Problem 5.56
Suggested follow-up conceptual questions:
- **Where is N larger than mg?**

Again, the net force must be inward (which is downward at the top of the Ferris wheel). Thus, at this position, the downward force (mg) must exceed the upward force (N).

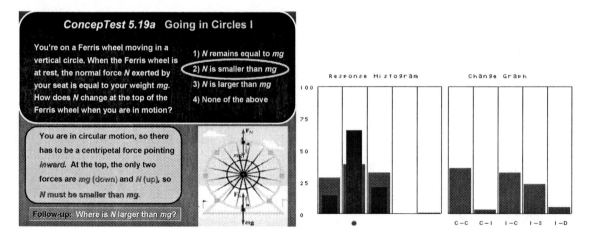

ConcepTest 5.19b: Going in Circles II
Difficulty Level: 4
Suggested follow-up numerical problem: Problem 5.54
Suggested follow-up conceptual questions:
- **What happens when the skier goes into a small dip?**

In this case, as in the previous question, the centripetal force must be directed in toward the center of the circle (which is downward at the top of the hill).   At that position, the weight and normal force are in opposite directions.

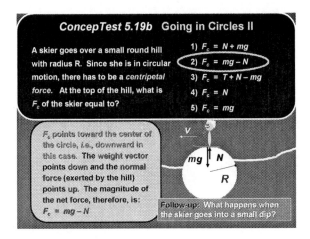

ConcepTest 5.19c: Going in Circles III
Difficulty Level: 4
Suggested follow-up numerical problem: Problems 5.80 and 5.87
Suggested follow-up conceptual questions:
- **What is F_c at the bottom of the ball's path?**

In this case, as in the previous questions, the centripetal force must be directed in toward the center of the circle (which is downward at the top of the ball's path).   At that position, the weight and tension force are in the same direction.

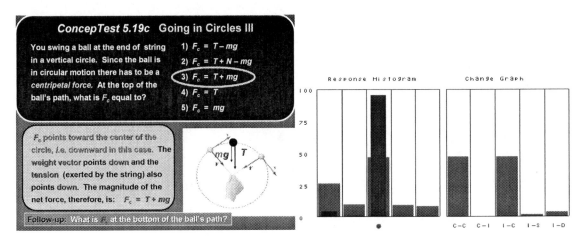

Conceptual Module 6.1
ConcepTest 6.1:   **To Work or Not to Work**
Difficulty Level: **1**

Work is a novel concept to the students. There is a belief that simply applying a force to an object constitutes work. This question emphasizes that the object must also have a certain displacement in order for work to be done.

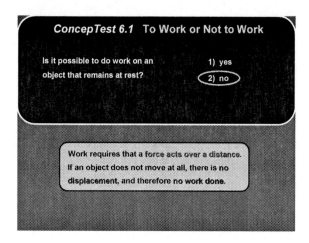

Conceptual Module 6.2   (four parts)
ConcepTest 6.2a: **Friction and Work I**
Difficulty Level: **2**
Suggested follow-up numerical problem: Problem 6.2

This question asks students to examine the relationship between the direction of the applied force and the direction of the displacement. Understanding the meaning of positive work or negative work is a distinction that the students should be able to make.

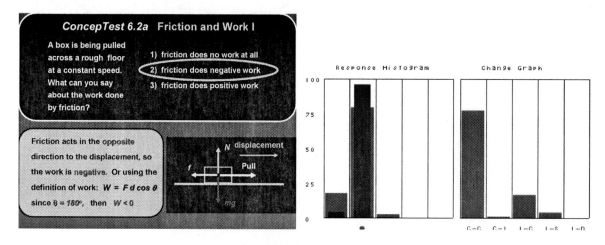

ConcepTest 6.2b: Friction and Work II
Difficulty Level: 3

The notion that friction "resists" motion may lead to the conclusion that friction can only do negative work. Examples of positive work by friction include a box moving on a conveyor belt or a crate in the back of a moving pickup truck.

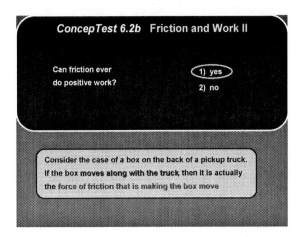

ConcepTest 6.2c: Play Ball!
Difficulty Level: 2
Suggested follow-up numerical problem: Problem 6.12
Suggested follow-up conceptual questions:

- **What about the work done by the ball on the catcher?**

This again deals with the directions of the force and the displacement in order to determine the sign of the work.

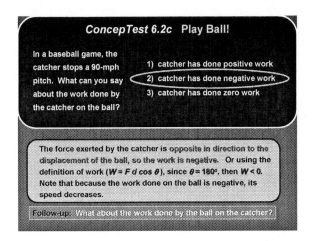

ConcepTest 6.2d: Tension and Work
Difficulty Level: 3
Suggested follow-up numerical problem: Problem 6.21
Suggested follow-up conceptual questions:
  • **Is there a force in the direction of the velocity?**

Finally, we examine the case where the applied force is perpendicular to the displacement, leading to a situation where zero work is done.

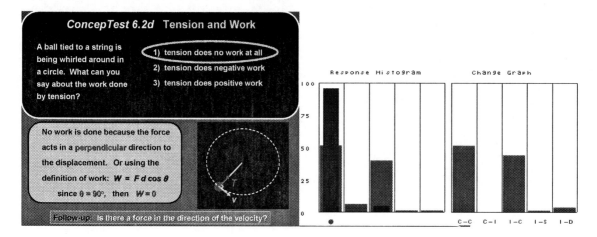

Conceptual Module 6.3
ConcepTest 6.3:   Force and Work
Difficulty Level: 4
Suggested follow-up numerical problem: Problem 6.7

This question requires a careful free-body diagram in order to address the forces on the box and which ones do non-zero work. Note that not all of the forces do non-zero work.

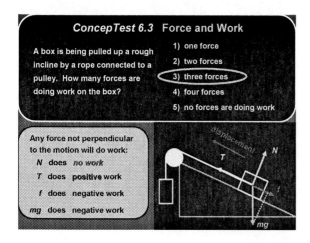

Conceptual Module 6.4
ConcepTest 6.4:   **Lifting a Book**
Difficulty Level: **3**
Suggested follow-up numerical problem: Problem 6.3
Suggested follow-up conceptual questions:
- **What would happen if F_{HAND} was greater than mg?**

Here the net work on an object is examined. Various forces may do work (positive or negative) on the object, but the net work is the sum of those separate components. Or, alternatively, the net work relates directly to the net force. Either way, if no net work is done, then the kinetic energy will not change.

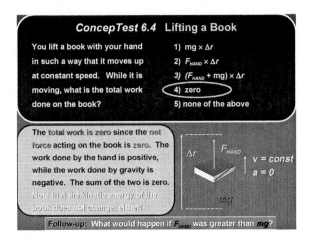

Conceptual Module 6.5   (two parts)
ConcepTest 6.5a: **Kinetic Energy I**
Difficulty Level: **2**
Suggested follow-up conceptual questions:
- **How would you achieve a KE increase of a factor of 2?**

This series of questions is intended to be a gentle introduction to kinetic energy. Here students are expected to recognize the fact that velocity is squared in the kinetic energy.

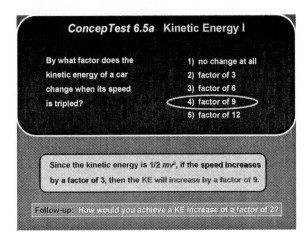

ConcepTest 6.5b: Kinetic Energy II
Difficulty Level: 3

In this case, the relation between mass and velocity in the expression for kinetic energy is being examined.

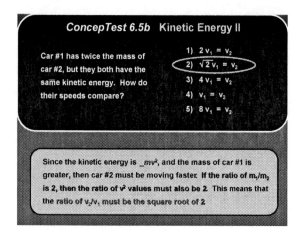

Conceptual Module 6.6 (two parts)
ConcepTest 6.6a: Free Fall I
Difficulty Level: 2
Suggested follow-up conceptual questions:
*   **How do the initial values of gravitational PE compare?**

In this case, the students must find the work done by gravity and then recognize that the only difference in the two cases is the mass. This also gives them a preview of the expression for gravitational potential energy.

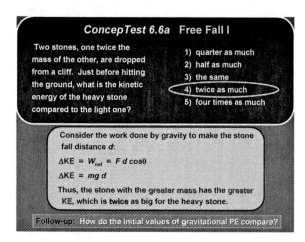

ConcepTest 6.6b: Free Fall II
Difficulty Level: 2

In this case, the students must realize that the final velocities of the two objects will be the same. Therefore, the kinetic energy ratio is directly related to the mass ratio, which independently confirms the result from the previous ConcepTest.

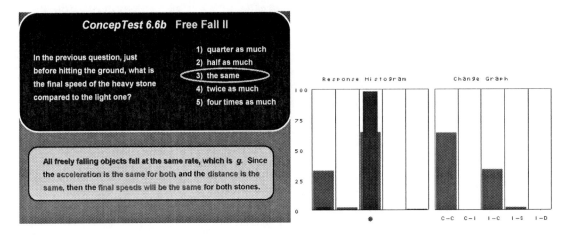

Conceptual Module 6.7
ConcepTest 6.7:   Work and KE
Difficulty Level: 2
Suggested follow-up numerical problem: Problem 6.11
Suggested follow-up conceptual questions:
- **What does it mean for negative work to be done on the child?**

The net work done by external forces leads to a change in kinetic energy. This relation is the so-called "work-kinetic energy" theorem and is crucial for students to understand.

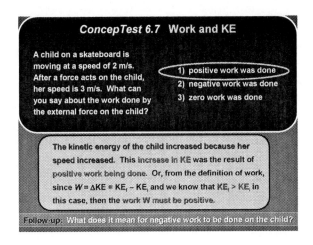

Conceptual Module 6.8 (three parts)
ConcepTest 6.8a: **Slowing Down**
Difficulty Level: **3**
Suggested follow-up numerical problem: Problem 6.90

The students are asked to relate work to the change in kinetic energy in order to calculate stopping distance. This question also has definite real-world implications, just to give a sense of how much more difficult it is to stop safely when moving at higher speeds.

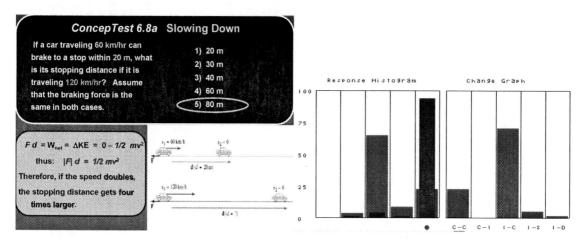

ConcepTest 6.8b: **Speeding Up I**
Difficulty Level: **4**
Suggested follow-up conceptual questions:
- **How much energy is required to stop the 60 mph car?**

In this case, a more careful assessment of the "work-kinetic energy" theorem is required. The intuitive notion that both accelerating stages take the same amount of energy is not true, and this is dictated largely by the square of the velocity in the kinetic energy.

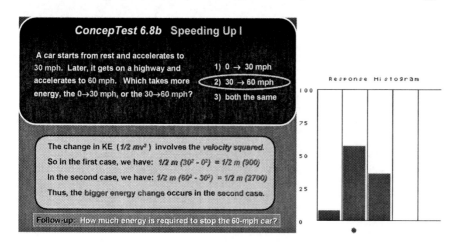

ConcepTest 6.8c: Speeding Up II
Difficulty Level: 4
Suggested follow-up conceptual questions:
  • **How much work is required to stop the 150 km/hr car?**

This question asks the students to quantify the energy difference between the two stages of acceleration. They must apply what they have learned from the previous ConcepTest to address this issue semi-quantitatively.

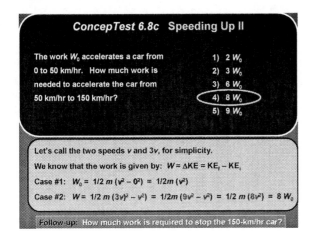

Conceptual Module 6.9 (two parts)
ConcepTest 6.9a: Work and Energy I
Difficulty Level: 4
Suggested follow-up numerical problem: Problem 6.85
Suggested follow-up conceptual questions:
  • **Which block has the greater magnitude of acceleration?**

This question addresses the relationship between work and kinetic energy in the case where the work is done by friction. The simplification that the blocks start with the same kinetic energy allows the students to focus on the determination of frictional work.

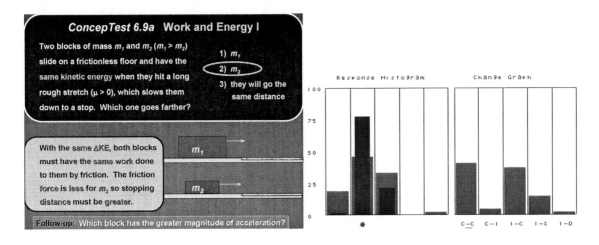

ConcepTest 6.9b: Work and Energy II
Difficulty Level: 3
Suggested follow-up numerical problem: Problem 6.89

In this case, the frictional force is constant, and the students must examine the kinetic energy part of the problem. Here the velocity dependence plays the major role.

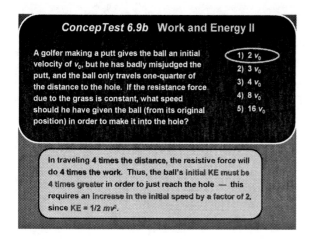

Conceptual Module 6.10
ConcepTest 6.10:   Sign of the Energy I
Difficulty Level: 1

This is a simple question relating to kinetic energy.

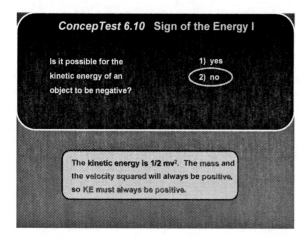

Conceptual Module 6.11 (three parts)
ConcepTest 6.11a: Time for Work I
Difficulty Level: 2

As a precursor to introducing power, a comparison is done between two cases where the time of application of the force is different. This does not affect the work at all.

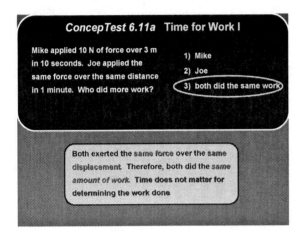

ConcepTest 6.11b: Time for Work II
Difficulty Level: 3
Suggested follow-up numerical problem: Problem 6.66

In this question, the relationship between work, time and power is examined.

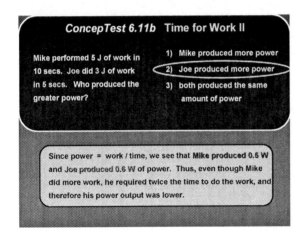

ConcepTest 6.11c: Power
Difficulty Level: 2
Suggested follow-up numerical problem: Problem 6.68

Power and work are not the same quantities. They are related, but not the same. Students often confuse the two concepts, and the distinction must be made clear.

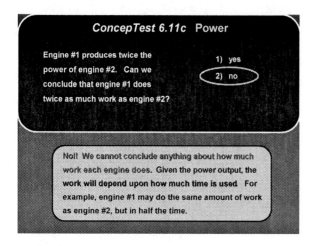

Conceptual Module 6.12 (two parts)
ConcepTest 6.12a: Electric Bill
Difficulty Level: 2
Suggested follow-up numerical problem: Problem 6.63

Power and work are not the same quantities. They are related, but not the same. Students often confuse the two concepts, and the distinction must be made clear. In this case, the units of energy (from an electric bill) carry the information to lead students to realize that they are paying for energy, not power.

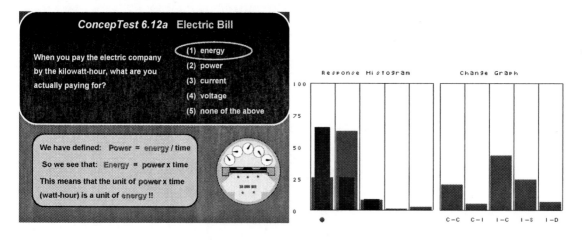

ConcepTest 6.12b: Energy Consumption
Difficulty Level: 2
Suggested follow-up numerical problem: Problem 6.64

Here again, the distinction between power and energy is emphasized. The total energy expended depends on the time that an appliance is in operation. Obviously, a higher-power device will use energy *faster*, but the total energy still depends on the time.

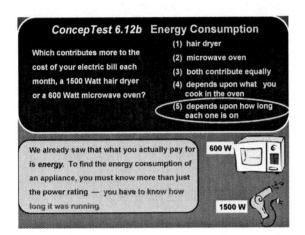

Conceptual Module 7.1
ConcepTest 7.1:   **Sign of the Energy II**
Difficulty Level: **2**
Suggested follow-up numerical problem: Problems 7.10 and 7.18

It is important for students to understand that the *actual value* of the gravitational potential energy is not that important – what is physically relevant is the *difference* between initial and final values (whatever they may be). The zero reference level for PE is arbitrary, and so it is certainly possible for the PE to be negative.

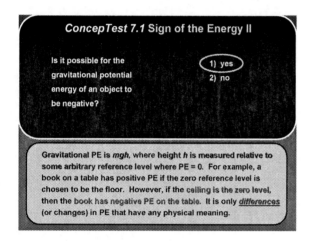

Conceptual Module 7.2
ConcepTest 7.2:   **KE and PE**
Difficulty Level: **2**
Suggested follow-up numerical problem: Problem 7.36
Suggested follow-up conceptual questions:
- **Does anything change physically by the choice of $y = 0$?**

This question continues to address the issue of the zero reference level for gravitational potential energy. Here students are asked to recognize that while the value of PE depends on the reference level, the ΔPE does not depend on that (and therefore KE does not).

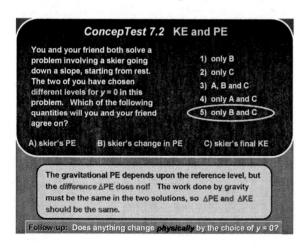

Conceptual Module 7.3
ConcepTest 7.3:   **Up the Hill**
Difficulty Level: **2**
Suggested follow-up numerical problem: Problems 7.1 and 7.51
Suggested follow-up conceptual questions:
- **How much more work do you do in taking the steeper path?**
- **Which path would you rather take? Why?**

The students must realize that the change in gravitational potential energy depends on the height difference between initial and final levels and is independent of the path taken to go from one point to another (because gravity is a conservative force). What does depend on the path is the force and the distance (related to work), while the work is unchanged.

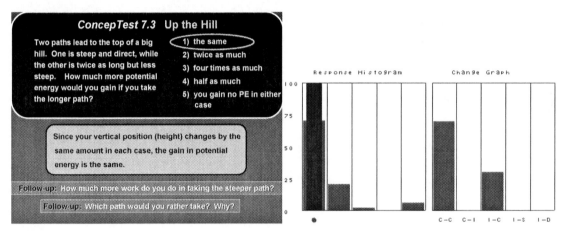

Conceptual Module 7.4
ConcepTest 7.4:   **Elastic Potential Energy**
Difficulty Level: **2**
Suggested follow-up numerical problem: Problem 7.8

The work has been defined as the change in potential energy. Using the relation for elastic potential energy, students are asked to determine the work for two different displacements, keeping in mind that elastic PE depends on the square of displacement.

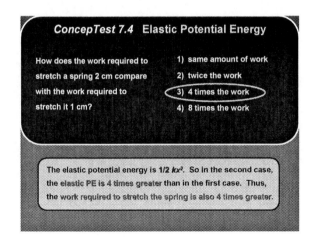

Conceptual Module 7.5
ConcepTest 7.5:   Springs and Gravity
Difficulty Level: 2
Suggested follow-up numerical problem: Problem 7.13

This question is a basic check on changes in potential energy, both gravitational and elastic. In the case of a vertical spring, both of these come into play.

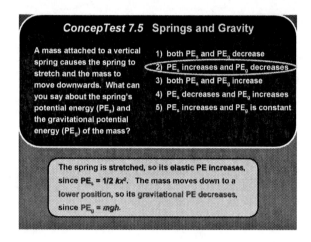

Conceptual Module 7.6
ConcepTest 7.6:   Down the Hill
Difficulty Level: 2
Suggested follow-up conceptual questions:
* **Which ball takes longer to get down the ramp?**

The kinetic energy is related to the change in potential energy. Here the gravitational PE depends on the height of the ramp, which is the same in all cases, so the KE must end up the same as well (and therefore, the speed).

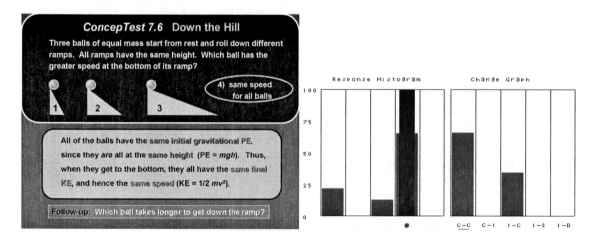

Conceptual Module 7.7 (two parts)
ConcepTest 7.7a: Runaway Truck
Difficulty Level: 3
Suggested follow-up numerical problem: Problem 7.31

This question examines conservation of energy, where potential energy is converted into kinetic energy. The dependence of these quantities on the relevant variables (in this case, height and velocity) is the principal concern here.

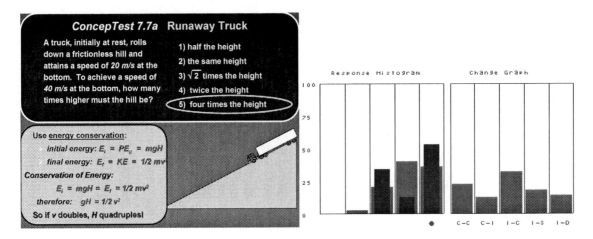

ConcepTest 7.7b: Runaway Box
Difficulty Level: 3
Suggested follow-up numerical problem: Problems 7.14 and 7.15

This question follows the same line of reasoning as the previous question, except that in this case, the elastic potential energy (instead of gravitational PE) is being related to kinetic energy.

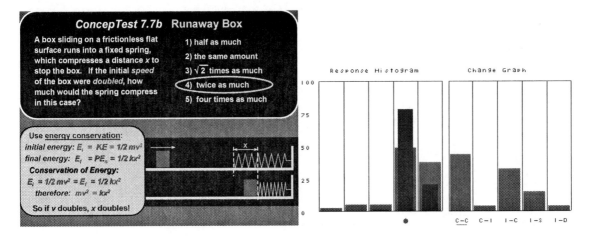

Conceptual Module 7.8 (two parts)
ConcepTest 7.8a: Water Slide I
Difficulty Level: 3
Suggested follow-up numerical problem: Problem 7.29

This question emphasizes the path independence of the potential energy. Both of the kids start at the same height, so their final velocities will be the same. The velocity does not depend on the shape of the slide (*i.e.*, the path taken).

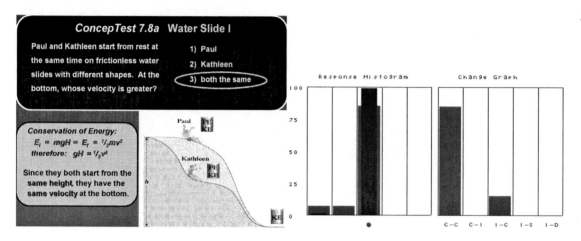

ConcepTest 7.8b: Water Slide II
Difficulty Level: 5

This follow-up question is somewhat tricky. In this case, when determining the travel time, the path actually does matter. Kathleen converts her gravitational potential energy into kinetic energy more quickly, which means that she has a greater velocity for most of the ride. Thus, she arrives at the bottom earlier.

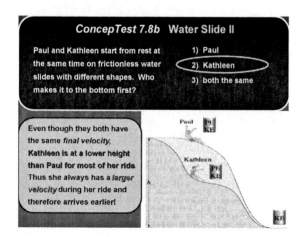

Conceptual Module 7.9
ConcepTest 7.9:   **Cart on a Hill**
Difficulty Level: 4
Suggested follow-up numerical problem: Problem 7.60

This question requires a careful consideration of energy conservation. The two velocities in the question cannot simply be added to obtain the answer.

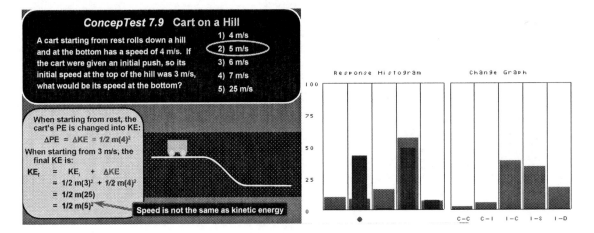

Conceptual Module 7.10 (two parts)
ConcepTest 7.10a: **Falling Leaves**
Difficulty Level: 4
Suggested follow-up numerical problem: Problem 7.46
Suggested follow-up conceptual questions:
- **What happens to the leaf's KE as it falls? What is net work done?**

In this case, the work done by non-conservative forces is involved. The leaf is falling at constant speed because there is a frictional force (air resistance); this constitutes the non-conservative force in the problem. Therefore, by the work-energy theorem, the final energy will be less than the initial energy.

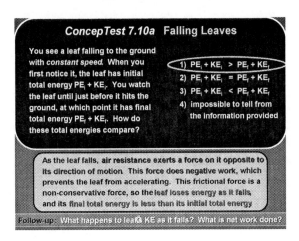

ConcepTest 7.10b: Falling Balls
Difficulty Level: 5
Suggested follow-up numerical problem: Problems 7.48 and 7.72
Suggested follow-up conceptual questions:
* **How does the force of air resistance compare to gravity when the ball reaches terminal velocity?**

In this case, again, a non-conservative force (air resistance) is playing a role. Since the ball has "lost" energy due to work by non-conservative forces, it will be moving slower at each point on the way down than it was at those same points on the way up. Thus, the downward trip will take a longer time.

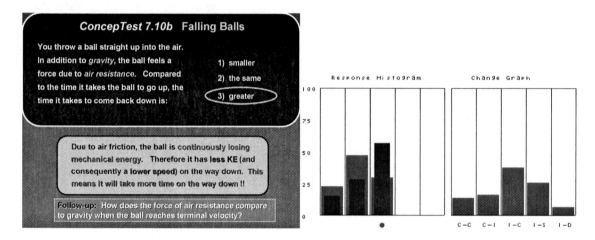

Conceptual Module 8.1
ConcepTest 8.1:   **Rolling in the Rain**
Difficulty Level: 2
Suggested follow-up numerical problem: Problem 8.87

This is a case of momentum conservation in its purest form. As the mass of the cart increases (due to the rain collecting), the velocity must decrease to maintain the same value of momentum. Note that the rain falling vertically does not exert any horizontal force on the rolling cart.

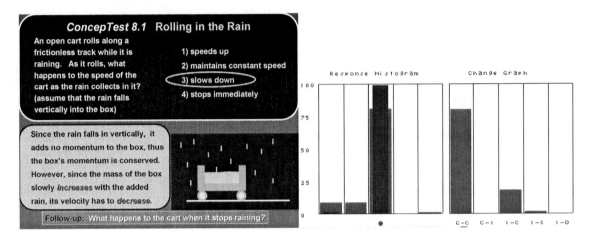

Conceptual Module 8.2 (three parts)
ConcepTest 8.2a: **Momentum and KE I**
Difficulty Level: 2

In the following questions, the students are asked to think about a system of particles and to draw conclusions about the energy and momentum. In this first case, the only way the kinetic energy (a scalar quantity) can be zero is for all velocities to be zero.

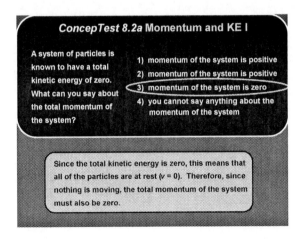

ConcepTest 8.2b: Momentum and KE II
Difficulty Level: 3

In this question, the total momentum can be zero even for finite velocities. The vector nature of momentum means that terms with equal and opposite momenta can cancel.

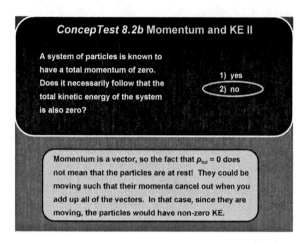

ConcepTest 8.2c: Momentum and KE III
Difficulty Level: 3

While both kinetic energy and momentum depend on mass and velocity, the dependence on these variables is different in each case. So equal momenta do not imply equal values of the mass and velocity, which is what would be necessary for the kinetic energies to be equal as well.

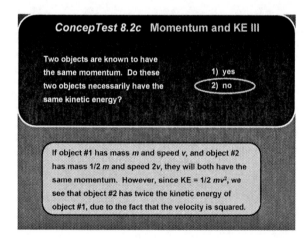

Conceptual Module 8.3 (two parts)
ConcepTest 8.3a: **Momentum and Force**
Difficulty Level: **2**
Suggested follow-up numerical problem: Problem 8.10

Force is related to the rate of change of momentum. This question is emphasizing the equivalence of these two quantities. This is essentially a restatement of Newton's Second Law.

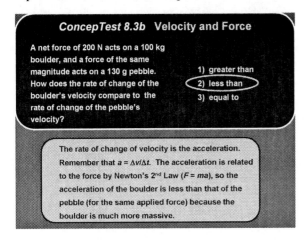

ConcepTest 8.3b: **Velocity and Force**
Difficulty Level: **3**

Using the relationship examined in the previous question, the students must now realize that momentum is related to mass and velocity in order to address the question of the rate of change of velocity (which is the acceleration).

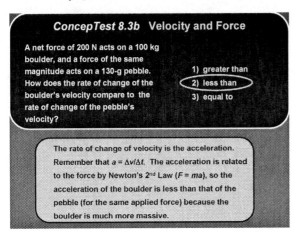

Conceptual Module 8.4
ConcepTest 8.4:   **Collision Course**
Difficulty Level: 2
Suggested follow-up conceptual questions:
- **Which one feels the larger acceleration?**

This question examines the relationship between momentum and force as it pertains to internal forces in a closed system. This also underscores the importance of Newton's Third Law in the discussion of momentum conservation.

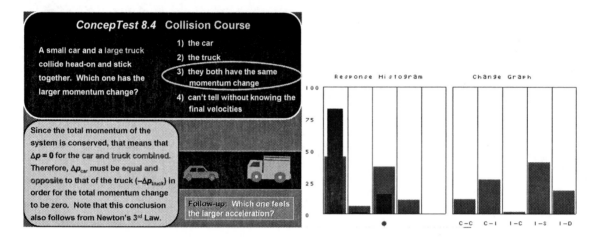

Conceptual Module 8.5 (two parts)
ConcepTest 8.5a: **Two Boxes I**
Difficulty Level: 2
Suggested follow-up numerical problem: Problem 8.19

Impulse is directly related to the change in momentum. In this case, the same force acting over the same time interval in two different situations (regardless of the mass) will give rise to the same momentum change, by the definition of impulse ($F \, \Delta t$).

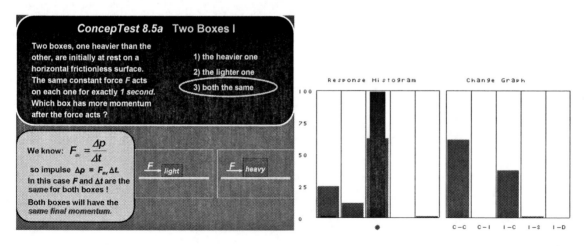

ConcepTest 8.5b: **Two Boxes II**
Difficulty Level: **3**
Suggested follow-up conceptual questions:
- **Which box has gone a larger distance after the force acts?**
- **Which box has gained more KE after the force acts?**

Here the students must break down the momentum into its relationship to mass and velocity in order to determine which box achieves the larger velocity. This result may be more intuitive to the students than the previous result.

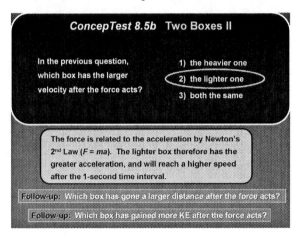

Conceptual Module 8.6
ConcepTest 8.6:   **Watch Out!**
Difficulty Level: **3**

This question may again lead to a non-intuitive result, but the fact remains that the momentum change is the same in both cases. The car will come to a dead stop in both cases, and the force can be related to the impulse (momentum change).

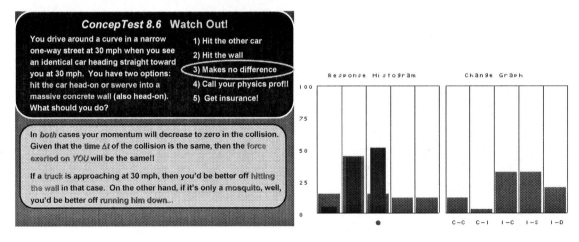

Conceptual Module 8.7
ConcepTest 8.7:   **Impulse**
Difficulty Level: **4**
Suggested follow-up numerical problem: Problem 8.23
Suggested follow-up conceptual questions:
- **Which one imparts the larger force to the floor?**

The impulse is related to the change in momentum. Students must understand that the case where an object rebounds (reverses momentum direction) has a large momentum change, whereas the case where an object comes to rest has a smaller momentum change.

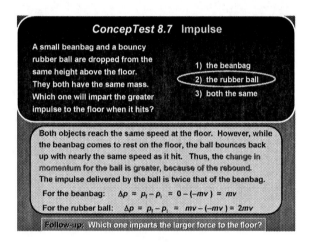

Conceptual Module 8.8
ConcepTest 8.8:   **Singing in the Rain**
Difficulty Level: **4**

This question examines the previous issue in more detail. Here the issue of force must be considered, but since the force is a part of the impulse, the extension is not so great. The fact that the hail "bounces off" and the rain does not is what leads to a larger force imparted by the hail.

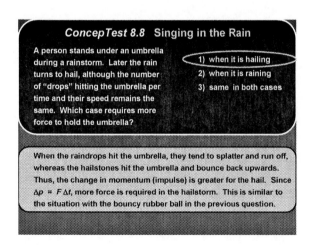

Conceptual Module 8.9 (two parts)
ConcepTest 8.9a: Going Bowling I
Difficulty Level: 3
Suggested follow-up numerical problem: Problem 8.20

This question examines the connection between momentum and impulse. Here the students are asked to break down the impulse into its dependence on the force and the time interval over which the force acts.

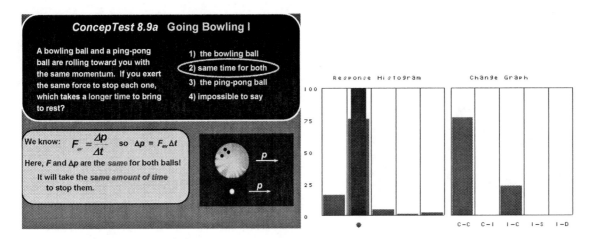

ConcepTest 8.9b: Going Bowling II
Difficulty Level: 5
Suggested follow-up numerical problem: Problem 8.19

This more complicated extension requires making the connection between kinetic energy and work. The kinetic energy must be inferred from the momentum, in this case, in order to draw a conclusion about the applied force and the distance (not the time, in this case!) over which it acts.

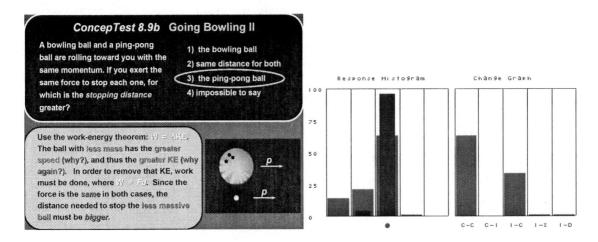

Conceptual Module 8.10 (two parts)
ConcepTest 8.10a: Elastic Collisions I
Difficulty Level: 4
Suggested follow-up numerical problem: Problem 8.44

In an elastic collision, the speed of approach before the collision equals the speed of recession after the collision. The students must compare the approach (same in each case) and the recession to determine the answer. Some reasonable assumptions have to be made about the final velocities of the two objects, which gives students a chance to make some independent judgements in the case of $m \ll M$.

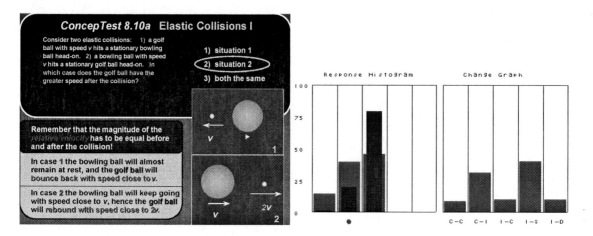

ConcepTest 8.10b: Elastic Collisions II
Difficulty Level: 5
Suggested follow-up numerical problem: Problem 8.39
Suggested follow-up conceptual questions:
*   **With initial drop height *h*, how high does the small rubber ball bounce up?**

This more difficult question relates to a popular classroom demonstration. Here again, the relative velocities must be considered in an elastic collision and some reasonable assumptions must be applied.

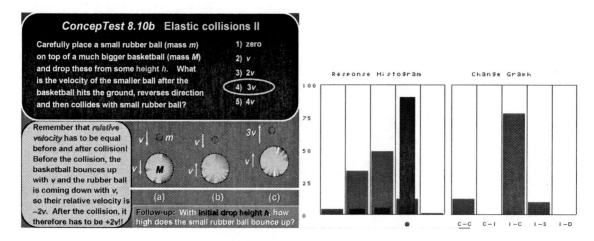

Conceptual Module 8.11
ConcepTest 8.11:   Golf Anyone?
Difficulty Level: 3

This revisits the question of the relative speeds in an elastic collision.

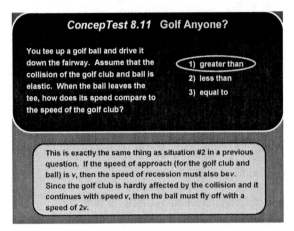

Conceptual Module 8.12 (two parts)
ConcepTest 8.12a: Inelastic Collisions I
Difficulty Level: 3
Suggested follow-up numerical problem: Problems 8.25 and 8.27

This is a straightforward application of momentum conservation in the case of an inelastic collision.

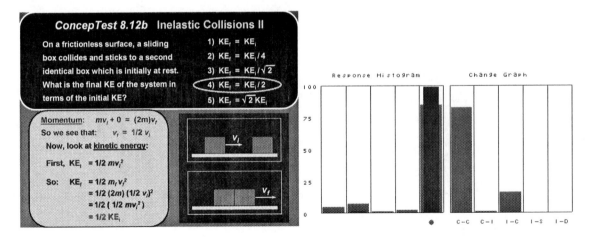

ConcepTest 8.12b: Inelastic Collisions II
Difficulty Level: 4
Suggested follow-up numerical problem: Problem 8.26

In this case, the students must extrapolate what they can deduce about the momentum (or actually, the velocity) to the issue of kinetic energy. This requires them to find the final velocity and then use it to compare the initial and final KE values.

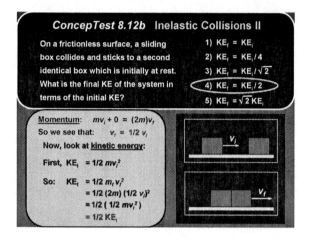

Conceptual Module 8.13 (two parts)
ConcepTest 8.13a: Nuclear Fission I
Difficulty Level: 2

This illustrates momentum conservation in an explosion. This first part establishes that both fragments have the same magnitude of momentum (equal and opposite), since the total momentum of the system must be zero.

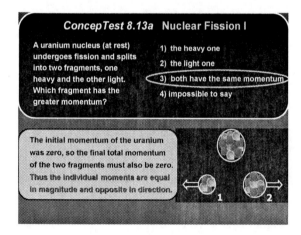

ConcepTest 8.13b: Nuclear Fission II
Difficulty Level: 3
Suggested follow-up numerical problem: Problem 8.32

In this part, the students must use what they have learned about the momenta of the fragments to deduce their respective velocities.

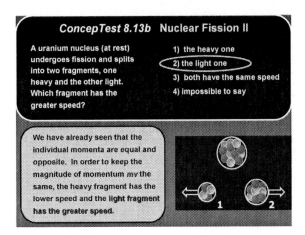

Conceptual Module 8.14 (two parts)
ConcepTest 8.14a: Recoil Speed I
Difficulty Level: 3
Suggested follow-up numerical problem: Problem 8.28

This question again examines momentum conservation in an explosion. In the previous ConcepTest, this was treated qualitatively. This case asks for a quantitative analysis.

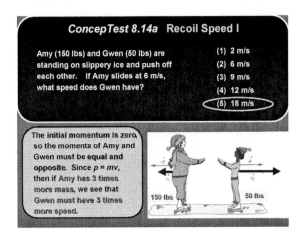

ConcepTest 8.14b: Recoil Speed II
Difficulty Level: 3
Suggested follow-up numerical problem: Problem 8.83

This is another quantitative question about momentum conservation in an explosion.

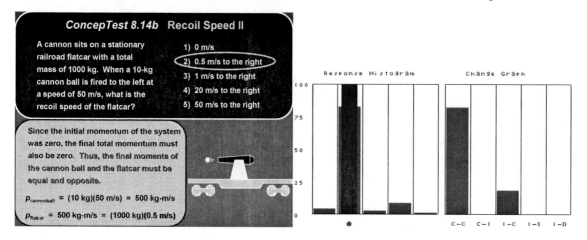

Conceptual Module 8.15
ConcepTest 8.15:   Gun Control
Difficulty Level: 3

This question illustrates that the potential for damage is related to the kinetic energy, not specifically the momentum. The recoil of a gun will have the same momentum as the bullet that was fired from the gun, but the kinetic energies can be vastly different due to the fact that KE involves the square of a velocity.

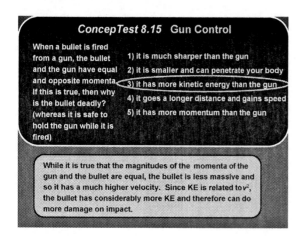

Conceptual Module 8.16 (two parts)
ConcepTest 8.16a: Crash Cars I
Difficulty Level: 3

This is a question of momentum conservation that must be answered by comparing the momenta of the oppositely directed cars.

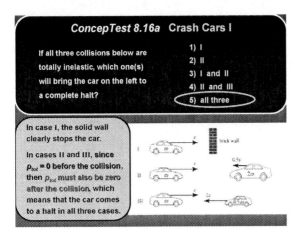

ConcepTest 8.16b: Crash Cars II
Difficulty Level: 4

Having established in the previous ConcepTest that the final velocities are zero in all cases, this next question investigates the damage done in the collisions. In this case, the relevant quantity is the loss of kinetic energy, which will depend heavily on the velocity, due to the fact that KE involves the square of the velocity.

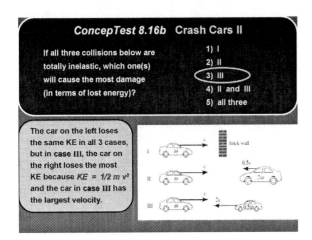

Conceptual Module 8.17
ConcepTest 8.17:   **Shut the Door!**
Difficulty Level: **4**
Suggested follow-up numerical problem: Problem 8.38

The issue of effectiveness relates to the one that will impart the greatest impulse (momentum change) to the door. As discussed in an earlier ConcepTest, the case where the ball rebounds will involve the greater momentum change, as opposed to the case where the ball simply comes to rest.

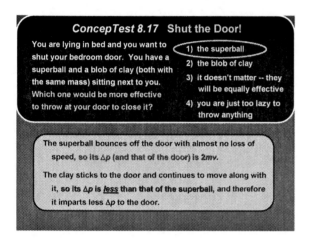

Conceptual Module 8.18
ConcepTest 8.18:   **Baseball Bat**
Difficulty Level: **3**
Suggested follow-up numerical problem: Problems 8.55, 8.61 and 8.69

The center of mass must be determined by considering the distribution of mass in an extended object. Here, with more mass concentrated in the thick part of the bat, the center of mass will be closer to that end (as opposed to being at the midpoint).

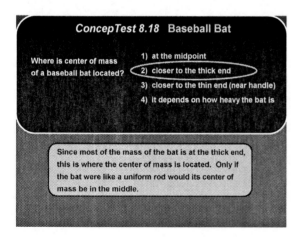

Conceptual Module 8.19
ConcepTest 8.19:   Motion of CM
Difficulty Level: 4
Suggested follow-up numerical problem: Problem 8.81

This is a question about the center of mass of a two-particle system, where one of the particles is moving. The location of the center of mass must be deduced as a function of time.

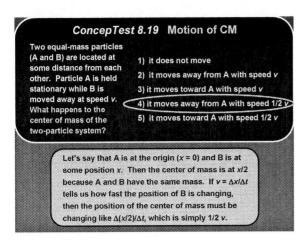

Conceptual Module 8.20
ConcepTest 8.20:   Center of Mass
Difficulty Level: 4
Suggested follow-up numerical problem: Problems 8.64 and 8.65

This question requires the center of mass of two separate extended objects to be identified, and then the overall center of mass to be determined. Since flipping the two semi-disks alters the mass distribution in the resulting shape (compared to the original disk), the center of mass will change.

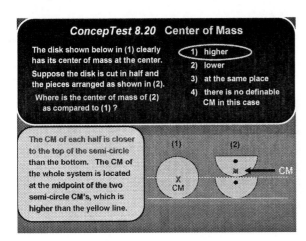

Conceptual Module 9.1 (two parts)
ConcepTest 9.1a: Bonnie and Klyde I
Difficulty Level: 1

Students must distinguish between angular velocity and linear velocity. For two objects on a rigid body that is rotating, the angular velocities are the same (even if the objects are at different radii).

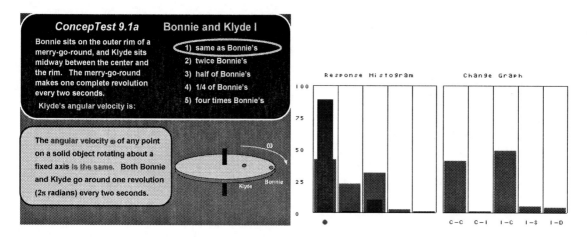

ConcepTest 9.1b: Bonnie and Klyde II
Difficulty Level: 2
Suggested follow-up numerical problem: Problems 9.6 and 9.8
Suggested follow-up conceptual questions:
* **Who has the larger centripetal acceleration?**

In this case, the linear velocity is examined. Here the position of the object relative to the center will matter. Objects at larger radii will move faster. Students should be able to relate this to their own experience with a rotating turntable (or merry-go-round) usually found in a playground.

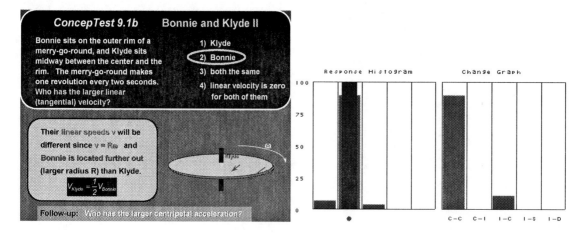

Conceptual Module 9.2
ConcepTest 9.2:   **Truck Speedometer**
Difficulty Level: 4
Suggested follow-up numerical problem: Problem 9.12

This question asks students to relate angular velocity to linear velocity. In this case, the speedometer actually measures angular velocity and then converts to linear velocity, assuming a particular tire radius. Students must realize that the larger tires will allow the truck to move faster (linearly) for a given angular velocity of the tires. Thus the speedometer will read too low.

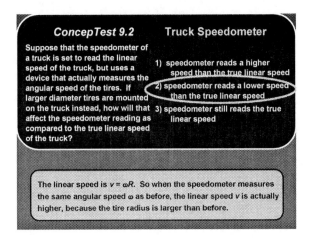

Conceptual Module 9.3 (two parts)
ConcepTest 9.3a: **Angular Displacement I**
Difficulty Level: 3
Suggested follow-up numerical problem: Problems 9.1 and 9.2

This question addresses rotational kinematics, which is quite analogous to linear kinematics. The angular displacement is related to the angular acceleration by the square of the time, so a time period that is half the original time will lead to an angular displacement that is a quarter of the original value.

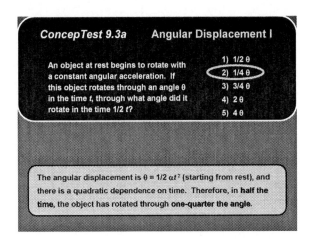

ConcepTest 9.3b: Angular Displacement II
Difficulty Level: 3
Suggested follow-up numerical problem: Problem 9.4

This question continues to address rotational kinematics. The angular velocity is linearly related to the angular acceleration, so a time period that is half the original time will lead to an angular velocity that is also half the original value.

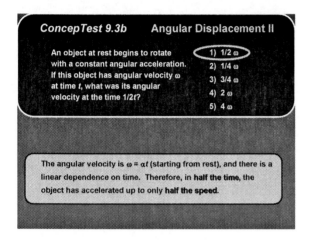

Conceptual Module 9.4
ConcepTest 9.4:   Using a Wrench
Difficulty Level: 2
Suggested follow-up numerical problem: Problems 9.38 and 9.39
Suggested follow-up conceptual questions:
  • **What is the difference between arrangement 1 and 4?**

Students often have a great deal of trouble with torque. In this question, the force is assumed fixed, so the issue here is the finding the largest lever arm. This is accomplished in the case where the force is applied at the greatest perpendicular distance from the axis of rotation. Cases #1 and #4 are, in fact, identical in this regard – the extension used in case #4 essentially gains nothing.

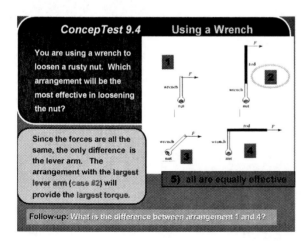

Conceptual Module 9.5
ConcepTest 9.5:   **Two Forces**
Difficulty Level: 2
Suggested follow-up conceptual questions:
- **If two torques are identical, does that mean their forces are identical as well?**

Torque is not the same as force. Clearly, force is involved, but the lever arm must also be taken into account. Thus, two equivalent torques do not necessarily imply that the forces are equal.

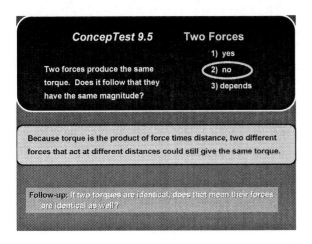

Conceptual Module 9.6
ConcepTest 9.6:   **Closing a Door**
Difficulty Level: 2
Suggested follow-up numerical problem: Problem 9.42
Suggested follow-up conceptual questions:
- **How large would the force have to be for F_4?**

Students often have difficulty identifying the lever arm when the force is not applied at right angles to the displacement vector from the axis of rotation. This question gives some practice for forces applied at the same position in space (but with different lever arms).

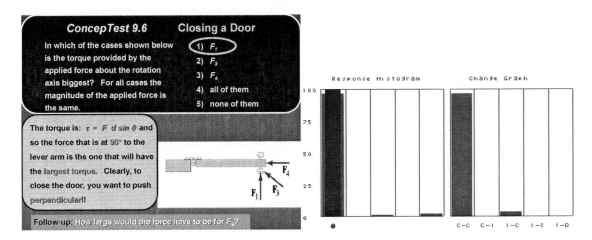

Conceptual Module 9.7
ConcepTest 9.7:   **Cassette Player**
Difficulty Level: **2**
Suggested follow-up numerical problem: Problem 9.47

In this question, the tension force in a rotating spool of tape is assumed constant, and the students are asked to examine the variation in torque as the effective lever arm changes. The students must recognize that the lever arm is decreasing as the spool empties, so the torque also decreases.

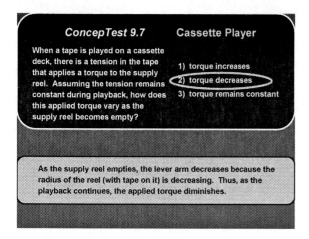

Conceptual Module 9.8 (two parts)
ConcepTest 9.8a: **Dumbbell I**
Difficulty Level: **2**

This question relates linear motion to rotational motion for a given applied force. The impulse $(F \, \Delta t)$ to the system is the same in both cases, so the motion of the center of mass will be the same also.

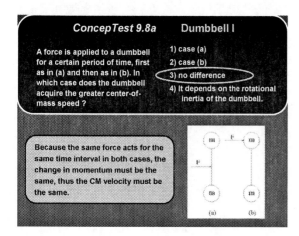

ConcepTest 9.8b: Dumbbell II
Difficulty Level: 3
Suggested follow-up numerical problem: Problem 9.22

In this follow-up question, students now have to account for the rotation of the dumbbell. Since the linear motions are the same in both cases, the translational energies will also be the same. The rotational motion of the dumbbell contributes additional energy to the system in case (b).

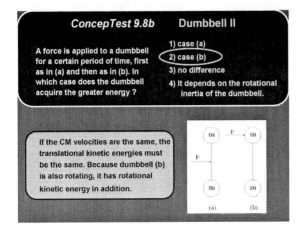

Conceptual Module 9.9
ConcepTest 9.9:   Moment of Inertia
Difficulty Level: 3
Suggested follow-up numerical problem: Problems 9.24 and 9.33

The moment of inertia depends upon the distribution of mass around an axis of rotation. Considering how this distribution affects the situation is often a challenge for students. The case in which more of the mass is located at a larger distance (the gold sphere) will have the larger moment of inertia.

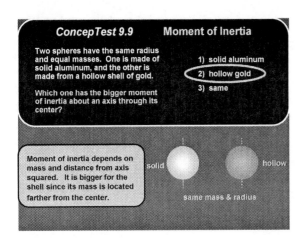

Conceptual Module 9.10
ConcepTest 9.10:   **Figure Skater**
Difficulty Level: 4
Suggested follow-up numerical problem: Problem 9.51
Suggested follow-up conceptual questions:
- **Where does the extra energy come from?**

The students must make the distinction between angular momentum and rotational energy. By angular momentum conservation, the skater speeds up her rotation by decreasing her moment of inertia. But the rotation KE depends upon the square of the angular speed, so this fact leads to an increase in rotational KE (the decrease in moment of inertia only enters as a linear term).

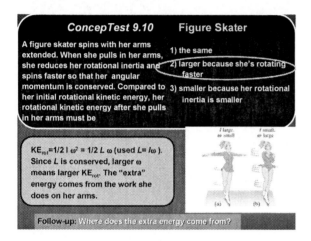

Conceptual Module 9.11
ConcepTest 9.11:   **Two Disks**
Difficulty Level: 4
Suggested follow-up numerical problem: Problem 9.19

This question also asks students to examine the moment of inertia and angular velocity in terms of the angular momentum and the rotational KE.

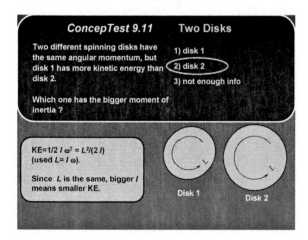

Conceptual Module 9.12
ConcepTest 9.12:   Spinning Bicycle Wheel
Difficulty Level: 2
Suggested follow-up numerical problem: Problem 9.49

This is a classic demonstration. In order to keep the angular momentum constant, when you flip the spinning bicycle wheel, the turntable must then rotate in the same direction in order to compensate for the "loss" of angular momentum. Students must realize that there are two contributions to the angular momentum in this question – the bicycle wheel and the turntable itself.

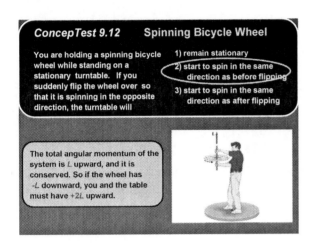

Conceptual Module 11.1
ConcepTest 11.1:   **Balancing Rod**
Difficulty Level: 4
Suggested follow-up numerical problem: Problem 11.1

This is a simple balancing problem, but one of the objects is an extended object (the rod). The students must realize that the rod can effectively be "replaced" by a point mass at the rod's center of mass, and then the answer is apparent.

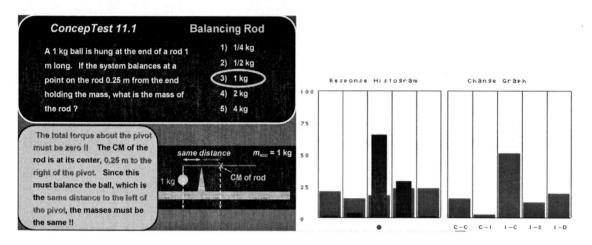

Conceptual Module 11.2
ConcepTest 11.2:   **Mobile**
Difficulty Level: 4
Suggested follow-up numerical problem: Problems 11.7 and 11.8

This is another balancing problem, but with multiple steps. As long as the students proceed systematically through the logical steps, starting with the bottom rod, they should be able to work out the values of the missing masses in order to get the total mass.

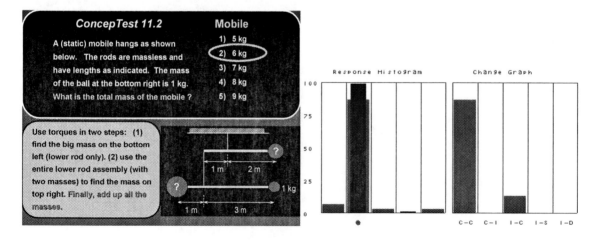

Conceptual Module 11.3 (two parts)
ConcepTest 11.3a: Tipping Over I
Difficulty Level: 2
Suggested follow-up numerical problem: Problems 11.9 and 11.10

The stability of an object depends on the position of the center of mass relative to the axis of rotation (for gravitational torques). If the object can rotate in order to lower its center of mass (and hence, reduce its gravitational PE), it will do so. This example also gives an illustration of the problems associated with a top-heavy large object.

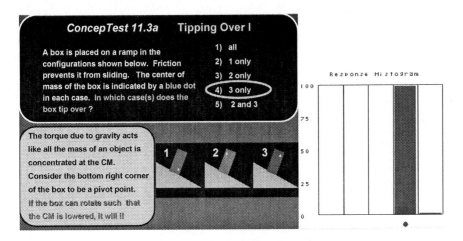

ConcepTest 11.3b: Tipping Over II
Difficulty Level: 4
Suggested follow-up numerical problem: Problems 11.12 and 11.13

Here again, the books will topple over if the center of mass of the entire system is out over the edge of the table. To deduce this position, the separate center of mass positions for each book must be considered and then used to find the overall center of mass.

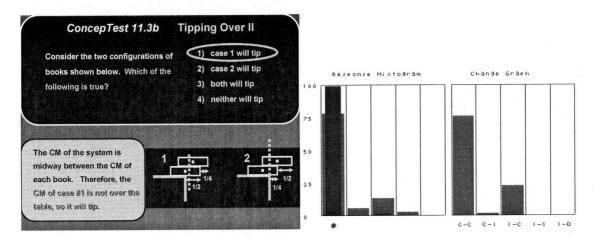

Conceptual Module 12.1 (two parts)
ConcepTest 12.1a: Earth and Moon I
Difficulty Level: 2
Suggested follow-up numerical problem: Problem 12.5

This is a review of Newton's Third Law, as it applies to the gravitational attraction between two bodies.

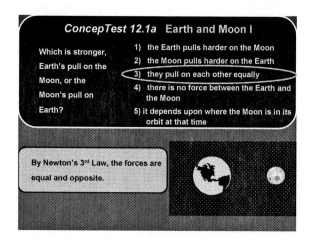

ConcepTest 12.1b: Earth and Moon II
Difficulty Level: 2
Suggested follow-up numerical problem: Problems 12.6 and 12.7
Suggested follow-up conceptual questions:
 • **What distance would increase the force by a factor of 2?**

This question examines the expression for Newton's Law of Gravitation. In particular, it is requiring students to recognize the inverse square nature of the force law.

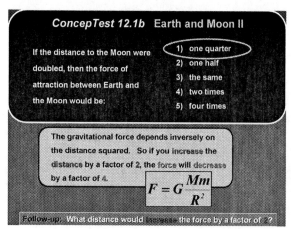

Conceptual Module 12.2
ConcepTest 12.2:   **Fly Me Away**
Difficulty Level: 3
Suggested follow-up numerical problem: **Problems 12.44 and 12.46**

Students must appreciate that the gravity they feel on the surface of Earth is simply a manifestation of the Law of Gravitation. If they were to increase their distance from the center of Earth (as in an airplane or on a mountaintop), then there would be a reduction in the effective force of gravity acting on them (*i.e.*, their weight).

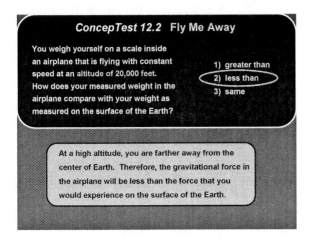

Conceptual Module 12.3
ConcepTest 12.3:   **Two Satellites**
Difficulty Level: 5
Suggested follow-up numerical problem: **Problem 12.13**

At first glance, this question may appear to be asking about something (centripetal force) that has nothing to do with gravity. However, students must recognize that the centripetal force is provided by gravity in this case (just as tension provides the centripetal force for a mass being whirled on a string). Realizing this, the answer is then a simple matter of comparing the square of the distances from the center of Earth.

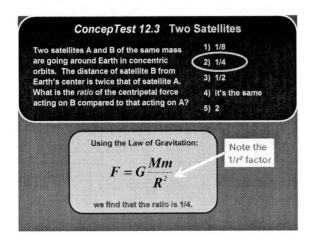

Conceptual Module 12.4
ConcepTest 12.4:   **Averting Disaster**
Difficulty Level: **4**
Suggested follow-up numerical problem: Problem 12.29
Suggested follow-up conceptual questions:
- **What happens to a satellite orbiting Earth as it slows?**

The notion of gravity as the "physical force" that provides the centripetal force for circular motion is critically important for students to appreciate. Many have probably not pondered the question of why the Moon doesn't fall into Earth, and it could be quite illuminating to realize that this is a consequence of the Moon's high orbital speed.

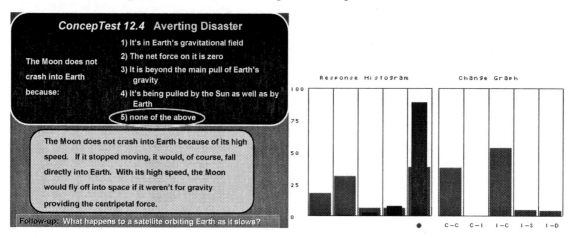

Conceptual Module 12.5
ConcepTest 12.5:   **In the Space Shuttle**
Difficulty Level: **4**
Suggested follow-up conceptual questions:
- **How weak is the value of *g* at an altitude of 300 km?**

There is a tendency to believe that astronauts float because they are not affected by gravity. In fact, this is far from the case – the value of *g* is only reduced by about 10% at an orbital height of 300 km. The "apparent" weightlessness arises due to the fact that the astronauts are in free fall.

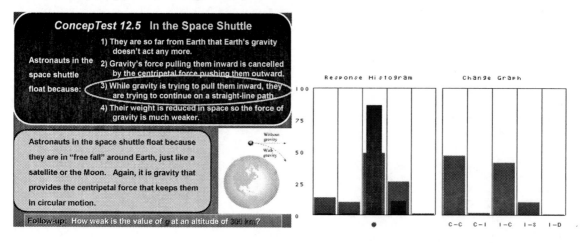

Conceptual Module 12.6
ConcepTest 12.6:   Guess My Weight
Difficulty Level: 4

This question addresses the fact that Earth is rotating and therefore all objects on the surface of Earth are in circular motion. This implies a net inwardly directed force, so when comparing the weight mg and the normal force N, the latter must be slightly less (and it is the normal force that a scale reads).

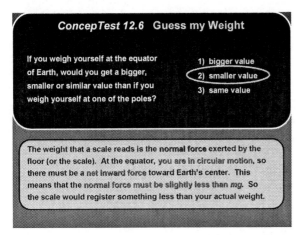

ConcepTest 12.6 Guess my Weight

If you weigh yourself at the equator of Earth, would you get a bigger, smaller or similar value than if you weigh yourself at one of the poles?

1) bigger value
2) smaller value
3) same value

The weight that a scale reads is the **normal force** exerted by the floor (or the scale). At the equator, you are in circular motion, so there must be a net inward force toward Earth's center. This means that the normal force must be slightly less than mg. So the scale would register something less than your actual weight.

Conceptual Module 12.7
ConcepTest 12.7:   Force Vectors
Difficulty Level: 3
Suggested follow-up numerical problem: Problem 12.70

This question addresses the vector nature of forces, coupled with the comprehension of the Law of Gravitation. The force vectors for the attraction to m and $2m$ must be estimated and then added vectorially to get the resultant.

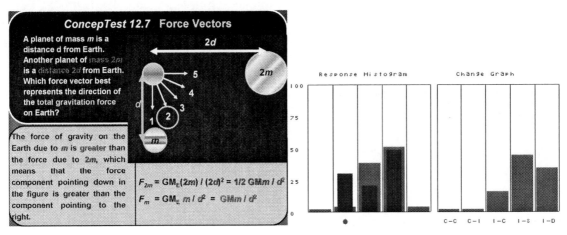

ConcepTest 12.7 Force Vectors

A planet of mass m is a distance d from Earth. Another planet of mass $2m$ is a distance $2d$ from Earth. Which force vector best represents the direction of the total gravitation force on Earth?

The force of gravity on the Earth due to m is greater than the force due to $2m$, which means that the force component pointing down in the figure is greater than the component pointing to the right.

$F_{2m} = GM_E(2m) / (2d)^2 = 1/2\ GM_Em / d^2$

$F_m = GM_E\ m / d^2 = GM_Em / d^2$

Response Histogram

Change Graph

C-C   C-I   I-C   I-S   I-D

Conceptual Module 13.1 (three parts)
ConcepTest 13.1a: Harmonic Motion I
Difficulty Level: 2
Suggested follow-up numerical problem: Problem 13.12

This question is intended to make sure students understand the meaning of a full cycle in simple harmonic motion, which is what is achieved in the time interval T. For example, a half cycle (where the mass returns to the equilibrium position for the first time) might be a common misconception for a full cycle.

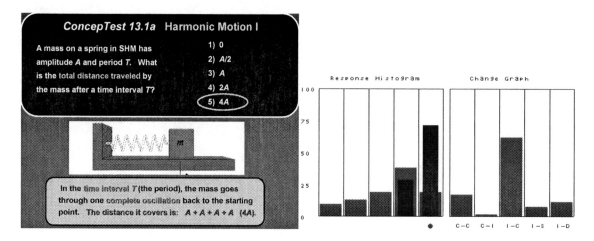

ConcepTest 13.1b: Harmonic Motion II
Difficulty Level: 2
Suggested follow-up conceptual questions:
- **What is the net displacement after a half of a period?**

This question addresses a similar issue, but is asking about the displacement (not the distance traveled). This underscores the central idea that a full cycle requires the mass to return to its original position.

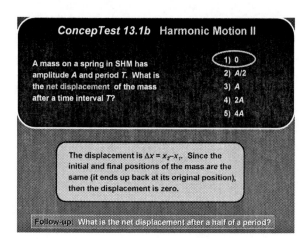

ConcepTest 13.1c: Harmonic Motion III
Difficulty Level: 3
Suggested follow-up numerical problem: Problem 13.17
Suggested follow-up conceptual questions:
- **What is the net displacement at this particular time?**

By recognizing what is meant by periodic motion and the idea of a complete cycle, the students should be able to extend what they have learned from ConcepTest 13.1a (above) to determine how long (in units of period T) it takes to cover a specific total distance.

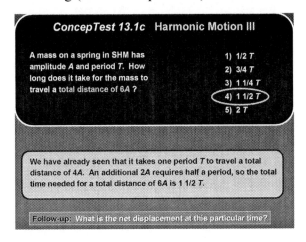

ConcepTest 13.1c Harmonic Motion III

A mass on a spring in SHM has amplitude A and period T. How long does it take for the mass to travel a total distance of $6A$?

1) 1/2 T
2) 3/4 T
3) 1 1/4 T
4) 1 1/2 T
5) 2 T

We have already seen that it takes one period T to travel a total distance of $4A$. An additional $2A$ requires half a period, so the total time needed for a total distance of $6A$ is 1 1/2 T.

Follow-up: What is the net displacement at this particular time?

Conceptual Module 13.2
ConcepTest 13.2:   Speed and Acceleration
Difficulty Level: 4
Suggested follow-up numerical problem: Problem 13.16
Suggested follow-up conceptual questions:
- **Where is acceleration a maximum?**

The students need to be familiar with the facts that the acceleration is maximum at the endpoints (where velocity is zero) and minimum at the equilibrium position (where velocity is a maximum). This question requires them to recognize these facts, such as there is no position where both acceleration and velocity are simultaneously zero.

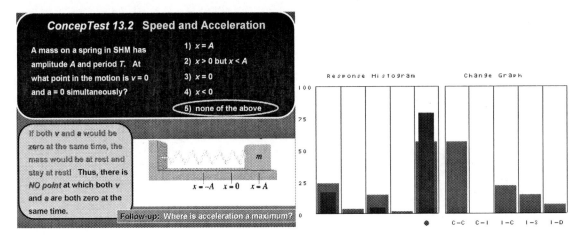

ConcepTest 13.2 Speed and Acceleration

A mass on a spring in SHM has amplitude A and period T. At what point in the motion is $v = 0$ and $a = 0$ simultaneously?

1) $x = A$
2) $x > 0$ but $x < A$
3) $x = 0$
4) $x < 0$
5) none of the above

If both v and a would be zero at the same time, the mass would be at rest and stay at rest! Thus, there is NO point at which both v and a are both zero at the same time.

$x = -A$ $x = 0$ $x = A$

Follow-up: Where is acceleration a maximum?

Response Histogram

Change Graph

Conceptual Module 13.3 (two parts)
ConcepTest 13.3a: Spring Combination I
Difficulty Level: 4
Suggested follow-up numerical problem: Problem 13.91

The idea of two springs in parallel is a more difficult concept and requires students to recognize that each spring will exert the same force at a given displacement. Thus, the forces from the two springs should add, and the total force will be the sum of the two.

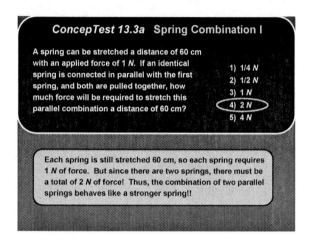

ConcepTest 13.3b: Spring Combination II
Difficulty Level: 5
Suggested follow-up numerical problem: Problems 13.34 and 13.85

The idea of two springs in series is also tricky and requires a more detailed analysis of the situation. Here each spring is only stretched half the total distance, so the force on each spring is half the original force (by Hooke's Law). However, since the springs are in series, the force exerted by the first spring is subsequently exerted on the second, so no additional force is needed beyond half the original force.

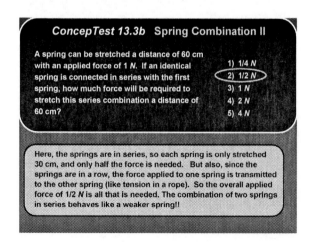

Conceptual Module 13.4

ConcepTest 13.4:   **To the Center of the Earth**
Difficulty Level: 3
Suggested follow-up numerical problem: Problem 13.47
Suggested follow-up conceptual questions:

- **Where is your acceleration zero?**

There are many examples of simple harmonic motion. This one is rather novel and is amusing to contemplate. The students should be able to reason that there will be zero force at the center (and a maximum velocity) and then a maximum force at the other end (where the person slows to a stop) – which makes this motion sound a lot like SHM.

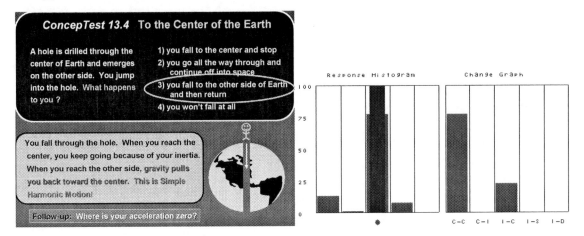

Conceptual Module 13.5 (two parts)

ConcepTest 13.5a: **Energy in SHM I**
Difficulty Level: 2
Suggested follow-up numerical problem: Problems 13.36 and 13.38
Suggested follow-up conceptual questions:

- **What happens if you double the amplitude?**

This question examines the dependence of the energy of a mass-spring system on specific variables, such as amplitude (yes) or mass (no).

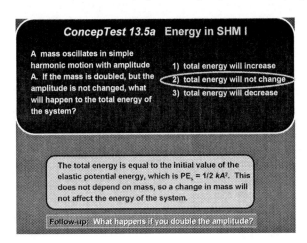

ConcepTest 13.5b: Energy in SHM II
Difficulty Level: 2
Suggested follow-up conceptual questions:
  • **Why do maximum speed and acceleration double?**

This question examines the dependence of various SHM quantities on the amplitude.   As it turns out, all but one of the listed quantities depend on mass, and the only one that depends on amplitude is the answer.

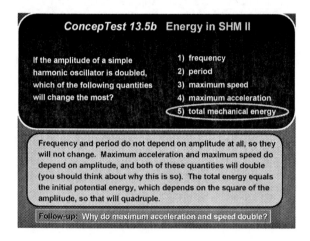

Conceptual Module 13.6 (two parts)
ConcepTest 13.6a: Period of a Spring I
Difficulty Level: 2
Suggested follow-up numerical problem: Problem 13.30
Suggested follow-up conceptual questions:
  • **What happens if the amplitude is doubled?**

This question examines the mass dependence of the period in a mass-spring system.

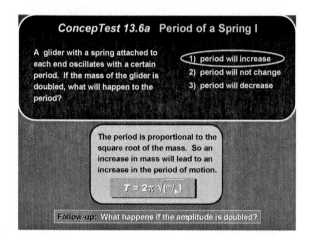

ConcepTest 13.6b: Period of a Spring II
Difficulty Level: 4

This question relates to an earlier one on parallel springs. We saw in the earlier case that the effective spring constant k increased. So in this case, the dependence of the period on the spring constant must be known in order to see the effect of the increased value of k.

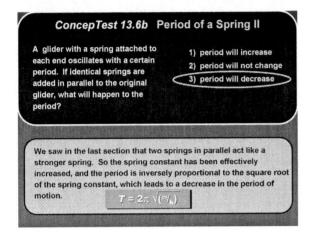

Conceptual Module 13.7 (three parts)
ConcepTest 13.7a: Spring in an Elevator I
Difficulty Level: 3

The vertical motion of the elevator could give rise to an "apparent" value of g that is different from usual. However, since g does not enter into the period for a mass-spring system, this is irrelevant and will not alter the period. However, it is worth pointing out that the constant vertical motion of the elevator will not alter the expected value of g.

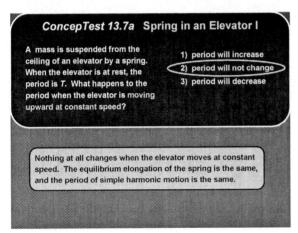

ConcepTest 13.7b: Spring in an Elevator II
Difficulty Level: 3
Suggested follow-up numerical problem:

In this case, the vertical motion of the elevator will give rise to an "apparent" value of g that is different from usual. However, since g does not enter into the period for a mass-spring system, this is irrelevant and will also not alter the period in this case.

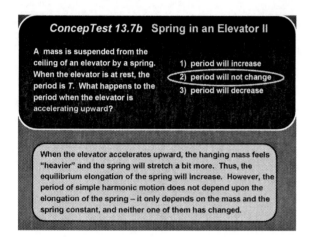

ConcepTest 13.7c: Spring on the Moon
Difficulty Level: 3
Suggested follow-up numerical problem: Problem 13.26
Suggested follow-up conceptual questions:
  • **Will the period be the same on any planet?**

In this case, the value of g is changed by going to the Moon. Again, since there is no dependence on g for the period of a mass-spring system, the period will not change.

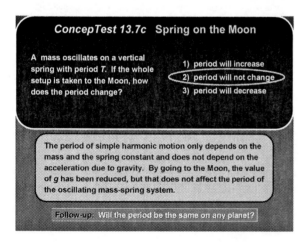

Conceptual Module 13.8 (two parts)
ConcepTest 13.8a: Period of a Pendulum I
Difficulty Level: 2
Suggested follow-up numerical problem: Problem 13.50
Suggested follow-up conceptual questions:
  - **What happens if the amplitude is doubled?**

This question addresses the dependence (or lack thereof, in this case) of the period of a pendulum on the mass of the pendulum bob.

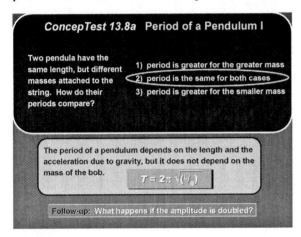

ConcepTest 13.8b: Period of a Pendulum II
Difficulty Level: 3
Suggested follow-up numerical problem: Problem 13.53

This question examines the dependence of the period of a pendulum on the length. The period scales as the square root of the length.

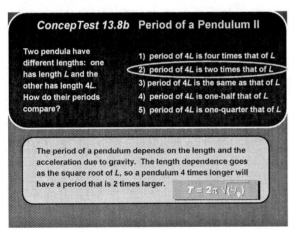

Conceptual Module 13.9
ConcepTest 13.9:   Grandfather Clock
Difficulty Level: 4
Suggested follow-up numerical problem: Problem 13.54

Since the length of a pendulum affects the period, a grandfather clock can be adjusted by changing the length of the swinging pendulum. In this question, the direction of the needed correction must be recognized, and then this must be applied to the expression for the period (in terms of length) in order to perform the appropriate length adjustment.

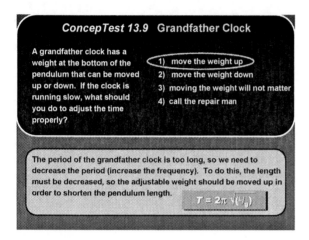

ConcepTest 13.9   Grandfather Clock

A grandfather clock has a weight at the bottom of the pendulum that can be moved up or down. If the clock is running slow, what should you do to adjust the time properly?

1) move the weight up
2) move the weight down
3) moving the weight will not matter
4) call the repair man

The period of the grandfather clock is too long, so we need to decrease the period (increase the frequency). To do this, the length must be decreased, so the adjustable weight should be moved up in order to shorten the pendulum length.

$$T = 2\pi \sqrt{\left(\tfrac{l}{g}\right)}$$

Conceptual Module 13.10 (three parts)
ConcepTest 13.10a: Pendulum in Elevator I
Difficulty Level: 3

The vertical motion of the elevator could give rise to an "apparent" value of g that is different from usual, and since the period of a pendulum does depend on g, this is entirely relevant in this case. However, the constant vertical motion of the elevator will not alter the expected value of g, so the period will not change.

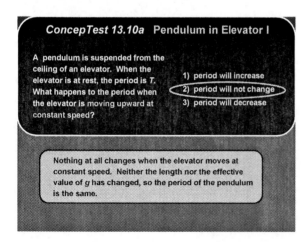

ConcepTest 13.10a   Pendulum in Elevator I

A pendulum is suspended from the ceiling of an elevator. When the elevator is at rest, the period is *T*. What happens to the period when the elevator is moving upward at constant speed?

1) period will increase
2) period will not change
3) period will decrease

Nothing at all changes when the elevator moves at constant speed. Neither the length nor the effective value of *g* has changed, so the period of the pendulum is the same.

ConcepTest 13.10b: Pendulum in Elevator II
Difficulty Level: 4

The upward acceleration of the elevator gives rise to an "apparent" value of g that is greater than usual. Since the period of a pendulum does depend on g, the period will be altered by this "increased" value of g. The sense of the effect on the period must be deduced from the expression for the pendulum period.

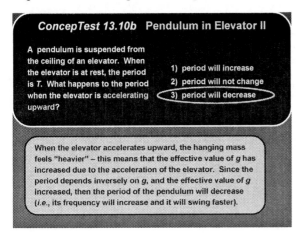

ConcepTest 13.10c: Pendulum in Elevator III
Difficulty Level: 4
Suggested follow-up numerical problem: Problem 13.87
Suggested follow-up conceptual questions:
  * **What can you do to return the pendulum to its original period?**

This is similar to the previous question, except that the value of g has been altered by going to the Moon. The only other difference is that in this case, g has decreased, while in the previous question, g was effectively increased.

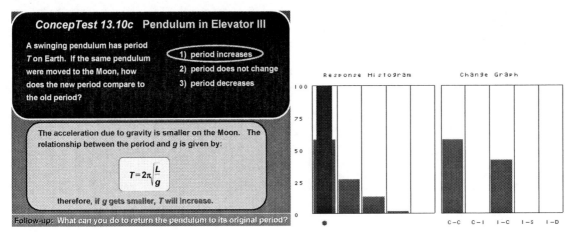

Conceptual Module 13.11
ConcepTest 13.11:   Damped Pendulum
Difficulty Level: 3
Suggested follow-up conceptual questions:
- **What is happening to the energy of the pendulum?**

The period of a pendulum does not depend on the amplitude, so even though the amplitude is diminishing in this question, the period is not affected.

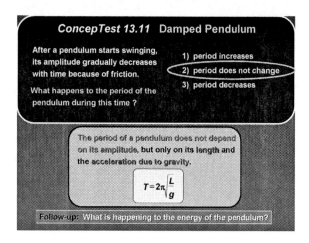

Conceptual Module 13.12
ConcepTest 13.12:   Swinging in the Rain
Difficulty Level: 3

Students must realize that when standing, you are effectively reducing the length of the pendulum constituted by you and the swing. Thus, a decrease in length will result in a subsequent decrease in period, as determined by the expression for the pendulum period.

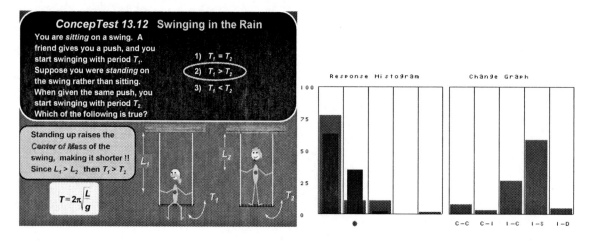

Conceptual Module 14.1
ConcepTest 14.1:   **Sound it Out**
Difficulty Level: **2**

Students may tend to think of waves mostly as transverse disturbances, and it is easy to visualize the amplitude in such cases. However, longitudinal waves are just as valid and also have an amplitude – this is a standard characteristic of any wave.

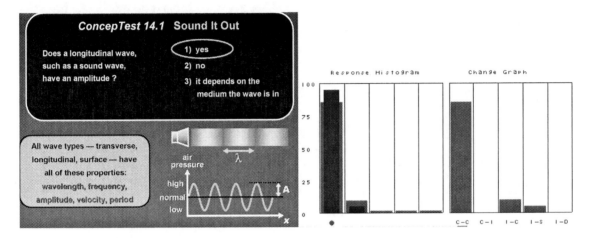

Conceptual Module 14.2
ConcepTest 14.2:   **The Wave**
Difficulty Level: **2**
Suggested follow-up conceptual questions:
- **What type of wave occurs when you toss a pebble in a pond?**

This is just another way of illustrating the nature of transverse waves. A transverse wave is characterized by a disturbance that is perpendicular to the actual direction of wave motion. In the case of the "wave" at a sporting event, the disturbance is vertical (people moving up and down) while the wave motion is horizontal.

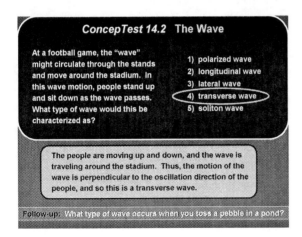

Conceptual Module 14.3 (two parts)
ConcepTest 14.3a: Wave Motion I
Difficulty Level: 4
Suggested follow-up numerical problem: Problems 14.1 and 14.2
Suggested follow-up conceptual questions:
   • **What is the acceleration of the particle at point A?**

This question examines the detailed nature of a transverse wave. Each particle on the string undergoes simple harmonic motion in the vertical direction. At the endpoints of that motion (such as point A), the particle is at rest momentarily.

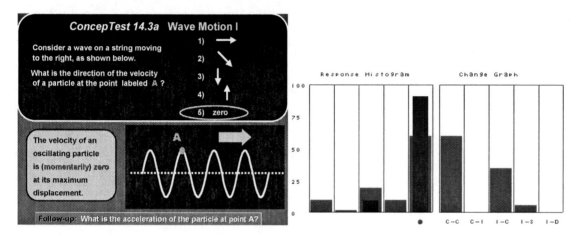

ConcepTest 14.3b: Wave Motion II
Difficulty Level: 5
Suggested follow-up numerical problem: Problem 14.14
Suggested follow-up conceptual questions:
   • **What is the acceleration of the particle at point B?**

In this case, the particle on the string (at B) is in motion, and the question is to recognize the direction of that motion. To accomplish this, the direction of wave motion must be taken into account as well.

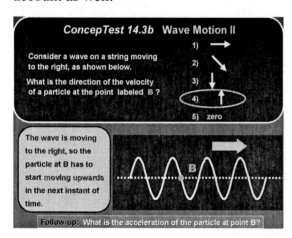

Conceptual Module 14.4
ConcepTest 14.4:   **Out to Sea**
Difficulty Level: 3
Suggested follow-up numerical problem: Problem 14.4

The question describes motion that corresponds to half a period, which the students must realize. What remains is for the students to compute the period based on the wave speed and the wavelength.

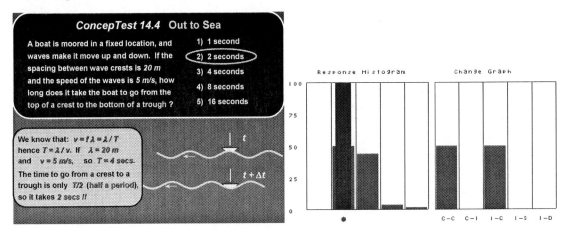

Conceptual Module 14.5
ConcepTest 14.5:   **Lunch Time**
Difficulty Level: 3
Suggested follow-up numerical problem:

This is a direct calculation of wavelength based on the wave speed and the frequency. The numbers are sufficiently simple that this can be done without a calculator. This "real life" example will reveal to the students the wavelength of standing waves in their microwave ovens (which can be tested).

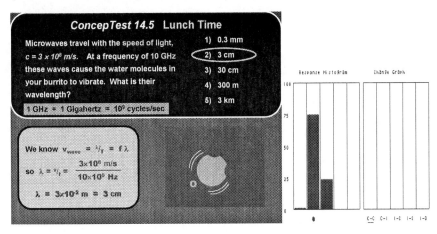

Conceptual Module 14.6 (three parts)
ConcepTest 14.6a: Wave Speed I
Difficulty Level: 2
Suggested follow-up numerical problem: Problems 14.3 and 14.68

This question examines the relationship of the wave speed to the tension. The greater the tension, the more rapidly a wave can move on the rope.

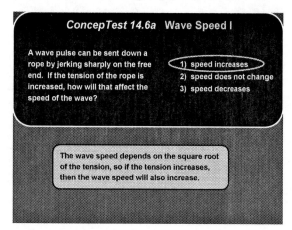

ConcepTest 14.6b: Wave Speed II
Difficulty Level: 3
Suggested follow-up numerical problem: Problem 14.6

This question examines the relationship of the wave speed to the mass density. The greater the mass density, the more slowly a wave will move on the rope.

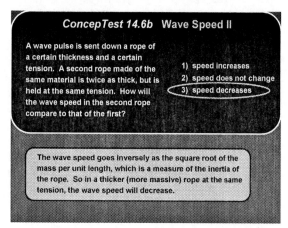

ConcepTest 14.6c: Wave Speed III
Difficulty Level: 5
Suggested follow-up numerical problem: Problem 14.8

This final question in the series also deals with the tension, but in a more realistic situation. Students must grasp a new concept, that is, that the tension in a hanging massive rope depends on the weight of rope below a given point. So the tension is increasing in the rope as the pulse rises. This increasing tension affects the wave speed as the pulse moves up.

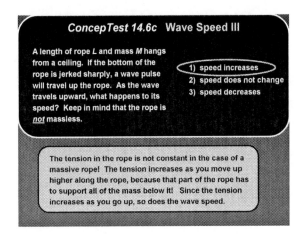

Conceptual Module 14.7 (two parts)
ConcepTest 14.7a: Sound Bite I
Difficulty Level: 2
Suggested follow-up numerical problem: Problem 14.12
Suggested follow-up conceptual questions:
 • **Does the wave speed increase or decrease in water?**

The wave speed depends entirely on the medium. The frequency, on the other hand, is determined by the actual vibrations of the source. The wavelength is a parameter that can change from one medium to another, depending upon changes in the wave speed.

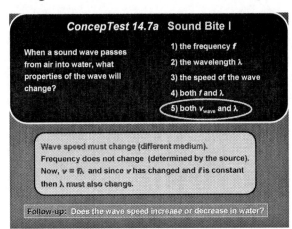

ConcepTest 14.7b: Sound Bite II
Difficulty Level: 3

This follow-up question is asking students to determine the sense of the wavelength change. By knowing how the wave speed will change, the effect on the wavelength can be deduced.

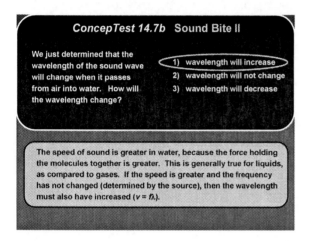

Conceptual Module 14.8 (three parts)
ConcepTest 14.8a: Speed of Sound I
Difficulty Level: 1
Suggested follow-up numerical problem: Problem 14.53

This question addresses the effect of the medium on the speed of sound. The solid medium will have the greater restoring force between particles in the medium, leading to a faster wave speed. This characteristic is akin to the tension in a rope, for the case of a transverse wave.

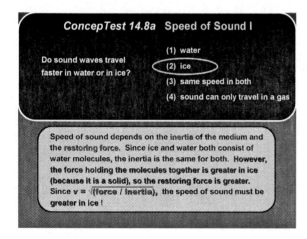

ConcepTest 14.8b: **Speed of Sound II**
Difficulty Level: **2**
Suggested follow-up numerical problem: **Problem 14.55**

The temperature dependence of the speed of sound is also related to the ease with which particles in the medium can "communicate" with each other. At higher temperatures, the air molecules are moving more quickly, so they are able to respond more rapidly to oscillations in the medium.

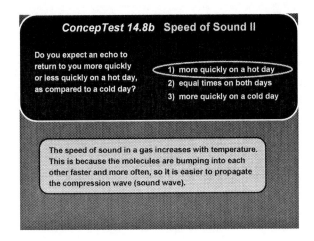

ConcepTest 14.8c: **Speed of Sound III**
Difficulty Level: **4**
Suggested follow-up numerical problem: **Problems 14.47, 14.69 and 14.75**
Suggested follow-up conceptual questions:

- **Why is the speed of sound greater in helium than in air?**

In this case, the wavelength is held fixed by the actual length of the vocal cords. The empirical observation in this problem is that the sound frequency is higher. That must therefore imply that the speed of sound is also higher, given the other conditions stated above.

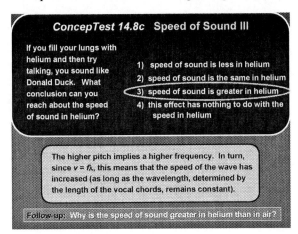

Conceptual Module 14.9
ConcepTest 14.9: **Wishing Well**
Difficulty Level: 4
Suggested follow-up numerical problem: Problem 14.46
Suggested follow-up conceptual questions:
- **How long does the sound take to travel the depth of the well?**

This is more a question of logic (or kinematics) than of sound speed. Assuming the transit time of the sound wave to be negligible compared to the fall time of the rock, the students are then simply comparing the fall times in the two cases. In the second case, the rock will cover the second half of the well much more quickly than the first half, so the time will be less than double the 1.5 seconds.

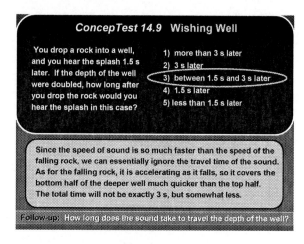

Conceptual Module 14.10 (two parts)
ConcepTest 14.10a: Sound Intensity I
Difficulty Level: 2
Suggested follow-up numerical problem: Problem 14.54
Suggested follow-up conceptual questions:
- **What distance would reduce the intensity by a factor of 100?**

This question emphasizes the inverse square relation of the intensity to the distance from the source.

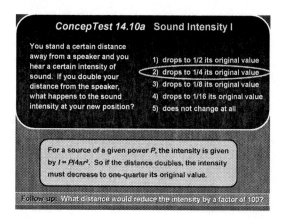

ConcepTest 14.10b: Sound Intensity II
Difficulty Level: 2

This question also relates to distance and intensity. In this case, the students must make some approximation for the square root of 10.

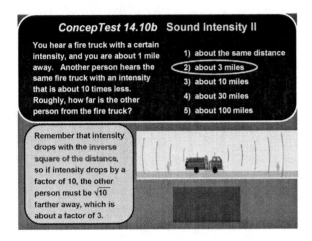

Conceptual Module 14.11 (three parts)
ConcepTest 14.11a: Decibel Level I
Difficulty Level: 4
Suggested follow-up numerical problem: Problems 14.48 and 14.49

This question deals with the addition of intensities and the relation of intensity to decibel level. While the intensities simply add, the decibel level involves a logarithm of the doubled intensity, so it will only change by a small amount.

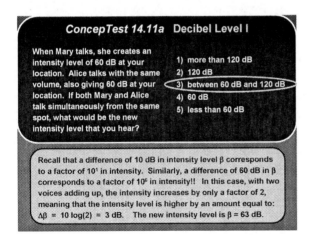

ConcepTest 14.11b: Decibel Level II
Difficulty Level: 4
Suggested follow-up numerical problem: Problems 14.51, 14.52 and 14.73
Suggested follow-up conceptual questions:
   • **What decibel level gives an intensity a million times greater?**

In this question, the decibel level is given first, and the intensity needs to be determined. This exercise emphasizes the connection between *factors of 10* in the intensity and *increments of 10* in the decibel level. This provides a guideline for students to quickly (and approximately) relate the two quantities.

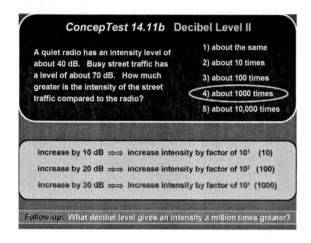

ConcepTest 14.11c: Decibel Level III
Difficulty Level: 2

This question addresses the meaning of the logarithm in the decibel level. The value of β can be zero only when $I/I_0 = 1$, which uniquely determines the value of the intensity at the point $\beta = 0$.

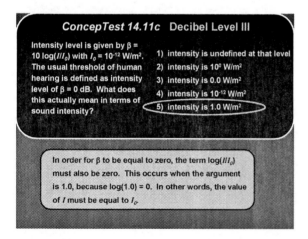

Conceptual Module 14.12 (three parts)
ConcepTest 14.12a: Pied Piper I
Difficulty Level: 2

The students must understand the relationship between the frequency (or wavelength) of a sound wave and the length of the pipe generating that sound. The longer pipe has the longer wavelength, but that must be translated into terms of frequency by the wave equation.

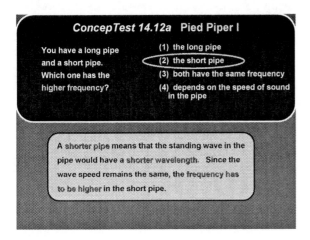

ConcepTest 14.12b: Pied Piper II
Difficulty Level: 2

This question also relates to frequency of sound and length of pipe. As described in this question, the situation can be demonstrated with a slide whistle, which allows a continuous change in length.

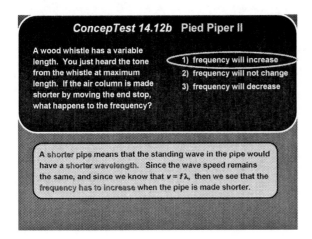

ConcepTest 14.12c: Pied Piper III
Difficulty Level: 2
Suggested follow-up conceptual questions:
 • **Why doesn't the wave speed change?**

In this case, the effective length of the pipe is changed by removing liquid from a soda bottle. Here the students must realize that the pipe is the column of air bounded by the top of the bottle and the surface of the liquid. Many students probably have some experience with this method of generating sound.

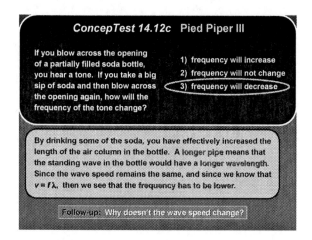

Conceptual Module 14.13
ConcepTest 14.13:   Open and Closed Pipes
Difficulty Level: 2
Suggested follow-up conceptual questions:
 • **What would you have to do to the pipe to increase the frequency?**

This question examines the comparison between an open and closed pipe of fixed length. The formation of standing waves in these pipes is central to understanding the differences between these two cases (which leads to the variations in frequency).

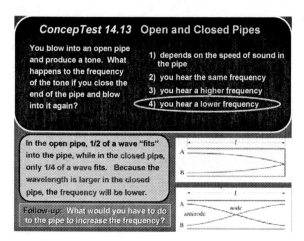

Conceptual Module 14.14
ConcepTest 14.14:   Out of Tune
Difficulty Level: 2
Suggested follow-up numerical problem: Problems 14.37, 14.40 and 14.41
Suggested follow-up conceptual questions:
- **To increase frequency, do you tighten or loosen the strings?**

This "real life" question asks students to recall the relation between frequency and wave speed, as well as the connection between wave speed and tension. Both of these relations are needed to address the issue of guitar tuning.

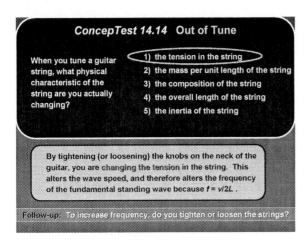

Conceptual Module 14.15 (three parts)
ConcepTest 14.15a: Doppler Effect I
Difficulty Level: 1
Suggested follow-up conceptual questions:
- **Where is the frequency lowest?**

In this question, the students must understand that higher frequencies correspond to more closely packed wavefronts (for a given wave speed). This question leads into the concept of Doppler Effect.

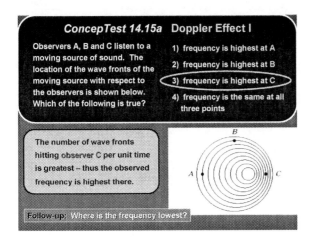

ConcepTest 14.15b: Doppler Effect II
Difficulty Level: 2
Suggested follow-up numerical problem: Problems 14.58 and 14.59

In this case, the Doppler Effect will play a role in determining the frequency due to the approaching sound source. The students should be able to relate this situation to the figure shown in the previous ConcepTest, which shows explicitly the bunching of wavefronts in front of a moving source.

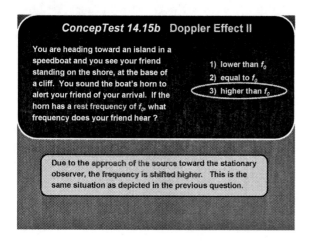

ConcepTest 14.15c: Doppler Effect III
Difficulty Level: 3
Suggested follow-up numerical problem: Problem 14.63

This question goes one step further by asking about the sound heard by an approaching observer. In this case, the source is fixed (sound bouncing off a stationary cliff) and it is the observer who is moving toward the source, which leads to another increase in frequency.

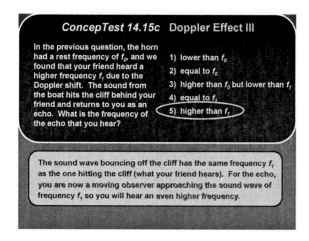

Conceptual Module 15.1
ConcepTest 15.1:   Interference
Difficulty Level: 3
Suggested follow-up numerical problem: Problems 15.22, 15.24 and 15.26
Suggested follow-up conceptual questions:

- **What if you move back by four meters?**

The concept of interference is embodied in the notion of waves being in phase or out of phase. This ConcepTest reveals this basic premise in the simple situation of two sources and an observer all located along a line.

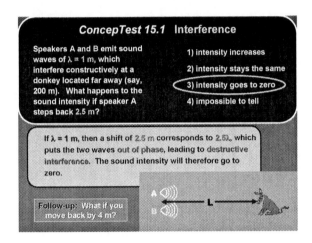

Conceptual Module 15.2 (two parts)
ConcepTest 15.2a: Standing Waves I
Difficulty Level: 4

This question relates a standing wave to the simple harmonic motion of the individual particles in the string. When the particles are at the endpoints, the velocity is zero (and the acceleration is maximum).

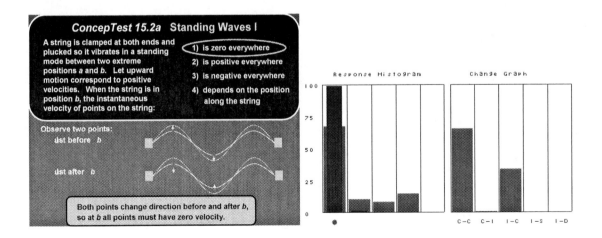

ConcepTest 15.2b: Standing Waves II
Difficulty Level: 4

In this case, the string is in the equilibrium position at all locations. That means that some particles are moving up and others are moving down, so the velocity of a particle does indeed depend upon its position along the string.

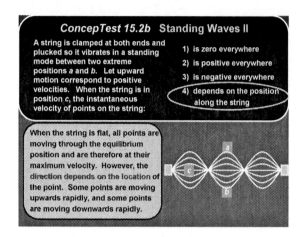

Conceptual Module 15.3
ConcepTest 15.3:   Beats
Difficulty Level: 3
Suggested follow-up numerical problem: Problems 15.16, 15.17 and 15.19

The beat frequency is the difference between the frequencies of the two interfering sounds. Students must be able to identify the trace that represents the higher beat frequency, which corresponds to the case of the largest difference between the two interfering sound waves.

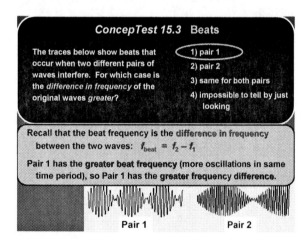

Conceptual Module 16.1
ConcepTest 16.1:   **Density**
Difficulty Level: **1**
Suggested follow-up numerical problem: **Problems 16.3 and 16.4**

Density is mass/volume and so a statement about the density does not necessarily reflect on the mass of the molecules. It could also be referring to the packing of those molecules – that is, more molecules can be packed in a given volume to achieve a higher density.

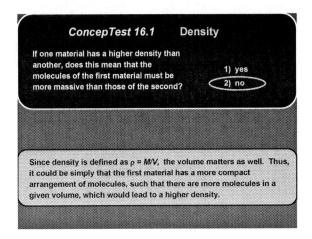

Conceptual Module 16.2
ConcepTest 16.2:   **Too Much Pressure**
Difficulty Level: **2**
Suggested follow-up numerical problem: **Problem 16.7**

Pressure is force/area, which is why, for a given force, the pin is more likely to puncture your skin than the blunt end of a pen. The force of the pin is concentrated over a smaller area, making the pressure much greater at the point of contact.

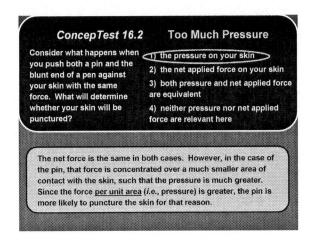

Conceptual Module 16.3
ConcepTest 16.3:   **On a frozen lake**
Difficulty Level: **2**

This question again addresses the concept of pressure. In this case, the force (your weight) is fixed, so the best thing that you can do is to spread that force over a larger area, which leads to a lower pressure on the ice at any one point.

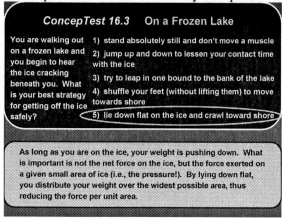

Conceptual Module 16.4
ConcepTest 16.4:   **Bubbling Up**
Difficulty Level: **3**
Suggested follow-up numerical problem: Problem 16.9

The students must recognize that the water pressure increases with depth, so as the bubble rises, the water pressure outside the bubble is diminishing. This allows the fixed volume of air in the bubble to expand. This also previews the ideal gas law, which is coming up in Chapter 17.

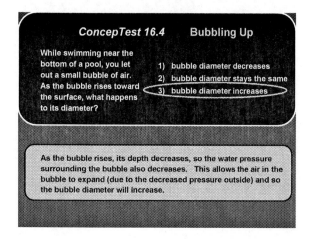

Conceptual Module 16.5
ConcepTest 16.5:   Three Containers
Difficulty Level: 1

The pressure depends only on the height of the container and not its shape. This issue also relates to the case where a variety of differently shaped vessels are connected together – the fluid level remains the same in all the vessels, regardless of their rather different shapes.

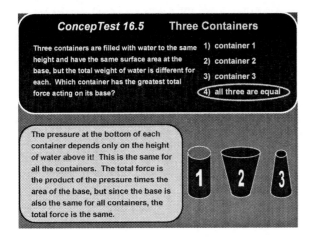

Conceptual Module 16.6
ConcepTest 16.6:   The Falling Bucket
Difficulty Level: 3

The students must recognize that when the can is in free fall, the fluid inside is "effectively weightless" and therefore cannot exert any pressure at the bottom of the can. Thus, the fluid flow will cease, due to the lack of water pressure in the can.

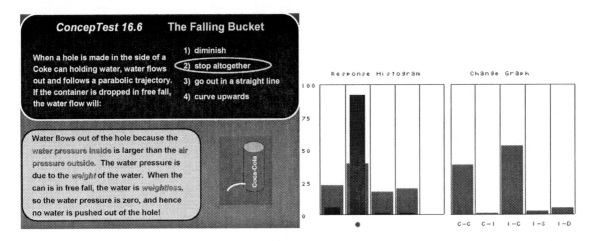

Conceptual Module 16.7 (three parts)
ConcepTest 16.7a: The Straw I
Difficulty Level: 2
Suggested follow-up conceptual questions:

* **Is it possible to sip liquid through a straw on the Moon?**

Students often think that "sucking on a straw" involves "pulling" the liquid up the straw, while in reality it is atmospheric pressure "pushing" the liquid from below. The drinker simply reduces the pressure at the top of the straw, and the atmosphere does the rest!

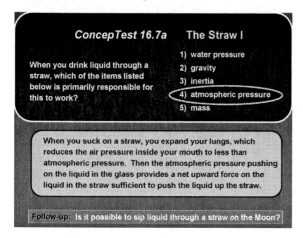

ConcepTest 16.7b: The Straw II
Difficulty Level: 4

This question examines the pressure difference at the top and bottom of a liquid inside a straw that is capped at the top. The students should be able to draw the free-body diagram of the liquid in order to realize that atmospheric pressure is counteracting both the water pressure and the pressure at the top.

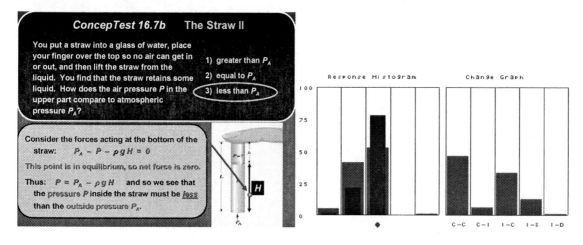

ConcepTest 16.7c: The Straw III
Difficulty Level: 3

Students often have a hard time distinguishing between force and pressure. In this question, the larger barometer does indeed require a larger force to raise the mercury column, but there is a larger area over which the atmospheric pressure can act. Thus, nothing changes, which may be a surprise to students!

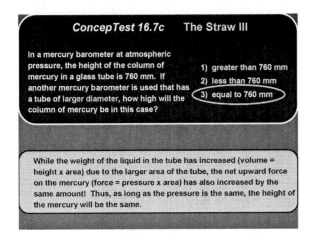

Conceptual Module 16.8
ConcepTest 16.8:   Thermometers
Difficulty Level: 2
Suggested follow-up numerical problem: Problems 16.6 and 16.12

Any liquid can serve as a barometer, but there is a practical limitation. A water barometer would require 10 m of height! In this question, this realization, coupled with the knowledge that the density of mercury is very high, leads to the practical solution of the everyday mercury barometer.

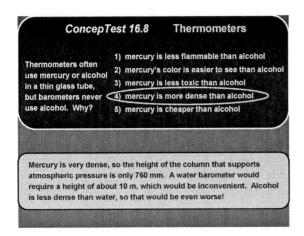

Conceptual Module 16.9
ConcepTest 16.9:   Two Bricks
Difficulty Level: 2

The notion that buoyancy is related to the volume of displaced fluid essentially derives from the pressure difference at the top and bottom of a submerged object. While it is true that brick #2 is in a region of higher overall pressure, the *pressure difference* is still the same between the top and bottom of the brick, regardless of its position in the tank! This realization helps demystify the concept of buoyancy for most students.

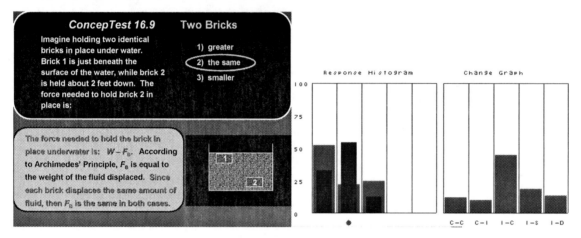

Conceptual Module 16.10 (two parts)
ConcepTest 16.10a: Cylinder and Pail I
Difficulty Level: 3

This question emphasizes Archimedes' Principle (buoyant force equals weight of displaced fluid). By submerging the aluminum cylinder, its "effective weight" is reduced, but the reduction is exactly equal to the water weight displaced, as demonstrated by pouring the displaced water back into the pail.

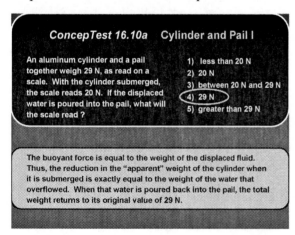

ConcepTest 16.10b: Cylinder and Pail II
Difficulty Level: 5
Suggested follow-up numerical problem: Problem 16.34

This is an interesting question involving buoyancy and Newton's Third Law. The buoyant force on the cylinder reduces its "effective weight," as described in the previous question. But this buoyant force must have a reaction force, by Newton's Third Law, and it is this reaction force that is registered by the scale reading for the water.

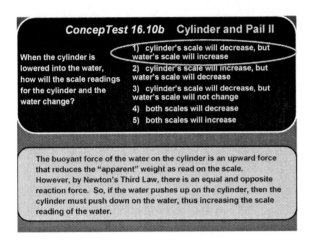

Conceptual Module 16.11
ConcepTest 16.11:   On Golden Pond
Difficulty Level: 4
Suggested follow-up numerical problem: Problem 16.25

This is actually a situation that most students have already experienced, but probably they have not given it much thought in the past. The question examines the difference between a floating object which displaces its own weight and a sinking object which displaces its own volume. For a massive object, this difference can be substantial.

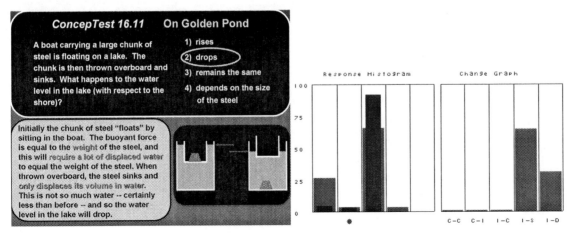

Conceptual Module 16.12 (four parts)
ConcepTest 16.12a: Archimedes I
Difficulty Level: 2
Suggested follow-up numerical problem: Problems 16.22, 16.23, 16.24 and 16.28

Students should already know that objects float in a fluid of higher density than the object. But there is a specific relation between the fraction of the object that is submerged and the density ratio. It should be intuitive, at least, that the smaller the density ratio, the less material that is actually submerged.

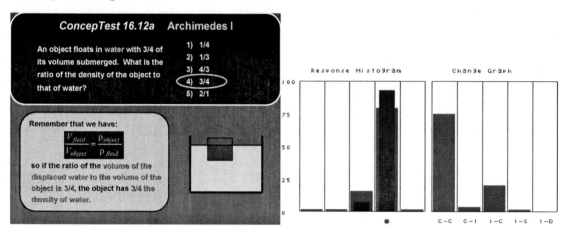

ConcepTest 16.12b: Archimedes II
Difficulty Level: 2

Using the information from the previous ConcepTest, students should realize that in this case, the object is actually denser than the fluid (oil) and will therefore sink.

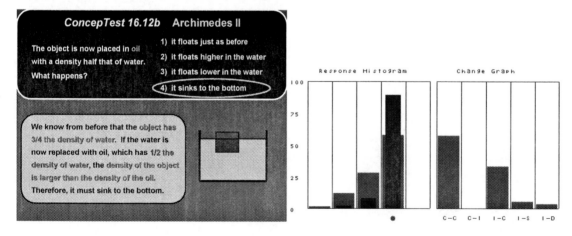

ConcepTest 16.12c: Archimedes III
Difficulty Level: 3

This question may seem rather obvious to students, since most of them will recognize that when covered with water, the block will still rise to the top and float. However, this is a setup for the following question, which leads to some surprising answers!

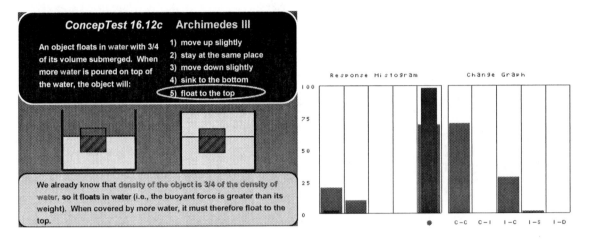

ConcepTest 16.12d: Archimedes IV
Difficulty Level: 4
Suggested follow-up numerical problem: Problem 16.33

This question is actually very similar to the previous one, but often elicits the opposite answer! Students tend to think that when the oil is on top of the block, it exerts a downward force, pushing the block lower (or having no effect). However, they fail to recognize that this logic directly contradicts their answer to the previous question (where water, which is more dense, was poured on top!).

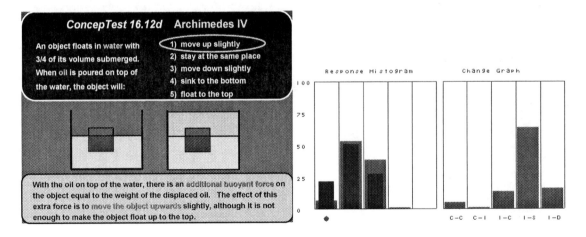

Conceptual Module 16.13 (two parts)
ConcepTest 16.13a: Helium Balloon I
Difficulty Level: 3
Suggested follow-up numerical problem: Problem 16.32

A helium balloon in helium gas will do the same thing as an air-filled balloon in air – it will sink! To determine the conditions of buoyancy, it is necessary to consider both the density of the object in question and the density of the surrounding fluid.

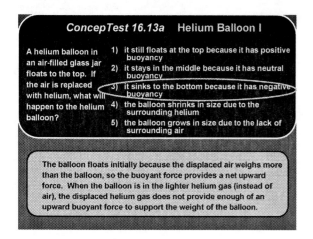

ConcepTest 16.13a   Helium Balloon I

A helium balloon in an air-filled glass jar floats to the top. If the air is replaced with helium, what will happen to the helium balloon?

1) it still floats at the top because it has positive buoyancy
2) it stays in the middle because it has neutral buoyancy
3) it sinks to the bottom because it has negative buoyancy
4) the balloon shrinks in size due to the surrounding helium
5) the balloon grows in size due to the lack of surrounding air

The balloon floats initially because the displaced air weighs more than the balloon, so the buoyant force provides a net upward force. When the balloon is in the lighter helium gas (instead of air), the displaced helium gas does not provide enough of an upward buoyant force to support the weight of the balloon.

ConcepTest 16.13b: Helium Balloon II
Difficulty Level: 4
Suggested follow-up numerical problem: Problem 16.35

Again, the relative densities of objects and fluids are being examined in this follow-up question. In this case, by lifting the jar, the bottom of the jar has an air-helium interface, on the surface of which the helium balloon will float. The helium balloon is still "lighter than air" so it will not sink into the air which is below the bottom of the jar (and the lighter helium, of course, stays in the jar!).

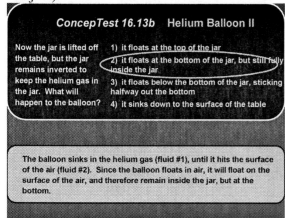

ConcepTest 16.13b   Helium Balloon II

Now the jar is lifted off the table, but the jar remains inverted to keep the helium gas in the jar. What will happen to the balloon?

1) it floats at the top of the jar
2) it floats at the bottom of the jar, but still fully inside the jar
3) it floats below the bottom of the jar, sticking halfway out the bottom
4) it sinks down to the surface of the table

The balloon sinks in the helium gas (fluid #1), until it hits the surface of the air (fluid #2). Since the balloon floats in air, it will float on the surface of the air, and therefore remain inside the jar, but at the bottom.

Conceptual Module 16.14 (two parts)
ConcepTest 16.14a: Wood in Water I
Difficulty Level: 4

This question examines the relation between buoyant force and weight of displaced fluid. By adding the wood, an amount of fluid equal to the weight of the wood is displaced (and spills out). So the overall scale reading will remain unchanged, since equal weights were simply exchanged.

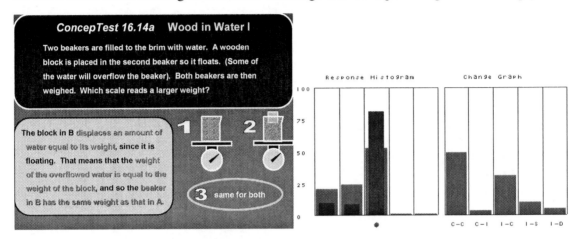

ConcepTest 16.14b: Wood in Water II
Difficulty Level: 2

This question focuses on the issue of weight. On the Moon, while both the weights of the block and the displaced water will be lower, they still will be equal, just as on Earth. So nothing has changed!

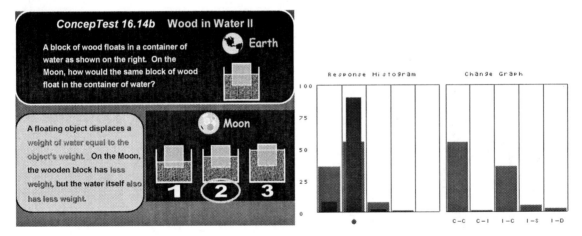

Conceptual Module 16.15 (three parts)
ConcepTest 16.15a: Fluid Flow
Difficulty Level: 3
Suggested follow-up numerical problem: Problems 16.39, 16.40 and 16.41

This question examines he continuity equation, which relates the cross-sectional area and the velocity of fluid flow. In this case, students must realize that the area will be dependent on the square of the radius of the pipe.

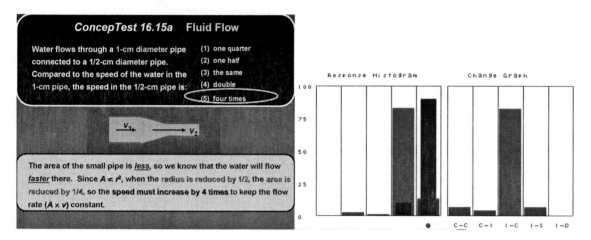

ConcepTest 16.15b: Blood Pressure I
Difficulty Level: 4
Suggested follow-up numerical problem: Problems 16.47 and 16.52

This question links the continuity equation with Bernoulli's equation. To determine the pressure (by Bernoulli), the fluid velocity must first be deduced based on the size of the pipe (by continuity).

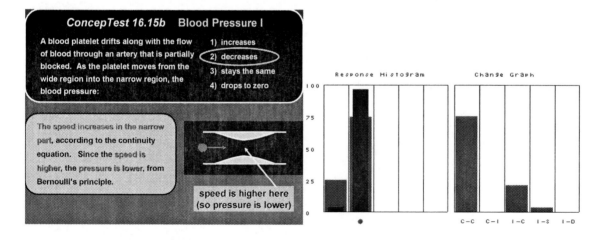

ConcepTest 16.15c: Blood Pressure II
Difficulty Level: 4
Suggested follow-up numerical problem: Problems 16.46, 16.50 and 16.53

This question examines other aspects of Bernoulli's equation, namely the dependence on gravitational potential energy. Since this relation is based on conservation of energy, both kinetic energy (assumed to be constant in this case) and gravitational PE come into play in this case.

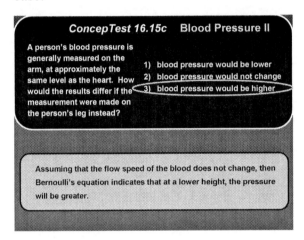

Conceptual Module 16.16
ConcepTest 16.16:   The Chimney
Difficulty Level: 3

There are many practical applications of Bernoulli's equation. This case of wind at the top of a chimney is similar to the case of an atomizer, where a rapidly flowing fluid creates a region of low pressure, which allows a fluid (or gas) to be drawn up a shaft from a region of higher pressure.

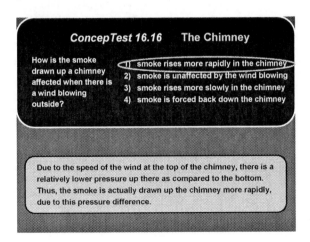

Conceptual Module 17.1
ConcepTest 17.1:   **Degrees**
Difficulty Level: 1
Suggested follow-up numerical problem: **Problems 17.6 and 17.7**

While the three principal temperature scales have different calibration points, they also have different size degree units. This question emphasizes the difference between the Fahrenheit and Celsius degrees, and the fact that Celsius and Kelvin scales only differ by an offset.

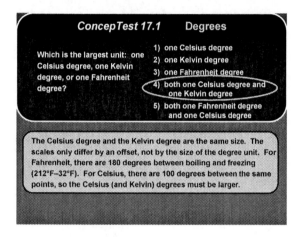

Conceptual Module 17.2
ConcepTest 17.2:   **Freezing Cold**
Difficulty Level: 2
Suggested follow-up numerical problem: **Problem 17.5**

The students should recognize that the Celsius and Kelvin scales only differ by any offset. Thus, there can never be a temperature at which the two scales give the same reading.

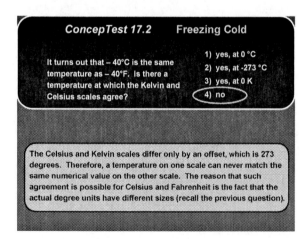

Conceptual Module 17.3
ConcepTest 17.3: **Thermometers**
Difficulty Level: 2
Suggested follow-up numerical problem: **Problems 17.22 and 17.27**
Suggested follow-up conceptual questions:
- **Is it possible to have the mercury first rise and later drop?**

This question addresses the concept of thermal expansion. While the glass, and then the mercury, expand in a certain time sequence, the fact that the thermal expansion coefficient of mercury is greater than glass means that it will expand by a greater amount for a given temperature change.

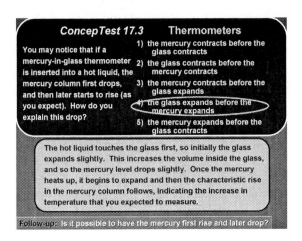

Conceptual Module 17.4
ConcepTest 17.4: **Glasses**
Difficulty Level: 2
Suggested follow-up numerical problem:

This is a "trick" that most of the students will know from practical experience in the kitchen. This question will give an indication of whether or not they understand why this "trick" works.

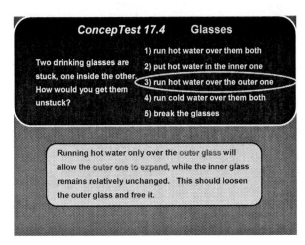

Conceptual Module 17.5 (two parts)
ConcepTest 17.5a: Steel Expansion I
Difficulty Level: 3
Suggested follow-up numerical problem: Problem 17.18

In this case, students must make the extrapolation from thermal expansion to an actual measurement. Here they must apply the expanded tape measure to a specific length in order to infer that the resulting measurements will, in fact, be too small.

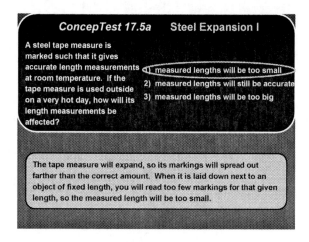

ConcepTest 17.5b: Steel Expansion II
Difficulty Level: 3
Suggested follow-up numerical problem: Problem 17.24

This is often a difficult question for students. The tendency is to believe that the metal "expands" into the hole, thus making it smaller. The analogy given, that of a circle sketched on a solid plate, generally convinces the students that the hole will, in fact, expand along with the rest of the plate.

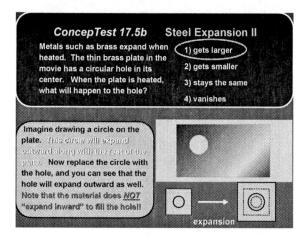

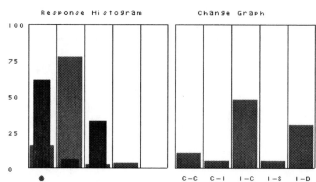

Conceptual Module 17.6 (two parts)
ConcepTest 17.6a: Steel Ring I
Difficulty Level: 4
Suggested follow-up numerical problem: Problem 17.26

In this case, the thermal expansion coefficients for different materials must be compared in order to arrive at the answer. The rod must be able to expand more than the ring (for a given temperature change) in order for the rod to touch the top of the ring, so the rod must have a higher coefficient.

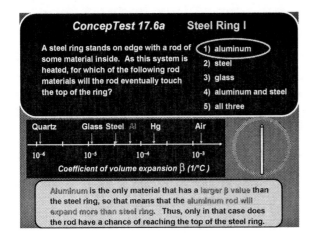

ConcepTest 17.6b: Steel Ring II
Difficulty Level: 4
Suggested follow-up numerical problem: Problem 17.25

This is the same type of comparative question. In this case, the two materials are given, and the action (heating or cooling) must be deduced. Students must realize that either the steel screws must shrink more or the aluminum parts must expand more (for a given temperature change) in order to loosen the stuck screws.

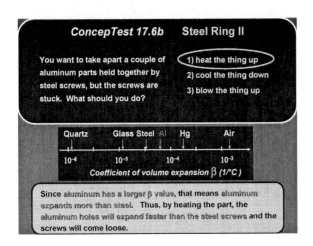

Conceptual Module 17.7
ConcepTest 17.7:   **Grandfather Clock**
Difficulty Level: **4**
Suggested follow-up numerical problem: **Problems 17.20 and 17.29**
Suggested follow-up conceptual questions:
    •   **Roughly by how much will it run slower?**

This question links thermal expansion with motion of a pendulum. Once students realize that the pendulum length will increase, the effect of this change on the period must be deduced.

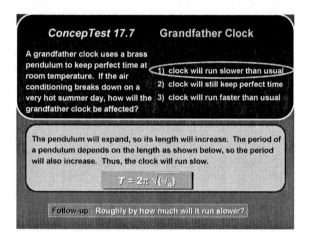

Conceptual Module 17.8 (two parts)
ConcepTest 17.8a: **Nitrogen and Oxygen I**
Difficulty Level: **1**
Suggested follow-up numerical problem: **Problems 17.34 and 17.35**

The definition of a mole is a fixed quantity of particles (Avogadro's number). This does not depend on the substance involved, so a mole of any quantity contains the same number of constituents.

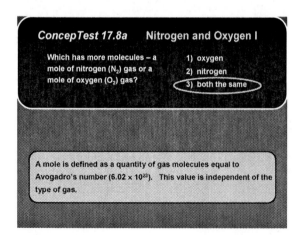

ConcepTest 17.8b: Nitrogen and Oxygen II
Difficulty Level: 2
Suggested follow-up numerical problem: Problems 17.36, 17.37 and 17.40
Suggested follow-up conceptual questions:
- **Which one will take up more space?**

This follow-up question now examines the mass of a mole of a gas. Since the number of particles is the same for each gas, the mass of the gas depends entirely on the masses of the individual molecules, which is larger for oxygen.

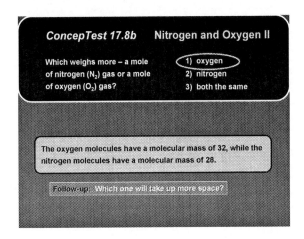

Conceptual Module 17.9 (three parts)
ConcepTest 17.9a: Ideal Gas Law I
Difficulty Level: 3
Suggested follow-up numerical problem: Problem 17.45

This question examines the ideal gas law. Students must learn to manipulate the parameters of the ideal gas law to simplify their problem-solving methods. In this case, the volume and temperature are held fixed, leaving a direct comparison between pressure (P) and moles (n) of gas.

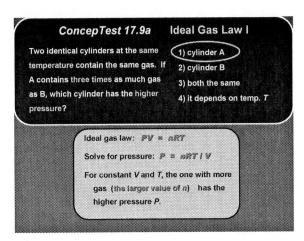

ConcepTest 17.9b: Ideal Gas Law II
Difficulty Level: 3
Suggested follow-up numerical problem: Problem 17.60

This is the same type of question for the ideal gas law, except that in this case, the volume and temperature are held fixed, leaving a direct comparison between temperature (T) and moles (n) of gas.

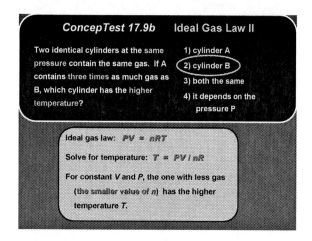

ConcepTest 17.9c: Ideal Gas Law III
Difficulty Level: 4
Suggested follow-up numerical problem: Problems 17.55 and 17.87

This is a slightly more complicated application of the ideal gas law, but it still follows the same logic. In this case, the question is quantitative and students must keep track of the volume and the number of moles of gas in order to deduce the pressure change.

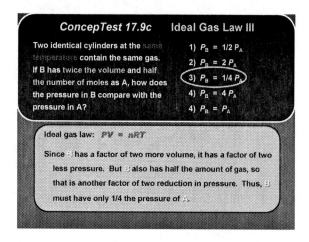

Conceptual Module 17.10
ConcepTest 17.10:   Soda Bottle
Difficulty Level: 3
Suggested follow-up numerical problem: Problem 17.42

This "real life" example has probably happened to many of the students. Here again, while they may have noticed a partially crushed plastic bottle in the refrigerator, they may not have given much thought to what might have caused this effect.

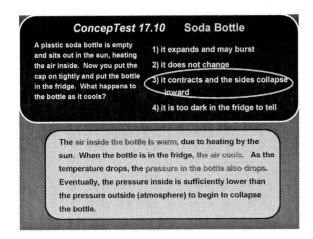

Conceptual Module 17.11
ConcepTest 17.11:   Balloon in Freezer
Difficulty Level: 3
Suggested follow-up numerical problem: Problem 17.88
Suggested follow-up conceptual questions:
- **What happens to the volume as the balloon rises in the air?**

This is the same type of question as the previous one. Using the ideal gas law, the students should deduce that the volume will decrease as the temperature decreases (at constant pressure).

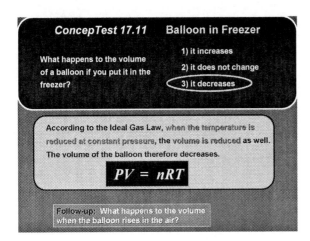

Conceptual Module 18.1 (two parts)
ConcepTest 18.1a: **Thermal Contact I**
Difficulty Level: **2**
Suggested follow-up numerical problem: Problem 18.6

The temperature change ΔT of each object as the combined system approaches thermal equilibrium will depend upon the mass m of the objects and their specific heats c. Since they are composed of the same material, only the masses matter in this case, and the less massive object will have the greater temperature change (based on $\Delta Q = m\, c\, \Delta T$).

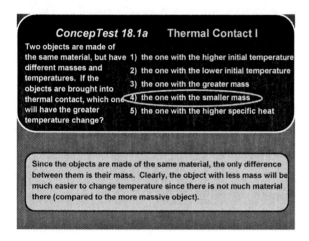

ConcepTest 18.2a: **Thermal Contact II**
Difficulty Level: **1**

As seen from the relationship $\Delta Q = m\, c\, \Delta T$, the temperature change depends on the mass and specific heat of an object, but it does *not* depend upon the initial temperature. The same amount of heat added to an object at 20°C or 80°C will still result in the same temperature change.

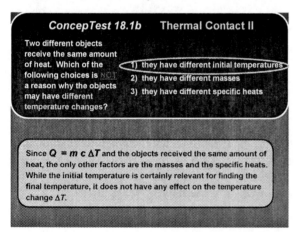

Conceptual Module 18.2
ConcepTest 18.2:   **Two Liquids**
Difficulty Level: 2

Based on the equal times of heating, students must infer that the same amount of heat was added to each liquid. Since the liquids have the same mass, the only variable in the problem is the specific heat. We can think of specific heat as a "thermal inertia" — the liquid with the higher specific heat will have a harder time changing temperature and will therefore have a lower ΔT.

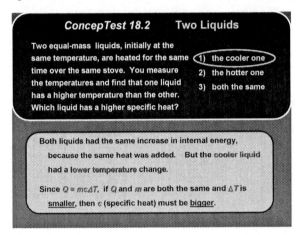

Conceptual Module 18.3 (two parts)
ConcepTest 18.3a: **Night on the Field**
Difficulty Level: 2

This again refers to specific heat and the fact that it is a type of "thermal inertia." The material with the lower specific heat (less "thermal inertia") will cool more rapidly; in this case, the soil.

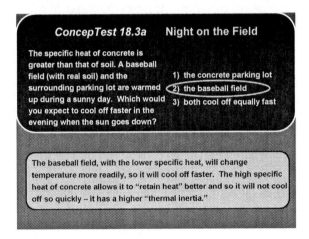

ConcepTest 18.3b: Night on the Beach
Difficulty Level: 4

This follow-up question introduces the concept of convection. The notion of specific heat dictates which material gets hotter during the day or cooler at night. The flow of air then must be considered (keeping in mind that hot air rises) in order to deduce the direction of the convection currents during the day or the night.

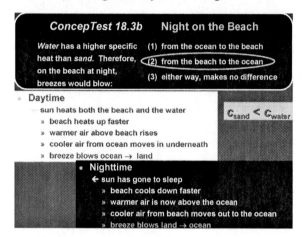

Conceptual Module 18.4
ConcepTest 18.4:   Calorimetry
Difficulty Level: 3

Calorimetry is based on the concept of energy conservation (heat loss = heat gain). In this case, with the two materials being the same, the temperature change of each will depend entirely upon the masses. Since equal masses would result in an equilibrium temperature right in the middle (50°C), the students must realize that the larger mass will have the smaller ΔT, so the final temperature must be closer to (but not equal to) the initial temperature of the larger mass.

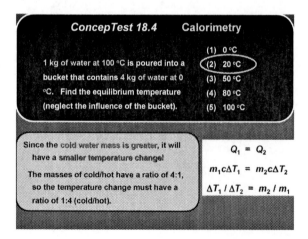

Conceptual Module 18.5
ConcepTest 18.5:   More calorimetry
Difficulty Level: 3
Suggested follow-up numerical problem: Problems 18.9 and 18.10

In this case, it is not the materials that are the same, but, rather, the masses. So the ΔT will depend on the different specific heats. The water has the higher specific heat, which means that it is more difficult to change its temperature. Therefore the final temperature will be closer to that of the water.

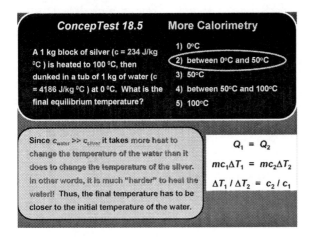

ConcepTest 18.5   **More Calorimetry**

A 1 kg block of silver ($c = 234$ J/kg $^{\circ}$C) is heated to 100 $^{\circ}$C, then dunked in a tub of 1 kg of water ($c = 4186$ J/kg $^{\circ}$C) at 0 $^{\circ}$C. What is the final equilibrium temperature?

1) 0°C
2) between 0°C and 50°C
3) 50°C
4) between 50°C and 100°C
5) 100°C

Since $c_{water} >> c_{silver}$ it takes more heat to change the temperature of the water than it does to change the temperature of the silver. In other words, it is much "harder" to heat the water! Thus, the final temperature has to be closer to the initial temperature of the water.

$$Q_1 = Q_2$$
$$mc_1 \Delta T_1 = mc_2 \Delta T_2$$
$$\Delta T_1 / \Delta T_2 = c_2 / c_1$$

Conceptual Module 18.6
ConcepTest 18.6:   Adding Heat
Difficulty Level: 1
Suggested follow-up conceptual questions:
- **Does that depend on the substance?**

This may be regarded as a "trick" question, but it is certainly representative of an important physical process. The notion of a phase change is specifically related to changing the "binding" of a substance and not changing the kinetic energy (related to temperature) of its constituent particles. This is a crucial distinction for students to make in order to fully understand what a phase change is.

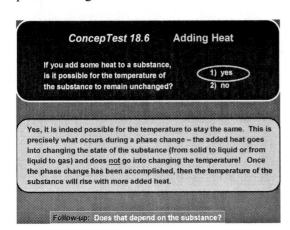

ConcepTest 18.6   **Adding Heat**

If you add some heat to a substance, is it possible for the temperature of the substance to remain unchanged?

1) yes
2) no

Yes, it is indeed possible for the temperature to stay the same. This is precisely what occurs during a phase change – the added heat goes into changing the state of the substance (from solid to liquid or from liquid to gas) and does <u>not</u> go into changing the temperature! Once the phase change has been accomplished, then the temperature of the substance will rise with more added heat.

Follow-up: Does that depend on the substance?

Conceptual Module 18.7
ConcepTest 18.7:   **Hot Potato**
Difficulty Level: **2**
Suggested follow-up conceptual questions:
- **How can you cook the potatoes faster?**

This question (again) relates to phase changes. When the water is boiling, a phase change is taking place, so the temperature of the water is *not increasing* as heat is added. Adding more heat will only make the phase change occur more rapidly (*i.e.*, faster boiling), but will still not alter the temperature of the water as long as the phase change is taking place. Thus, the potatoes will *not* cook faster.

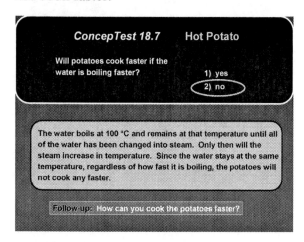

Conceptual Module 18.8
ConcepTest 18.8:   **Water and Ice**
Difficulty Level: **3**
Suggested follow-up numerical problem: Problems 18.7 and 18.95
Suggested follow-up conceptual questions:
- **How much more water at 50°C water would you need?**

Both temperature changes and phase changes must be taken into account here. The heat released by the 50°C water as it cools down to 0°C goes into melting the ice (which does not completely melt.)

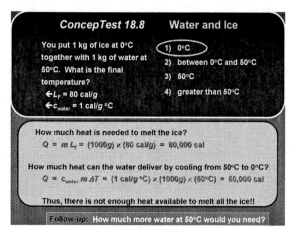

Conceptual Module 18.9

ConcepTest 18.9:   Ice and Steam
Difficulty Level: 4
Suggested follow-up numerical problem: Problem 18.96
Suggested follow-up conceptual questions:

- **How much more ice would you need?**

This follow-up question is similar to the previous one in the sense that temperature changes and phase changes need to be considered. In this case, due to the very high value of the heat of vaporization of water (540 cal/g), there is actually more than enough steam to not only melt all of the ice, but also to raise the temperature of the melted ice (0°C water) up to 100°C, and still have steam to spare!

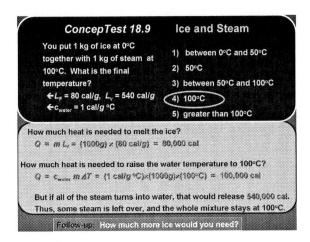

Conceptual Module 18.10

ConcepTest 18.10:   You're in Hot Water!
Difficulty Level: 2

At first glance, the fact that both the water and the steam are at the same temperature suggests that they will both burn equally. However, the key point here is that when the steam condenses into water, it releases the heat of vaporization, which is a very large quantity of heat. So, bearing that in mind, the steam is therefore much more likely to cause severe burns than the hot water.

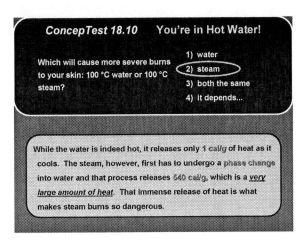

Conceptual Module 18.11
ConcepTest 18.11: **Spring Break**
Difficulty Level: **2**

Evaporation is essentially a cooling process, which is why we sweat. In order to vaporize the water on your skin, the heat of vaporization must be absorbed from your body, which is why you tend to cool off. This evaporation is much more likely to take place in a dry climate (like Phoenix) where the air is not already saturated with moisture. So you will tend to feel cooler in the drier environment, where a more effective evaporation process can take place.

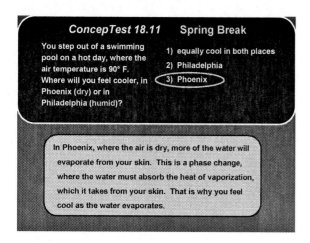

Conceptual Module 18.12
ConcepTest 18.12: **Heat Conduction**
Difficulty Level: **2**
Suggested follow-up numerical problem: Problem 18.15

The higher the thermal conductivity of a surface, the faster it can draw (conduct) heat away from your body. The metal surface will always feel cooler (compared to bare concrete or a rug); this is a direct result of its higher thermal conductivity.

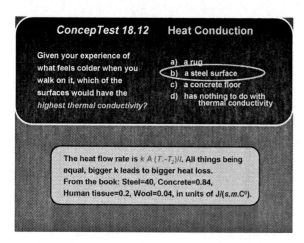

Conceptual Module 18.13
ConcepTest 18.13:   Radiation
Difficulty Level: 3
Suggested follow-up numerical problem: Problems 17.71 and 17.72

This is a direct application of the Stefan-Boltzmann Law. According to that relationship, the radiated energy depends on T^4, so if the temperature drops by a factor of 2, the energy will correspondingly drop by a factor of 16.

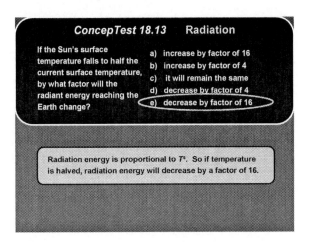

Conceptual Module 20.1
ConcepTest 20.1:   Free Expansion
Difficulty Level: 2

This question examines the First Law of Thermodynamics. In this case, with no work done and no heat added, the total energy of the system must remain constant (this is essentially a restatement of conservation of energy). Thus, if the energy of the system does not change, the temperature will not change.

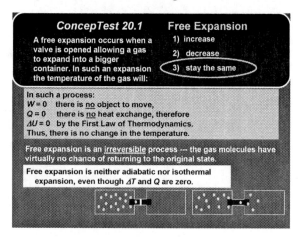

Conceptual Module 20.2
ConcepTest 20.2:   Work
Difficulty Level: 2

This question is designed to familiarize students with a P-V diagram. The area under the P-V curve represents the work done by a gas. Since the top curve (expansion at high pressure) corresponds to positive work and the lower curve (compression at low pressure) corresponds to negative work, it is clear that the net work is positive.

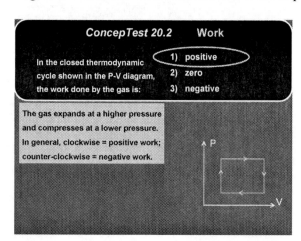

Conceptual Module 20.3

ConcepTest 20.3: **Heat Engine**
Difficulty Level: 3
Suggested follow-up numerical problem: Problems 20.7, 20.8 and 20.9
Suggested follow-up conceptual questions:
- **What would you need to change to make it a Carnot engine?**

Students must get a sense of idealized and real processes and understand the efficiency that pertains to each. The Carnot efficiency denotes an ideal efficiency corresponding to a reversible process. In this case, the actual efficiency is less than the Carnot efficiency, so this situation describes a real process, which is by definition irreversible.

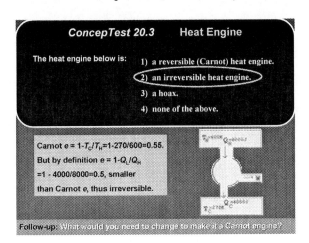

Conceptual Module 21.1 (two parts)
ConcepTest 21.1a: **Electric Charge I**
Difficulty Level: 1
Suggested follow-up numerical problem: Problems 21.10 and 21.29
Suggested follow-up conceptual questions:
- **What does the picture look like if the two balls are oppositely charged?**
- **What about if both balls are neutral?**

The repulsion of the two charged balls indicates only that they have the same type of charge, but it is impossible to distinguish between two positive or two negative balls. Either case will result in a repulsion as shown in the figure.

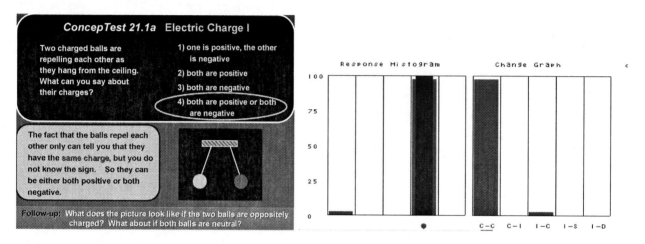

ConcepTest 21.1b: **Electric Charge II**
Difficulty Level: 2
Suggested follow-up numerical problem: Problems 21.7 and 21.8

This is an exercise in logic, as it pertains to like and unlike charges. Students must deduce from the first figure that the green and pink balls have the same charge and from the second figure that the green and yellow balls also have the same charge. These deductions should lead them to the final conclusion that all the balls have the same charge.

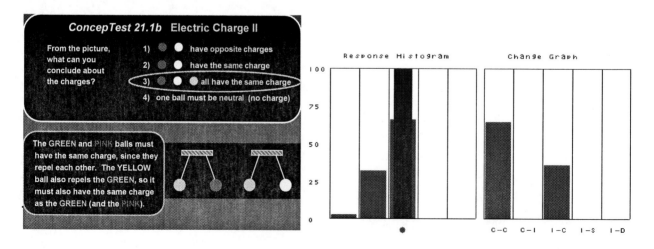

Conceptual Module 21.2 (two parts)

ConcepTest 21.2a: Conductors I
Difficulty Level: 2
Suggested follow-up conceptual questions:

- **What happens if the metal ball is replaced by a plastic ball?**

This question addresses the concept of induction. Students must realize that the metal ball need not be charged in order to be attracted to the charged rod. The separation of mobile charges (induction) in the metal conductor will also give rise to a net attraction between the two objects.

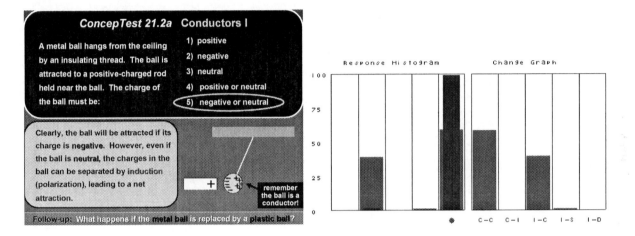

ConcepTest 21.2b: Conductors II
Difficulty Level: 2
Suggested follow-up numerical problem: Problem 21.4
Suggested follow-up conceptual questions:

- **What will happen when the conductors are reconnected with a wire?**

This question also relates to induction. The separation of charges that is achieved when the conducting balls are linked together can be "locked" in place by cutting the connection between the balls. The students must understand that the near ball will have an opposite charge to the rod, since these charges are attracted when the rod is brought close.

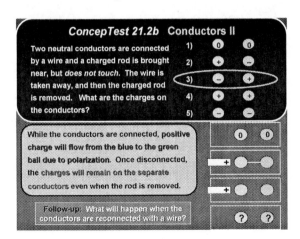

Conceptual Module 21.3 (three parts)
ConcepTest 21.3a: Coulomb's Law I
Difficulty Level: 2
Suggested follow-up numerical problem: Problems 21.18 and 21.19

This question is intended to begin familiarizing students with Coulomb's Law, which is symmetric in the two charges that are interacting. The answer to this question can also be deduced from Newton's Third Law, since the forces must be equal and opposite.

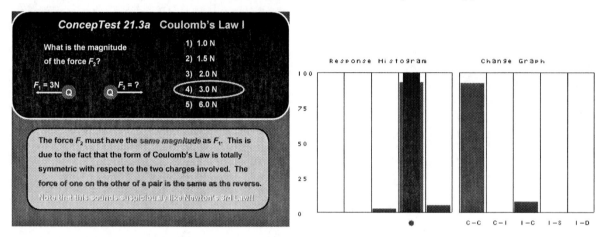

ConcepTest 21.3b: Coulomb's Law II
Difficulty Level: 3
Suggested follow-up numerical problem: Problems 21.20 and 21.21
Suggested follow-up conceptual questions:
- **Now what is the magnitude of F_2?**

Continuing with Coulomb's Law, the students should be able to determine the new force on the charges when one of them is increased. The force simply scales as the product of the charges, so changing one charge by a certain factor will change the force by that same factor.

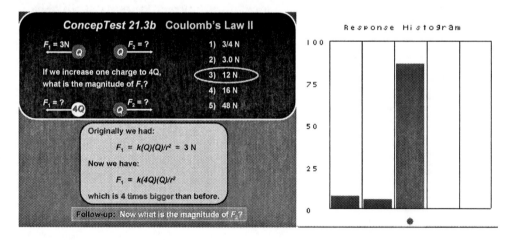

ConcepTest 21.3c: Coulomb's Law III
Difficulty Level: 3
Suggested follow-up numerical problem: Problems 21.26 and 21.64
Suggested follow-up conceptual questions:
   • **What is the force if the original distance is halved?**

This question examines the distance dependence of Coulomb's Law. Using the inverse square law, an increase in distance by a factor of 3 will lead to a decrease in force by a factor of 9.

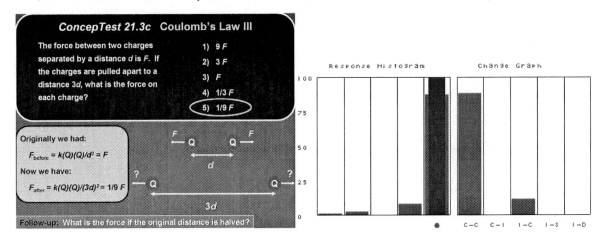

Conceptual Module 21.4 (three parts)
ConcepTest 21.4a: Electric Force I
Difficulty Level: 3
Suggested follow-up conceptual questions:
   • **What happens if both charges are +Q? Where would the $F = 0$ point be in this case?**

Superposition of electric fields and forces is a common difficulty for students. This question requires the students to consider the vector addition of two forces for a "virtual" charge that can be either positive or negative. In the end, it does not matter, but this is a realization that the students need to make for themselves. In essence, they are actually finding the point where the net electric field is zero.

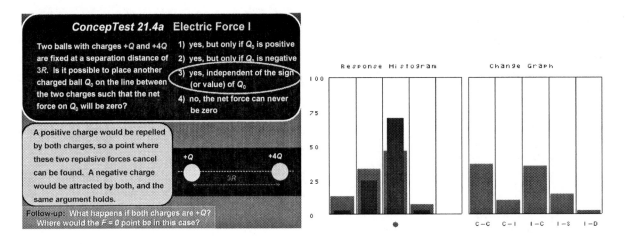

ConcepTest 21.4b: Electric Force II
Difficulty Level: 4
Suggested follow-up numerical problem: Problems 21.34 and 21.38

This follow-up question asks students to address the previous case quantitatively. Now they have to determine the actual position where the net force is zero, taking into account the relative sizes and positions of the two charges. Students should easily be able to see that the point must be closer to the smaller charge, but then it is a matter of evaluating the specific position.

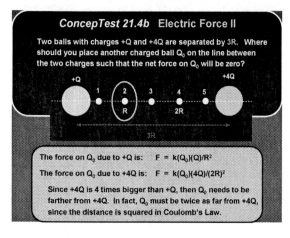

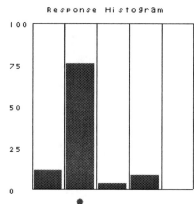

ConcepTest 21.4c: Electric Force III
Difficulty Level: 3
Suggested follow-up numerical problem: Problem 21.35
Suggested follow-up conceptual questions:
- **What happens if one charge is +Q and the other is –Q?**

This examines an alternate case to that of ConcepTest 21.4a where the charges now have opposite signs. This means that the position of zero force cannot be in between the charges and in fact must be off to one side or the other. Again, this question previews the upcoming introduction of electric field.

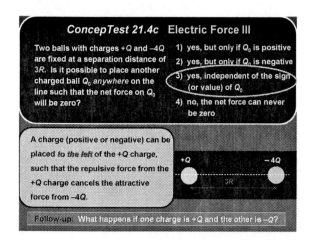

Conceptual Module 21.5 (three parts)
ConcepTest 21.5a: Proton and Electron I
Difficulty Level: 2
Suggested follow-up conceptual questions:
- **Which particle feels the larger force at any one moment?**

This is a question relating to the distance dependence of Coulomb's Law. Due to the inverse square law, as the separation between the charges decreases, the force between them will increase. While this result may seem obvious, students do not often have the experience of a non-constant force acting.

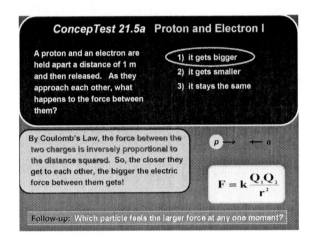

ConcepTest 21.5b: Proton and Electron II
Difficulty Level: 3
Suggested follow-up numerical problem: Problem 21.28

This is a reminder of earlier work with Newton's Second Law. At any one moment, the force on each particle is the same, but the one with the smaller mass will have the larger acceleration ($F = ma$).

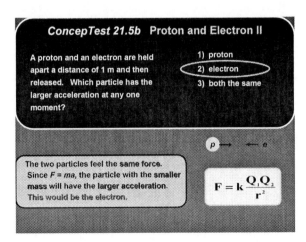

ConcepTest 21.5c: Proton and Electron III
Difficulty Level: 3
Suggested follow-up conceptual questions:
- **Which particle will be moving faster when they meet?**

For this final question, the students must utilize their answer for acceleration in the previous question to recognize that if the electron accelerates faster, it will cover more distance more rapidly, and so the two particles will meet much closer to the original proton position (and *not* in the middle!).

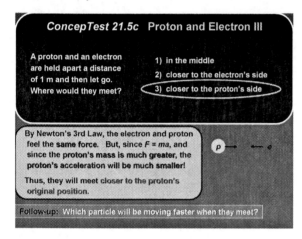

Conceptual Module 21.6
ConcepTest 21.6:   Forces in 2D
Difficulty Level: 4
Suggested follow-up numerical problem: Problems 21.40, 21.41 and 21.43
Suggested follow-up conceptual questions:
- **What happens if the yellow charge would be +3Q?**

This is a problem relating to Coulomb's Law in two dimensions. Here the students have to perform a vector addition with two forces that they must first determine from Coulomb's Law. In this case, the distances are the same, so the variation in the two forces is related to the magnitude of the charges.

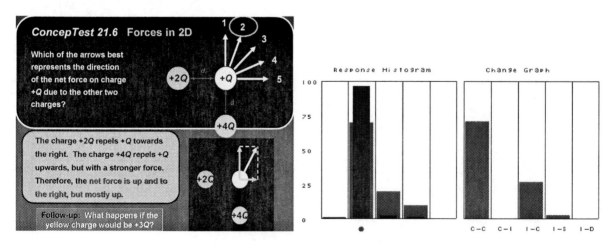

Conceptual Module 22.1
ConcepTest 22.1: **Electric Field**
Difficulty Level: 3
Suggested follow-up numerical problem: Problems 22.1 and 22.3
Suggested follow-up conceptual questions:
- **If your distance is doubled, what must you do to the charge to maintain the same E field at your new position?**

This question examines the expression for electric field strength in terms of the charge and distance. Related to Coulomb's Law, this also involves an inverse square law for the distance, which must be taken into account in this problem to obtain the correct answer.

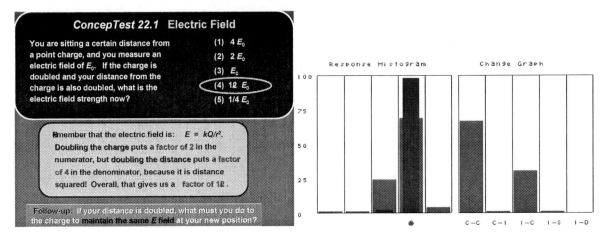

Conceptual Module 22.2 (two parts)
ConcepTest 22.2a: **Field and Force I**
Difficulty Level: 2

Students have tremendous difficulty understanding that there can be an electric field at an empty point in space. There is a tendency to think that a charge must be at the field location. To emphasize that the electric field only has to do with the source charge, this question places two different charges (which are irrelevant) at the field location and asks for the electric field in both cases.

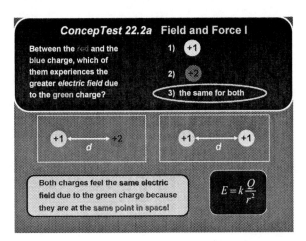

ConcepTest 22.2b: Field and Force II
Difficulty Level: 3
Suggested follow-up numerical problem: Problem 22.6

Following on the previous question, this one now asks for the force. In this case, the charge located at the field position is relevant ($F = qE$). So while the field is the same at the position of the red or blue charges, the force on those charges is different, depending on the value of those charges. This series of questions is intended to clarify the difference between electric field and electric force.

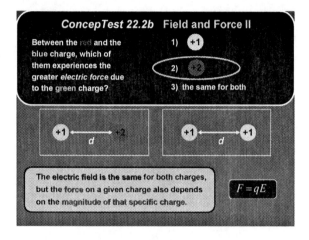

Conceptual Module 22.3 (three parts)
ConcepTest 22.3a: Superposition I
Difficulty Level: 4
Suggested follow-up numerical problem: Problems 22.7 and 22.8
Suggested follow-up conceptual questions:
  • **What if the lower charge was +2C?**
  • **What if both charges were +2C?**

This question examines the superposition of electric field vectors for the simple case of two point charges. Students must recognize that the field points toward the negative charges and that the superposition in this symmetric case leads to a net leftward force.

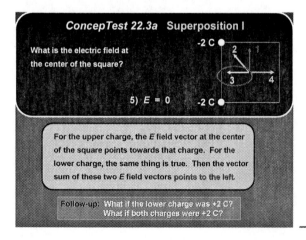

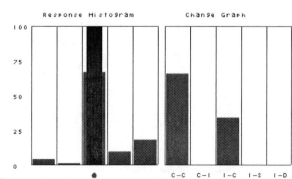

ConcepTest 22.3b: Superposition II
Difficulty Level: 4
Suggested follow-up numerical problem: Problem 22.2 and 22.4
Suggested follow-up conceptual questions:
- **What if the upper two charges were +2C?**
- **What if the right-hand charges were +2C?**

In this case, the superposition involves four charges. Still, the situation is symmetric, and so in this case, the net electric field is zero at the center. In fact, the sign of the charges will not matter, as long as they are all the same sign.

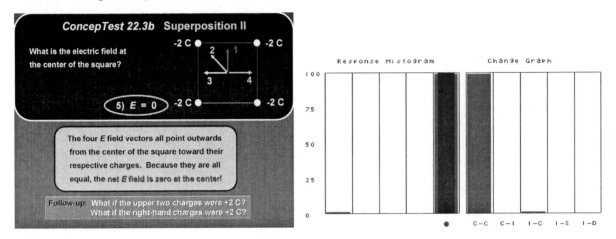

ConcepTest 22.3c: Superposition III
Difficulty Level: 4
Suggested follow-up numerical problem: Problem 22.5
Suggested follow-up conceptual questions:
- **What if all three charges reversed their signs?**

This last question involves a case of superposition that is not so symmetric. The effect of the two closer positive charges compared to the more distant single negative charge has to be taken into account. Both distances from the field point and directions of the contributions must be considered.

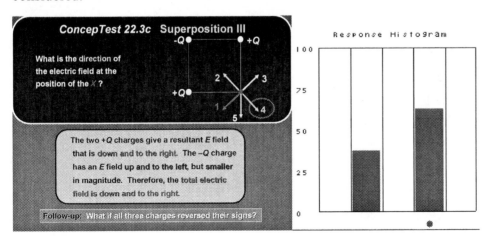

Conceptual Module 22.4
ConcepTest 22.4:   **Find the Charges**
Difficulty Level: 4
Suggested follow-up conceptual questions:
- **How would you get the *E* field to point toward the right?**

This question employs a different tactic. Here the electric field is given, and something must be inferred about the charges that have created that field. Using the superposition practice from the previous series of questions, students should be able to reconstruct the nature of the charges.

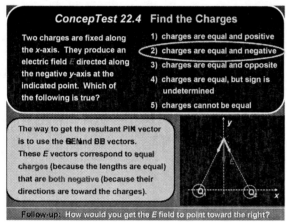
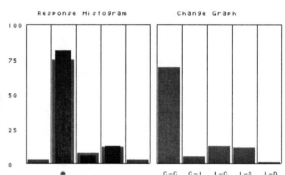

Conceptual Module 22.5
ConcepTest 22.5:   **Uniform Electric Field**
Difficulty Level: 3
Suggested follow-up numerical problem: Problem 22.39
Suggested follow-up conceptual questions:
- **What if the charge is placed at a different position in the field?**

The force on a charge in a uniform electric field depends on the magnitude of the charge ($F = qE$). So if the charge varies by a certain factor, then the force will change by the same factor.

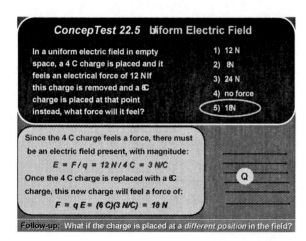

Conceptual Module 22.6 (two parts)
ConcepTest 22.6a: Electric Field Lines I
Difficulty Level: 1

To help with the understanding of electric field lines, the students must interpret a field plot with regard to the charges that created it. In this case, this primarily relates to the sign of the charges, which is determined by viewing the direction of the electric field vectors.

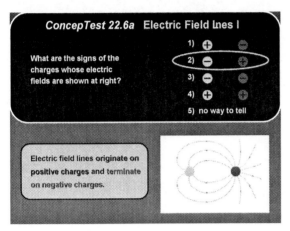

ConcepTest 22.6b: Electric Field Lines II
Difficulty Level: 2
Suggested follow-up numerical problem: Problems 22.12, 22.14, and 22.15
Suggested follow-up conceptual questions:
   • **What is the red/green ratio of magnitudes for the two charges?**

In this follow-up question, the students must now make a judgement about the relative magnitude of the two charges, based on the density of field lines in the vicinity of each charge.

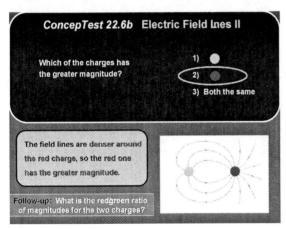

Conceptual Module 24.1 (three parts)
ConcepTest 24.1a: Electric Potential Energy I
Difficulty Level: 1

Students must realize that the electric force depends on the charge of the particle in the uniform field, and that the electron and proton have the same magnitude of charge. So the forces will have the same magnitude, although the directions will be opposite because the particles have opposite charges.

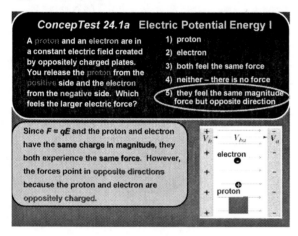

ConcepTest 24.1b: Electric Potential Energy II
Difficulty Level: 2

Again reminding the students of Newton's Second Law: while the forces on the proton and electron may be the same, the accelerations of each particle are quite different, with the less massive particle experiencing the greater acceleration ($F = ma$).

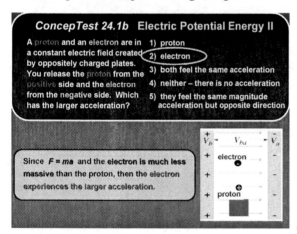

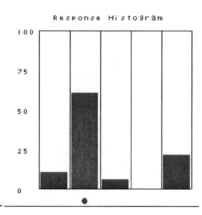

ConcepTest 24.1c: **Electric Potential Energy III**
Difficulty Level: **3**
Suggested follow-up numerical problem: Problems 24.3, 24.4 and 24.24

The initial electrostatic potential energy is converted into kinetic energy as the particle moves. Since the initial PE is the same for both particles ($PE = qV$), the final kinetic energy will also be the same.

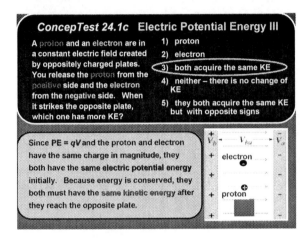

Conceptual Module 24.2
ConcepTest 24.2: **Work and Potential Energy**
Difficulty Level: **4**
Suggested follow-up numerical problem: Problems 24.5 and 24.9

The work to assemble a charge distribution is equivalent to the total electrostatic potential energy. The electrostatic PE of a charge configuration must be determined by adding the PE contributions pairwise. For the first case, there is only one contribution (but with a larger charge involved), whereas for the second case, there are three contributions. By treating these contributions quantitatively, it works out that the second case has the higher electrostatic PE.

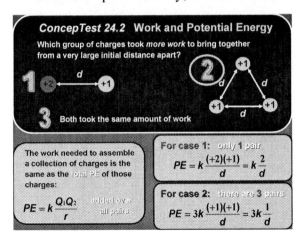

Conceptual Module 24.3 (two parts)
ConcepTest 24.3a: **Electric Potential I**
Difficulty Level: 3
Suggested follow-up numerical problem: Problem 24.25

Unlike the electric field, which is a vector, the electric potential is a scalar quantity. So in this case, the contributions to the potential simply add numerically (not vectorially). In this question, the difference in the relative contributions arises due to the distances, where the positive charge is closer to point A.

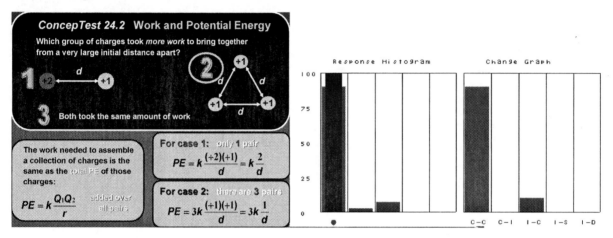

ConcepTest 24.3b: **Electric Potential II**
Difficulty Level: 3
Suggested follow-up numerical problem: Problems 24.11 and 24.12
Suggested follow-up conceptual questions:
* **What is the potential at the origin of the *x-y* axes?**

In this follow-up question, point B is equidistant between a positive and a negative charge, so the contributions to the potential are equal and opposite (and therefore add up to zero).

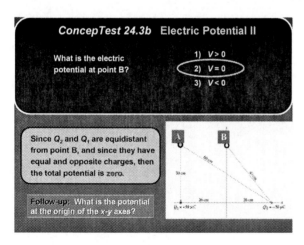

Conceptual Module 24.4
ConcepTest 24.4:   Hollywood Square
Difficulty Level: 4
Suggested follow-up numerical problem: Problem 24.18
Suggested follow-up conceptual questions:
  - **What is the direction of the electric field at the center?**

This question allows students to confront the differences between electric field and electric potential. The square configuration of charges is a case they have seen before, but now they are asked about both the field and the potential. In the former, the vector nature leads to a non-zero result, but in the latter, the scalar nature ends up giving zero potential.

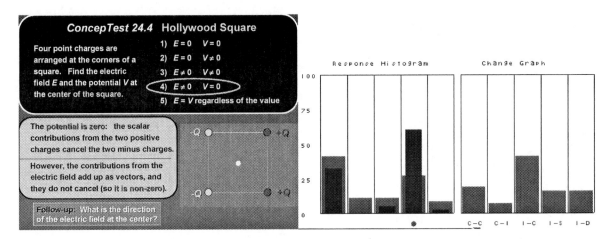

Conceptual Module 24.5 (three parts)
ConcepTest 24.5a: Equipotential Surfaces I
Difficulty Level: 3
Suggested follow-up conceptual questions:
  - **What is the direction of the electric field at all four points?**

This question serves as a lead-in for the concept of equipotential surfaces. All of the points shown are equidistant from both charges, so the net potential at each point will be zero.

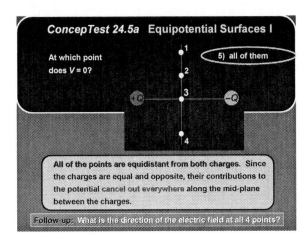

ConcepTest 24.5b: Equipotential Surfaces II
Difficulty Level: 3
Suggested follow-up numerical problem: Problem 24.37

This question is examining the concept of equipotential surfaces. As in the previous question, as long as all of the points along the surface are equidistant from the equal and opposite charges, the potential contributions will always cancel out. For an equipotential on the *x*-axis, this is only true in case #1.

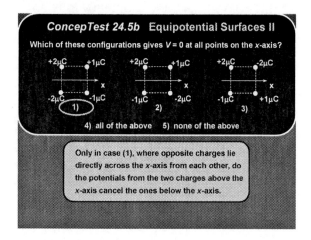

ConcepTest 24.5c: Equipotential Surfaces III
Difficulty Level: 3
Suggested follow-up conceptual questions:
*   **Where is *V* = 0 for configuration #2?**

This is essentially the same question as the previous one, except that the equipotential surface being sought is perpendicular to the previous case.

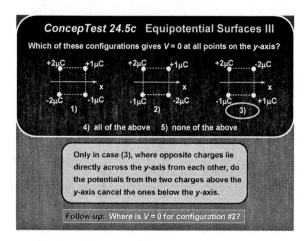

Conceptual Module 24.6

ConcepTest 24.6:   **Equipotential of Point Charge**

Difficulty Level: **2**

Suggested follow-up numerical problem: Problem 24.31

Suggested follow-up conceptual questions:

- **Which point has the smallest potential?**

This question is asking about the equipotential surfaces of a point charge. In this case, such a surface is characterized by its radius, since the situation is spherically symmetric about the point charge.

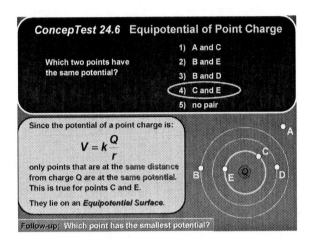

Conceptual Module 24.7 (two parts)

ConcepTest 24.7a: **Work and Electric Potential I**

Difficulty Level: **2**

The concept of work is central to the notion of equipotentials and electric fields. It requires no work to move along an equipotential, while moving along a field line involves positive (or negative) work. In this question, students must be able to distinguish between the cases above and realize that moving a positive charge *against* the electric field will require the most work. This is analogous to the case of lifting a rock vertically upwards, against Earth's gravitational field.

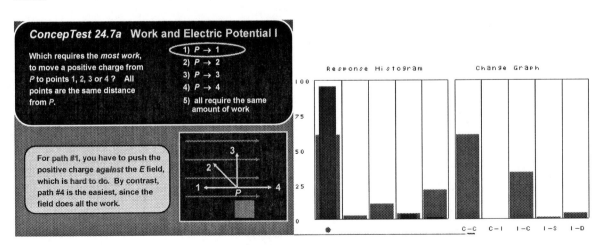

ConcepTest 24.7b: Work and Electric Potential II
Difficulty Level: 2
Suggested follow-up conceptual questions:
*   **Which path requires the least work?**

As mentioned in the previous question, moving along an equipotential surface requires no work. Thus, the students must be able to identify the equipotentials for a uniform electric field, and then recognize that these surfaces provide the path of zero work.

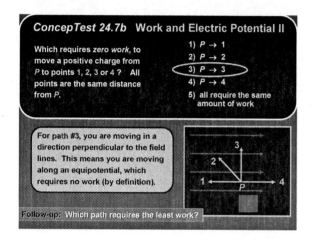

Conceptual Module 25.1
ConcepTest 25.1:   **Capacitors**
Difficulty Level: 2
Suggested follow-up numerical problem: Problems 25.3 and 25.4

This is a direct application of $Q = CV$ for capacitors. Since the capacitors are identical, then the only other parameter that the charge depends on is the voltage. A higher voltage will supply more charge.

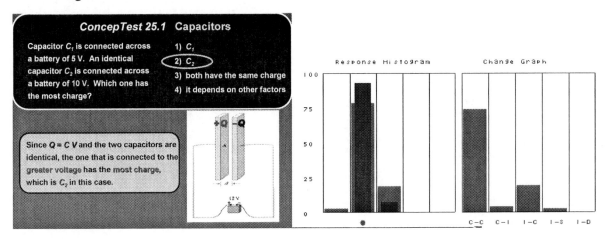

Conceptual Module 25.2 (three parts)
ConcepTest 25.2a: **Varying Capacitance I**
Difficulty Level: 3
Suggested follow-up numerical problem: Problem 25.5

The capacitance depends exclusively on geometrical factors such as plate area and separation. The relationship between these two quantities must be understood in the context of how they affect the capacitance.

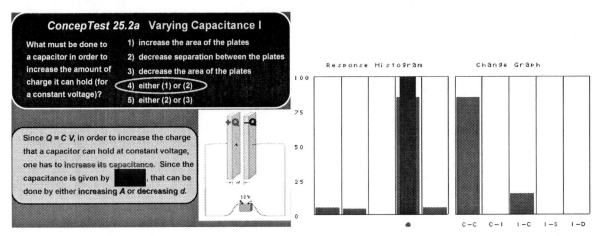

441

ConcepTest 25.2b: Varying Capacitance II
Difficulty Level: 3
Suggested follow-up conceptual questions:
- **How do you increase the charge?**

This question addresses the cause-and-effect relationship between capacitance and charge. The students must first realize that leaving the battery connected means that the voltage remains fixed. So the increase in the plate spacing, which leads to a corresponding decrease in the capacitance, will result in a decrease in charge (using $Q = CV$ which can be rewritten as $V = Q/C$ or $C = Q/V$).

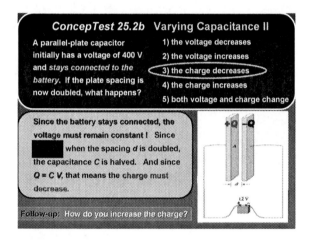

ConcepTest 25.2c: Varying Capacitance III
Difficulty Level: 3
Suggested follow-up numerical problem: Problem 25.10

In this follow-up question, with the battery disconnected, the charge must remain fixed. So the increase in the plate spacing, which leads to a corresponding decrease in the capacitance, will result in an increase in voltage (using $Q = CV$ which can be rewritten as $V = Q/C$ or $C = Q/V$).

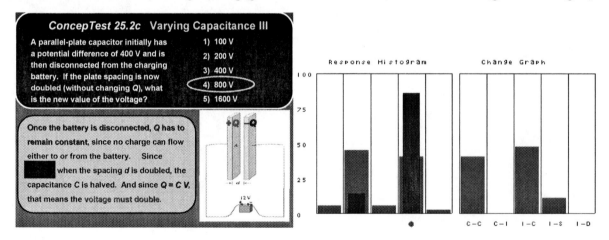

Conceptual Module 25.3 (three parts)
ConcepTest 25.3a: Capacitors I
Difficulty Level: 3
Suggested follow-up numerical problem: Problem 25.33

This is a direct application of the rules for equivalent capacitance of combinations. In this case, two series capacitors are combined in parallel with another single capacitor, so there are two steps that the students must account for.

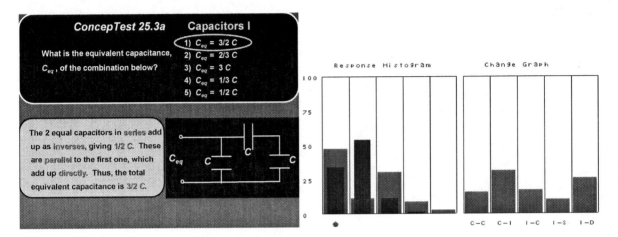

ConcepTest 25.3b: Capacitors II
Difficulty Level: 4
Suggested follow-up conceptual questions:
  • **What is the current in this circuit?**

This question addresses the issue of voltage in capacitor combinations. Students should recognize immediately that V_1 must be the battery voltage. Then the voltages V_2 and V_3 must add up to the battery voltage, so each of them individually must be less than V_1.

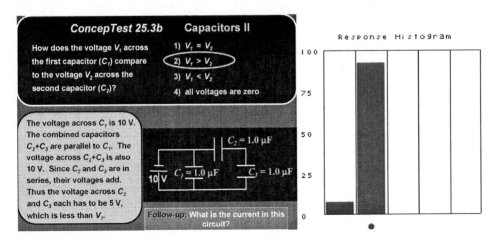

ConcepTest 25.3c: Capacitors III
Difficulty Level: 4
Suggested follow-up numerical problem: Problems 25.36 and 25.37

This question addresses the issue of charge in capacitor combinations. Students must utilize what they have learned in the previous question about the voltages to deduce the charges in the present case.

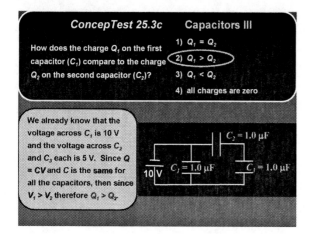

Conceptual Module 26.1
ConcepTest 26.1: **Connect the Battery**
Difficulty Level: 2

The concept of a complete circuit is very important to emphasize when discussing DC circuits. The notion that current must flow through a complete loop is often missed by students. For example, simply touching the bulb to the battery (case #1) will not light the bulb, but many students may think otherwise. Moreover, case #2 may appear to be a loop, but it is certainly not a complete circuit.

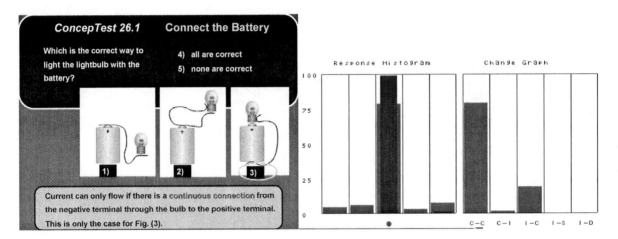

Conceptual Module 26.2
ConcepTest 26.2: **Ohm's Law**
Difficulty Level: 1
Suggested follow-up numerical problem: Problem 26.46
Suggested follow-up conceptual questions:
- **Where could this situation occur?**

Ohm's Law is a linear relationship between voltage and current. There are, however, devices that do not follow Ohm's Law, and it is useful to point out this distinction to the students (*i.e.*, that not every device necessarily obeys Ohm's Law).

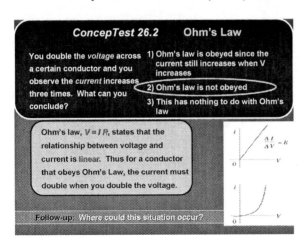

Conceptual Module 26.3 (two parts)
ConcepTest 26.3a: Wires I
Difficulty Level: 3
Suggested follow-up numerical problem: Problems 26.24 and 26.25

This question examines the relationship of resistance to the geometry of a wire. Since the resistance depends inversely (but linearly) on the area, the students must realize that the area involves the square of the radius (or diameter). This is why a factor of 4 in resistance relates to a factor of ½ in diameter.

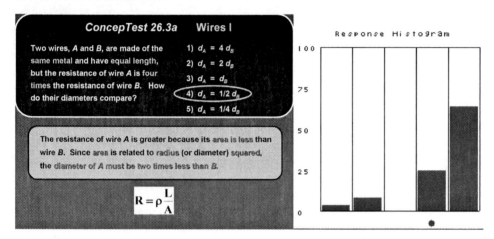

ConcepTest 26.3b: Wires II
Difficulty Level: 4
Suggested follow-up numerical problem: Problems 26.23 and 26.83

This is a tricky problem in which students must realize that to preserve the volume of the wire, then when the length is doubled, the area is halved. These two factors in the expression for resistance lead to an overall increase in resistance by a factor of 4.

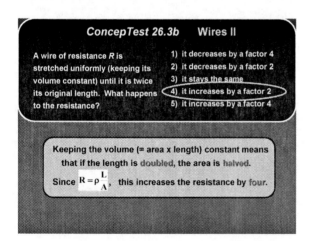

Conceptual Module 26.4 (two parts)
ConcepTest 26.4a: Series Resistors I
Difficulty Level: 3
Suggested follow-up numerical problem: Problem 26.47
Suggested follow-up conceptual questions:
- **What would be the potential difference if $R = 1\ \Omega, 2\ \Omega, 3\ \Omega$**

For series resistors, the individual voltages add to give the total (battery) voltage. In this case, with three equal resistors, the voltages are simply 1/3 of the total voltage. This gives the students a gentle warm up to the concept of resistors in series and the associated voltages.

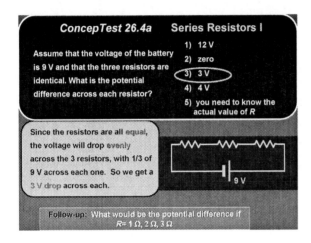

ConcepTest 26.4b: Series Resistors II
Difficulty Level: 3
Suggested follow-up numerical problem: Problems 26.49 and 26.51
Suggested follow-up conceptual questions:
- **What happens if the voltage is doubled?**

In this follow-up question, the resistors are no longer equal, so the voltage drops will have to scale with the magnitudes of the resistors.   A simple way to treat this is to look at the ratio of resistors and realize that the voltages must be in that same ratio.

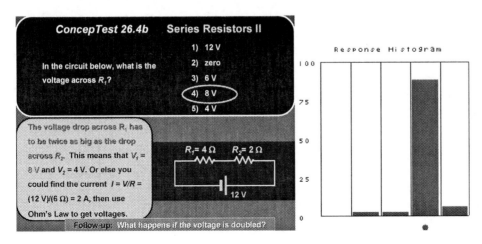

Conceptual Module 26.5 (two parts)
ConcepTest 26.5a: Parallel Resistors I
Difficulty Level: 3
Suggested follow-up numerical problem: Problem 26.50
Suggested follow-up conceptual questions:
  • **What is the total current through the battery?**

This is a simple application of Ohm's Law. Knowing the voltage across R_1 (which is simply the battery voltage) and the value of R_1 gives the current immediately. The parallel combination does not actually enter into this problem at all.

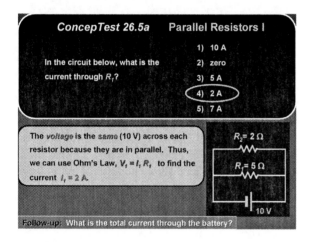

ConcepTest 26.5b: Parallel Resistors II
Difficulty Level: 4
Suggested follow-up numerical problem: Problems 26.76 and 26.86
Suggested follow-up conceptual questions:
  • **What happens to the current through each resistor?**

In parallel circuits, the voltage across each parallel element is the same, and so the current drawn by each element contributes to an ever-increasing total current as more elements are added. The students may have the notion that a battery is a constant current source, which is not true.

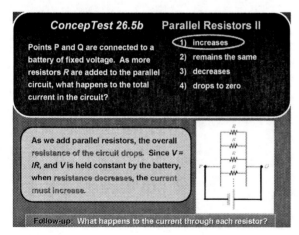

Conceptual Module 26.6 (two parts)
ConcepTest 26.6a: Short Circuit I
Difficulty Level: 3
Suggested follow-up conceptual questions:
- **Doesn't the wire have SOME resistance?**

The wire is connected in parallel with the lightbulb, and the current will split based on the resistance of the branches. If the wire has nearly zero resistance, then nearly all of the current will flow through that branch. The current clearly does not split up evenly between the wire and the lightbulb.

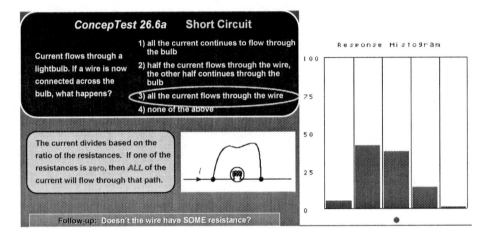

ConcepTest 26.6b: Short Circuit II
Difficulty Level: 4
Suggested follow-up conceptual questions:
- **What happens to bulb B?**

By connecting the wire, the overall resistance of the circuit decreases, which in turn increases the total current flowing through the circuit (the total voltage is held fixed by the battery). When the current increases, bulb A will be brighter than before. The modification to the circuit near bulb B has an impact on the entire circuit, not just bulb B.

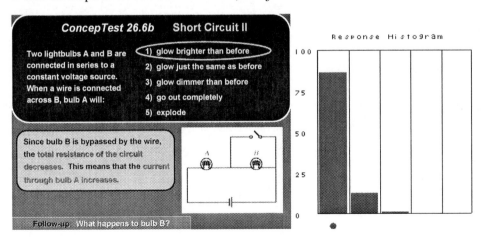

Conceptual Module 26.7 (two parts)
ConcepTest 26.7a: **Circuits I**
Difficulty Level: 4
Suggested follow-up numerical problem: Problem 26.48

This question addresses the total power ($P = IV$) in a circuit. In each case, the total voltage is the same, but the total current is greater in the parallel combination. Thus the power dissipated by the parallel circuit will be greater, which means that the lightbulbs will be brighter.

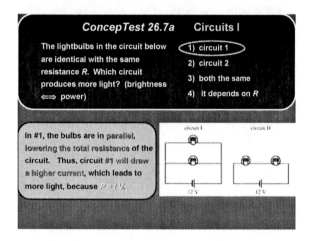

ConcepTest 26.7b: **Circuits II**
Difficulty Level: 5
Suggested follow-up numerical problem: Problems 26.55 and 26.56
Suggested follow-up conceptual questions:
  • **What is the total current in the circuit?**

This quantitative question examines the power dissipated in specific branches of a circuit. The students must obtain either the voltage or the current for each lightbulb in order to compare the power dissipated by each element. In this case, since $P = I^2R$, then the smaller current (by a factor of 2) in the bottom branch leads to a reduction in power by a factor of 4 (due to the I^2 term).

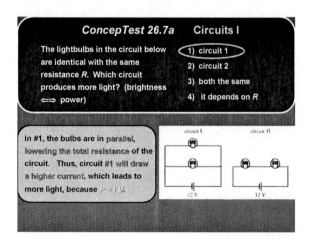

Conceptual Module 26.8 (two parts)
ConcepTest 26.8a: **More Circuits I**
Difficulty Level: **4**
Suggested follow-up conceptual questions:

- **What happens to the current through R_3?**

Here again, a change somewhere in the circuit affects the entire circuit. By closing the switch, the equivalent resistance of the parallel combination is changed, affecting the overall current in the circuit. By reducing the parallel resistance, the current in the circuit increases and therefore so does V_1.

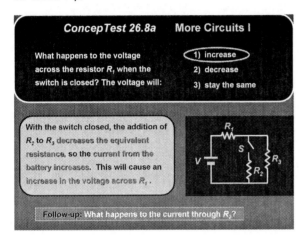

ConcepTest 26.8b: **More Circuits II**
Difficulty Level: **4**
Suggested follow-up conceptual questions:

- **What happens to the current through R_4?**

In this question, several steps are necessary, which follow from the previous question. We just saw that when the current in the circuit increases, then V_1 increases – but that means that the voltage across the parallel combination must decrease, since the total voltage is constant (from the battery). The voltage across the combination is also the voltage across any element in the combination.

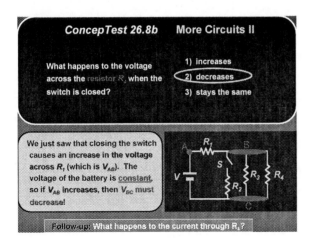

ConcepTest 26.9:   Even More Circuits
Difficulty Level: 4
Suggested follow-up numerical problem: Problem 26.57
Suggested follow-up conceptual questions:
- **Which one has the smallest voltage drop?**

In this question, the students must be able to do some basic qualitative circuit analysis. Realizing that the current is the same through both combinations (because they are in series) leads to an examination of each combination and the way the current will split in each case. The 2:1 ratio of resistors in the second group favors R_5 as the resistor with the greatest current.

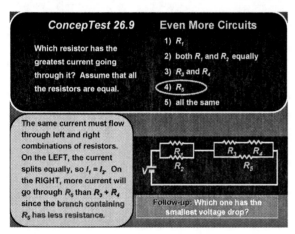

Conceptual Module 26.10
ConcepTest 26.10:   Dimmer
Difficulty Level: 3
Suggested follow-up conceptual questions:
- **Why does the voltage not change?**

Students must recognize that the voltage is constant for appliances in the house. With this in mind, the current must be changed in order to operate the dimmer. This is achieved by changing the resistance. It is impossible to change only one parameter in Ohm's Law without changing something else.

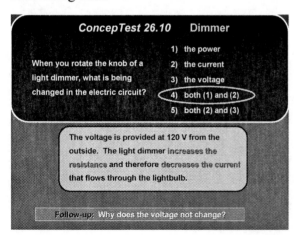

Conceptual Module 26.11 (two parts)
ConcepTest 26.11a: Lightbulbs
Difficulty Level: 3
Suggested follow-up numerical problem: Problem 26.65
Suggested follow-up conceptual questions:
- **Which one carries the greater current?**

Given that the voltage in a typical household circuit is constant, then the power of a light bulb must be related to the current through it, which is determined by the resistance. Since $P = IV = V^2/R$, and since the voltage is constant, then the lower power comes about from a higher resistance.

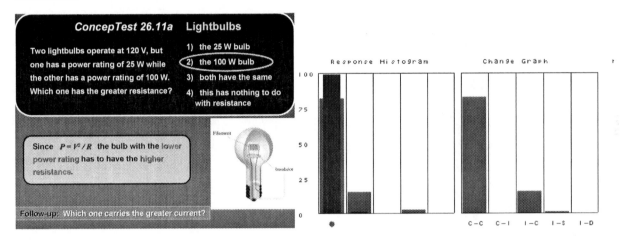

ConcepTest 26.11b: Space Heaters I
Difficulty Level: 3
Suggested follow-up numerical problem: Problem 26.78
Suggested follow-up conceptual questions:
- **Which one carries the greater current?**

This question relates to the same issue of power and resistance (for constant voltage). Again, using the expression for power $P = V^2/R$, the lower resistance heater will have the higher power (more heat).

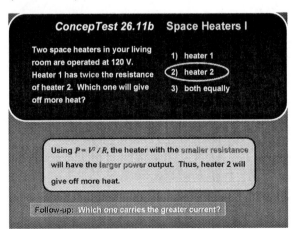

Conceptual Module 27.1
ConcepTest 27.1:   **Junction Rule**
Difficulty Level: 2
Suggested follow-up numerical problem: Problems 27.15 and 27.16

This question addresses the junction rule, which states that the total current entering a point must equal the total current leaving that point. By inspecting the currents shown, the students should be able to deduce the value of the missing current.

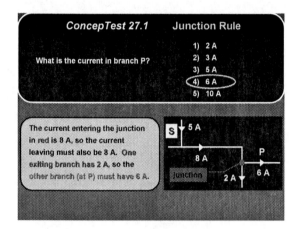

Conceptual Module 27.2
ConcepTest 27.2:   **Kirchhoff's Rule**
Difficulty Level: 5
Suggested follow-up numerical problem: Problem 27.11 and 27.24
Suggested follow-up conceptual questions:
- **What happens if the bottom battery is replaced by a 24 V battery?**

This question requires a reasonable insight into what is going on in the original circuit. Knowing that the total voltage is 24 V and that this total will drop evenly (12 V each) across the two equal resistors leads to the conclusion that the potential must be 12 V at the point between the two resistors. Since this is the same value of the potential between the batteries, the result is that nothing happens.

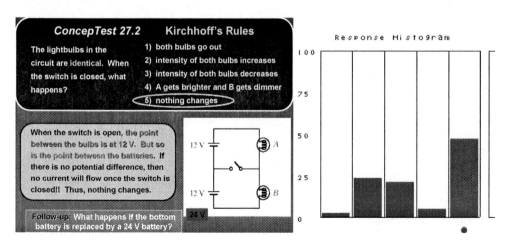

Conceptual Module 27.3
ConcepTest 27.3: **Wheatstone Bridge**
Difficulty Level: 5
Suggested follow-up numerical problem: Problem 27.47

A Wheatstone Bridge operates by adjusting the value of a variable resistor so as to "balance" the bridge and make the current in the ammeter zero. In this case, as before, the students must realize that the potentials at points (a) and (b) are the same, which means that no current will flow. Actually, this equality of potential is due to the ratio of resistors in each branch being the same and does not require the resistors to have the exact same values themselves.

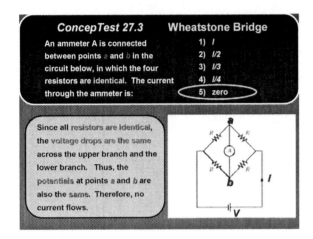

Conceptual Module 27.4
ConcepTest 27.4: **More Kirchhoff's Rules**
Difficulty Level: 4
Suggested follow-up numerical problem: Problems 27.29 and 27.32

In this question, the students must work to set up a valid loop equation for one of the possible loops in the circuit shown. This is an exercise in identifying the proper signs of voltage drops and voltage gains as the current goes through batteries and resistors in the directions shown.

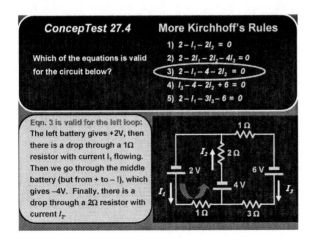

Conceptual Module 28.1 (four parts)
ConcepTest 28.1a: Magnetic Force I
Difficulty Level: 3
Suggested follow-up numerical problem: Problems 28.4 and 28.5

This is a direct application of the right-hand rule for determining the direction of the magnetic force on a moving charged particle.

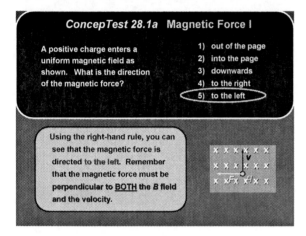

ConcepTest 28.1b: Magnetic Force II
Difficulty Level: 3
Suggested follow-up numerical problem: Problem 28.6

This is a direct application of the right-hand rule for determining the direction of the magnetic force on a moving charged particle.

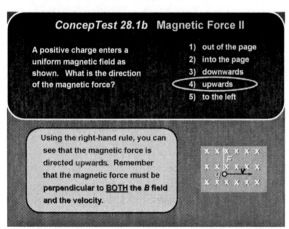

ConcepTest 28.1c: Magnetic Force III
Difficulty Level: 3
Suggested follow-up numerical problem: Problems 28.7 and 28.9

This is a direct application of the right-hand rule for determining the direction of the magnetic force on a moving charged particle.

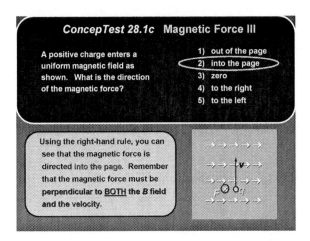

ConcepTest 28.1d: Magnetic Force IV
Difficulty Level: 2

In this final question, the velocity is parallel to the magnetic field, so there will be no magnetic force. This comes directly from the expression $F = qvB(\sin\theta)$ for the magnitude of the magnetic force.

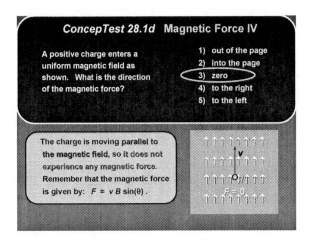

Conceptual Module 28.2
ConcepTest 28.2:   Atomic Beams
Difficulty Level: 2
Suggested follow-up conceptual questions:
- **What charge would follow path #3?**
- **What charge would follow path #1?**

To some extent, this is a "trick" question. Since atoms are neutral, they will not experience any magnetic force. Thus their paths will be undeflected by the presence of the magnetic field.

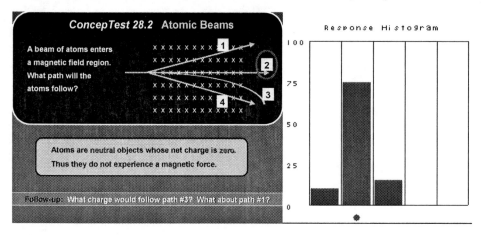

Conceptual Module 28.3
ConcepTest 28.3:   Magnetic Field
Difficulty Level: 3
Suggested follow-up numerical problem: Problem 28.3
Suggested follow-up conceptual questions:
- **What would happen to a beam of atoms?**

This question addresses the right-hand rule, but in reverse. That is, in this case, the force is indicated and the students must work backwards to infer the direction of the magnetic field. By realizing that the field must be perpendicular to both the force and the velocity will reduce the choices down to two.

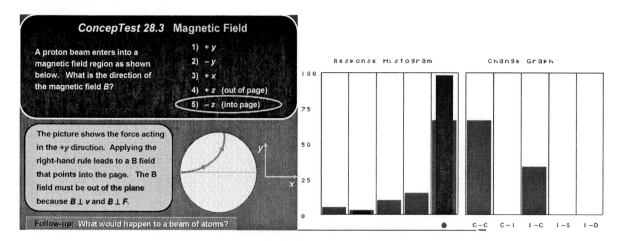

Conceptual Module 28.4 (two parts)
ConcepTest 28.4a: Mass Spectrometer I
Difficulty Level: 3
Suggested follow-up numerical problem: Problems 28.34 and 28.35
Suggested follow-up conceptual questions:
- **What is the sign of the charges in the picture?**

In addition to using the expression for radius of curvature in a magnetic field, students may also notice that the larger charge will have the larger force (if velocity and *B* field are fixed) and therefore will also have the larger acceleration (if mass is fixed), which results in the tighter circle as the trajectory.

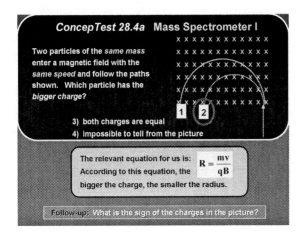

ConcepTest 28.4b: Mass Spectrometer II
Difficulty Level: 2

This question relates to work and kinetic energy. The students have seen this type of question before, in terms of circular motion. When the force acts perpendicular to the direction of motion (as it does for magnetic forces), no work is done and therefore the kinetic energy does not change.

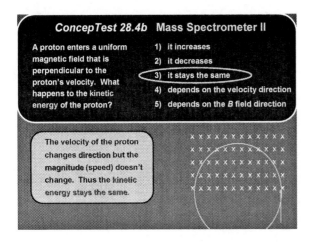

Conceptual Module 28.5
ConcepTest 28.5:   Velocity Selector
Difficulty Level: 4
Suggested follow-up numerical problem: Problems 28.39 and 28.40

This question links the electric and magnetic forces on a charged particle. First, the electric force must be determined. Then, knowing that the magnetic force must act in the opposite direction, the students must invoke the right-hand rule to infer the direction of the magnetic field that will accomplish this.

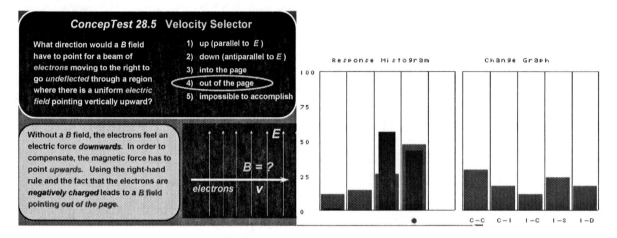

Conceptual Module 28.6 (two parts)
ConcepTest 28.6a: Magnetic Force on a Wire I
Difficulty Level: 3
Suggested follow-up numerical problem: Problems 28.43, 28.44 and 28.45

This is an exercise in the right-hand rule, where in this case the moving charges are a current in a wire. This changes nothing with regard to the direction of the force, but helps students realize that there is no difference between a single moving charge and a current (which consists of many moving charges).

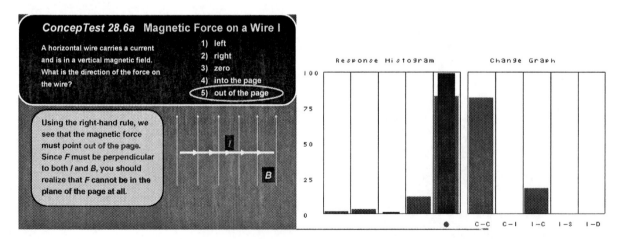

ConcepTest 28.6b: **Magnetic Force on a Wire II**
Difficulty Level: **2**

In this follow-up question, the current is parallel to the direction of the magnetic field, so there is no magnetic force. This comes directly from the expression $F = ILB(\sin\theta)$ for the magnitude of the magnetic force.

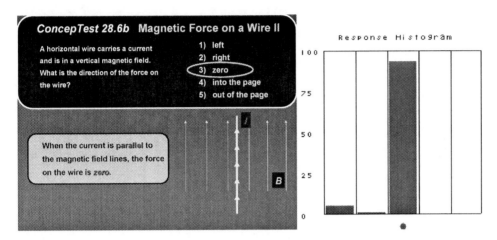

Conceptual Module 28.7

ConcepTest 28.7a: **Magnetic Force on a Loop I**
Difficulty Level: **4**
Suggested follow-up numerical problem: **Problems 28.51 and 28.80**

In this question, the right-hand rule must again be applied. By finding an outward force on one of the legs, students may be able to use symmetry arguments to deduce that each leg will also experience an outward force, such that the vector sum of all the four outward forces will be zero.

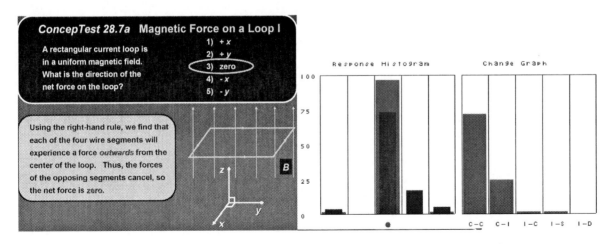

ConcepTest 28.7b: Magnetic Force on a Loop II
Difficulty Level: 4
Suggested follow-up numerical problem: Problems 28.59 and 28.60

In this case, the right-hand rule leads to opposite forces on each of the two legs, but the directions of these forces are not in the plane of the loop. Thus, while the loop will not undergo any translational motion, it will in fact rotate. This is a precursor to the introduction of motors, which utilize the same combination of forces in conjunction with an alternating current in the loop.

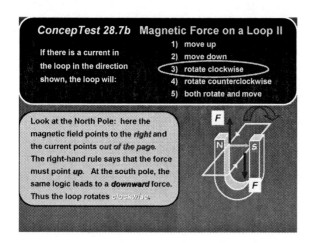

Conceptual Module 29.1 (two parts)
ConcepTest 29.1a: Magnetic Field of a Wire I
Difficulty Level: 4
Suggested follow-up numerical problem: Problems 29.1 and 29.2

This question deals with the magnetic field of a straight wire and the superposition of two separate forces. In this case, the students must find the direction of the field from each wire and then perform the vector addition of the two forces to obtain the resultant.

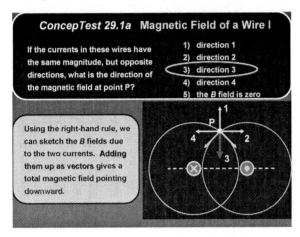

ConcepTest 29.1b: Magnetic Field of a Wire II
Difficulty Level: 4

This follow-up question includes four wires, instead of two, and is asking for the case in which the net magnetic field is largest. In cases #1 and #3, the similar currents at opposite corners of the square will end up canceling, such that these cases give a net field of zero. It is only in case #2 that the field contributions add up to a maximum value.

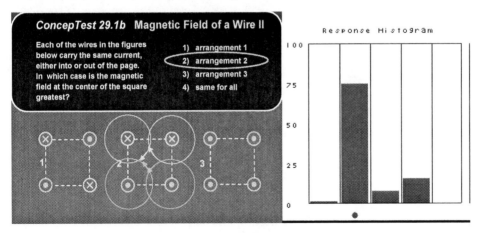

Conceptual Module 29.2 (two parts)
ConcepTest 29.2a: Field and Force I
Difficulty Level: 4
Suggested follow-up numerical problem: Problems 29.4 and 29.19

This question involves two separate parts. First, the students must ascertain the direction of the magnetic field due to the wire at the position of the charge. Second, knowing that field and the velocity of the moving charge, the students must then apply the right-hand rule to obtain the direction of the force.

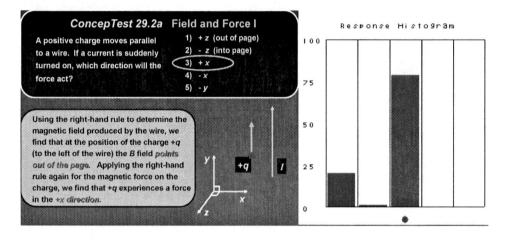

ConcepTest 29.2b: Field and Force II
Difficulty Level: 4
Suggested follow-up numerical problem: Problems 29.3 and 29.6
Suggested follow-up conceptual questions:
- **What happens when one of the currents is turned off?**

This question is very similar to the previous one, except for the fact that the moving charge has now been replaced by a current in a wire. The same steps must be applied, and the students will arrive at the well-known result that two wires carrying current in the same direction will attract each other.

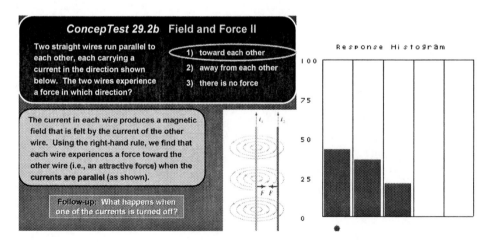

Conceptual Module 29.3
ConcepTest 29.3:   Current Loop
Difficulty Level: 4
Suggested follow-up numerical problem: Problems 29.46, 29.47 and 29.53

This is an exercise to get the students to derive for themselves the direction of the magnetic field at the center of a current loop. The simplest case of a current loop is a square loop, which is given in this question. After obtaining this result, a new version of the right-hand rule will soon be introduced to give directly the direction of the magnetic field inside a current loop.

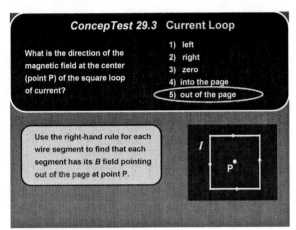

Conceptual Module 30.1 (two parts)
ConcepTest 30.1a: Magnetic Flux I
Difficulty Level: 1

The concept of magnetic flux is troublesome for students, but an understanding of this concept is necessary for the subsequent work on electromagnetic induction. In this question, some of the various ways in which the magnetic flux can be varied are examined.

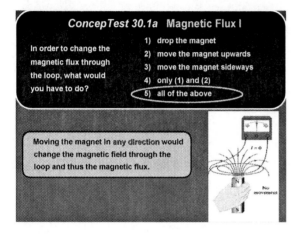

ConcepTest 30.1b: Magnetic Flux II
Difficulty Level: 1

This follow-up question continues to explore the ways in which the magnetic flux can be varied.

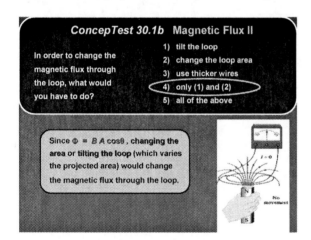

Conceptual Module 30.2 (two parts)
ConcepTest 30.2a: Moving Bar Magnet I
Difficulty Level: 3
Suggested follow-up conceptual questions:
- **What happens if the magnet is stationary and the loop moves?**

The next series of questions examines the concept of electromagnetic induction, mainly in terms of the direction of the induced current as given by Lenz's Law. In each situation, the students must identify two specific things: (1) the initial direction of the flux and (2) the sense of the change in flux. These two facts will then dictate the direction of the induced current, which will act to oppose the change.

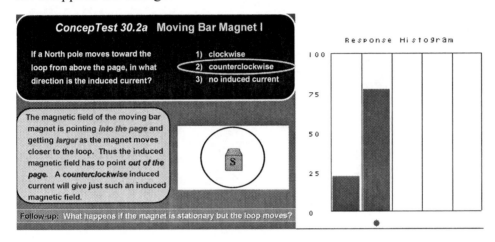

ConcepTest 30.2b: Moving Bar Magnet II
Difficulty Level: 2

In this case, the initial flux through the loop is zero, since it is in the same plane as the magnet. So even though the magnet is moving, the flux through the loop remains zero (*i.e.*, does not change).

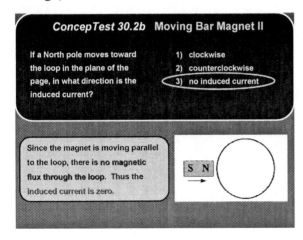

Conceptual Module 30.3 (three parts)
ConcepTest 30.3a: Moving Wire Loop I
Difficulty Level: 2
Suggested follow-up conceptual questions:
- **What happens if the loop moves out of the page?**

In this case, even though the loop is moving, the flux through the loop is not changing. Thus, there will be no induced current.

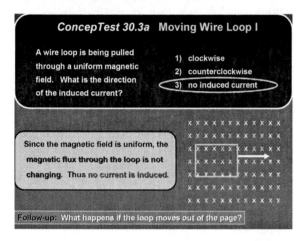

ConcepTest 30.3b: Moving Wire Loop II
Difficulty Level: 3
Suggested follow-up numerical problem: Problem 30.7
Suggested follow-up conceptual questions:
- **What happens when the loop is completely out of the field?**

In this follow-up question, the loop is emerging from the field region, so the flux is indeed changing. Thus, there will be an induced current, whose direction must be determined by using Lenz's Law.

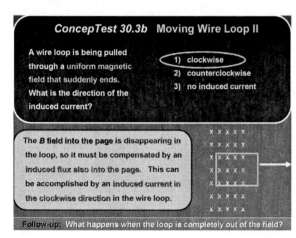

ConcepTest 30.3c: Moving Wire Loop III
Difficulty Level: 3
Suggested follow-up numerical problem: Problems 30.3, 30.5, and 30.6
Suggested follow-up conceptual questions:
- **What if the loop stops moving while the field increases?**

In this case, the magnetic flux is also changing, but this is due to an explicit variation in the strength of the magnetic field. Again, Lenz's Law must be used to determine the direction of the induced current.

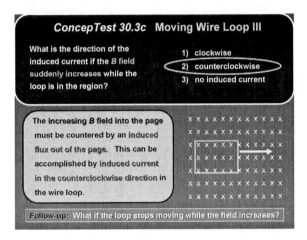

Conceptual Module 30.4
ConcepTest 30.4:   Shrinking Wire Loop
Difficulty Level: 3
Suggested follow-up numerical problem: Problem 30.16
Suggested follow-up conceptual questions:
- **What if the *B* field is oriented at 90° to its present direction?**

In this case, the flux is changing due to a variation in the area of the loop.

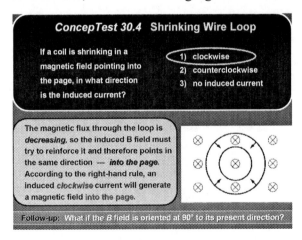

Conceptual Module 30.5
ConcepTest 30.5:   Rotating Wire Loop
Difficulty Level: 3
Suggested follow-up numerical problem: Problems 30.10, 30.12, and 30.17

It is also possible to change the flux through the loop by varying its orientation. In this case, the angle between the loop and the magnetic field is changing as the loop rotates, which leads to a corresponding variation in the flux. This is a preview of how a generator works.

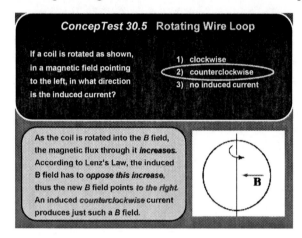

Conceptual Module 30.6 (two parts)
ConcepTest 30.6a: Voltage and Current I
Difficulty Level: 3

The induced voltage is determined by Faraday's Law, which involves the number of turns of wire in the loop. In this case, the two-turn loop will have twice the induced voltage as the single-turn loop.

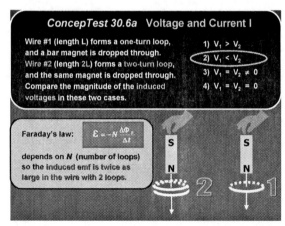

ConcepTest 30.6b: Voltage and Current II
Difficulty Level: 4

This follow-up question now brings in Ohm's Law to relate the current to the voltage. In the previous question, the voltages were different by a factor of 2, due to the number of turns. But the resistances of the loops will also be in that ratio, so in the end, the resulting currents will be the same.

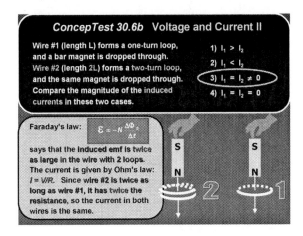

Conceptual Module 30.7 (two parts)
ConcepTest 30.7a: Falling Magnet I
Difficulty Level: 4
Suggested follow-up conceptual questions:

* **What happens in case 2 if you flip the magnet so that the South pole is on the bottom as the magnet falls?**

This is a classic demonstration, where a magnet is dropped through a long, hollow aluminum rod. The magnet takes significantly longer to fall through than an unmagnetized piece of metal. This question should be asked before showing the demonstration.

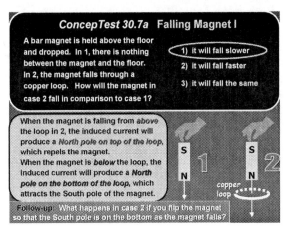

ConcepTest 30.7b: Falling Magnet II
Difficulty Level: 4

In this follow-up question, students must ponder the source of energy to make the induced current. Realizing that the falling magnet moves slower should lead the students to the conclusion that the "lost" kinetic energy is what accounts for the additional energy for the induced current.

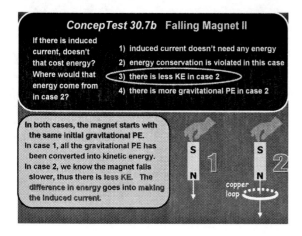

Conceptual Module 30.8 (two parts)
ConcepTest 30.8a: Loop and Wire I
Difficulty Level: 3
Suggested follow-up numerical problem: Problems 30.8 and 30.13

In this question, the magnetic field must first be deduced by examining the long straight wire. The fact that the field decreases with distance is what leads to a change in flux as the loop moves away.

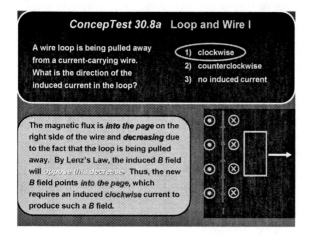

ConcepTest 30.8b: **Loop and Wire II**
Difficulty Level: **2**

In this follow-up question, the direction of motion of the loop is now parallel to the wire. While it is true that the loop is covering a region of non-uniform magnetic field, its motion in that field is such that the flux does not change, so there is no induced current.

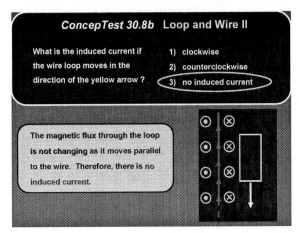

Conceptual Module 30.9

ConcepTest 30.9:   **Motional EMF**
Difficulty Level: **3**
Suggested follow-up numerical problem: **Problems 30.29, 30.56, 30.60, and 30.70**
Suggested follow-up conceptual questions:
- **What direction is the magnetic force on the rod as it moves?**

The concept of motional EMF can be understood in terms of changing flux through a loop, as shown in this question. As the area of the loop effectively changes (as the rod moves), the flux is changing and therefore gives rise to an induced current.

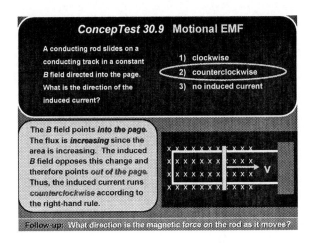

Conceptual Module 30.10
ConcepTest 30.10:   Generators
Difficulty Level: 1
Suggested follow-up numerical problem: Problems 30.51 and 30.52

This is a direct application of the generator equation, which includes the frequency ω in the amplitude. As the rotation rate increases, the frequency increases but so does the amplitude of the generator.

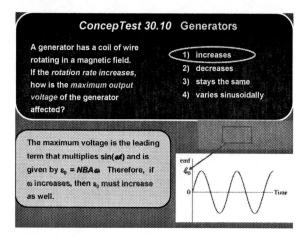

Conceptual Module 30.11
ConcepTest 30.11:   Magic Loop
Difficulty Level: 3

This question is intended to introduce the idea of a motor. The direction of current flow in the loop (which is given in this problem) leads to a net torque on the loop. In the case of a motor, the current is provided by an external source and is alternating current (AC), which is synchronized with the rotation of the loop.

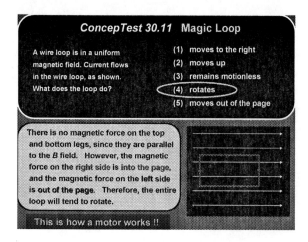

Conceptual Module 33.1 (three parts)
ConcepTest 33.1a: Transformers I
Difficulty Level: 3
Suggested follow-up numerical problem: Problems 33.1, 33.3 and 33.5

The students have to apply the transformer relation twice in order to determine the output voltage of the second transformer. The ratio of primary/secondary voltages is just the same as the ratio of turns in the transformer coils.

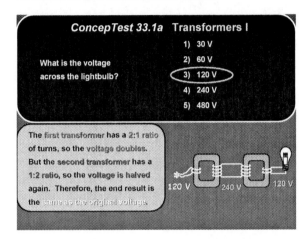

ConcepTest 33.1b: Transformers II
Difficulty Level: 3
Suggested follow-up numerical problem: Problems 33.4, 33.7 and 33.8

While the voltage of a step-down transformer is reduced, the output current is increased by the same factor. This comes from conservation of energy, such that the input power must equal the output power in a transformer. In this case, since the output voltage has decreased by a factor of 2 (given by the ratio of turns of wire), the output current must be doubled.

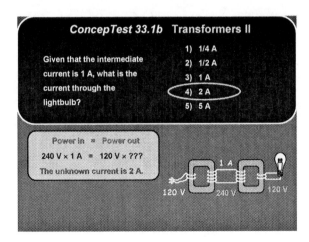

ConcepTest 33.1c: Transformers III
Difficulty Level: 2

This is a "trick" question where the students must realize that a transformer can only work with an AC input current. In this case, a DC battery will not give any changing magnetic flux in the transformer core, so there will be no induced output voltage.

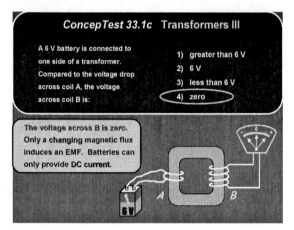

Conceptual Module 34.1 (three parts)
ConcepTest 34.1a: EM Waves I
Difficulty Level: 2

The induced EMF depends entirely on the changing flux through the loop and not on the composition of the loop itself. This is a precursor to introducing the students to the concept of electromagnetic waves, in which an induced alternating voltage can be produced in empty space by an alternating magnetic field (and vice versa).

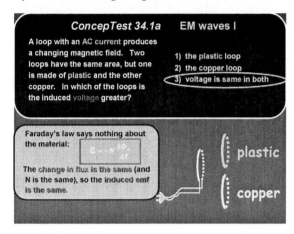

ConcepTest 34.1b: EM Waves II
Difficulty Level: 3

When asking about the current in the loop, now the material becomes relevant in terms of the resistance of the loop itself. The current is determined by Ohm's Law ($V = IR$), and the material with the lower resistance (in this case, copper) will carry the higher current.

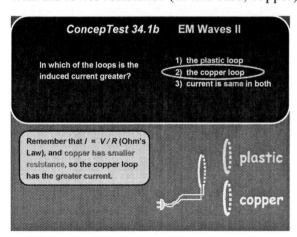

ConcepTest 34.1c: EM Waves III
Difficulty Level: 2

This follow-up question touches on the concept of EM waves. In this case, the plastic loop is replaced by a "loop of air" and the electric field inside both "loops" is seen to be the same. Here, again, the type of material (or even the presence of a material) has no bearing on the induced electric field created by the changing magnetic field.

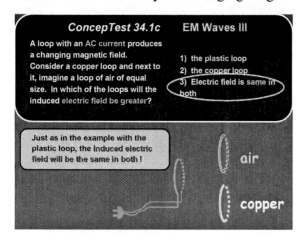

Conceptual Module 34.2
ConcepTest 34.2:   Oscillations
Difficulty Level: 2
Suggested follow-up numerical problem: Problems 34.5 and 34.13

The electric field, magnetic field and direction of motion of an EM wave are mutually perpendicular. In this case, two of the above are specified (electric field and travel direction), and the students must use this fact about EM waves to infer the direction of the third (magnetic field).

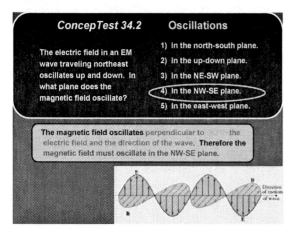

Conceptual Module 34.3
ConcepTest 34.3: TV antennas
Difficulty Level: 2
Suggested follow-up numerical problem: Problem 34.47

Students have probably seen both types of antennas, but have not given much thought to their shapes. The straight antenna is designed to pick up electric oscillations in the vertical direction, since charges can oscillate up and down the antenna. On the other hand, the circular antenna is designed to pick up magnetic oscillations in the horizontal direction, since this changing magnetic field will induce a current in the loop through which the flux is oscillating.

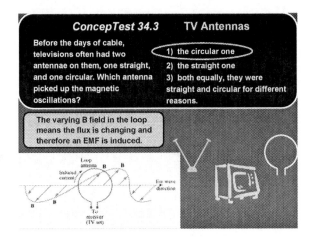

Conceptual Module 34.4
ConcepTest 34.4: Radio antennas
Difficulty Level: 2
Suggested follow-up numerical problem: Problem 34.49

Since the transmitter antenna is vertical, the electric field of the EM wave is also vertical. In order to allow charges to oscillate due to electric forces, the receiving antenna must also be oriented vertically.

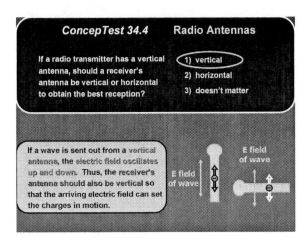

Conceptual Module 34.5
ConcepTest 34.5:   **Heat Insulation**
Difficulty Level: **2**

We are accustomed to detecting visible light, but in this case, the students are asked to make the extrapolation to the case of infrared light. Bright spots would be characterized by high intensities of radiation, and since human bodies are warm, they emit infrared radiation. These are the spots that would appear bright in infrared spectrum.

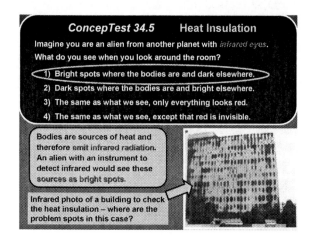

Conceptual Module 34.6
ConcepTest 34.6:   **Superman**
Difficulty Level: **3**

This question intends to get students to make the distinction between transmission and reception of EM waves. We see things because our eyes receive visible radiation that is reflected from objects. With no light source present, we cannot see (for example, we cannot see objects in a totally dark room). Thus, unless Lois Lane was irradiated by an external source of x-rays, then Superman would not be able to see her (since there is no reflected x-ray radiation).

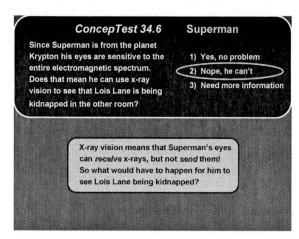

Conceptual Module 34.7
ConcepTest 34.7:   Polarization
Difficulty Level: 4
Suggested follow-up numerical problem: Problems 34.57, 34.56, and 34.54

Transmission of light through polarizers depends on the angle between adjacent elements, as given by Malus's Law. In cases #1 and #3, there are two adjacent perpendicular elements, which will cancel any transmitted light. However, in case #2, the intermediate 45° element will rotate the plane of polarization such that it can get through the last polarizer.

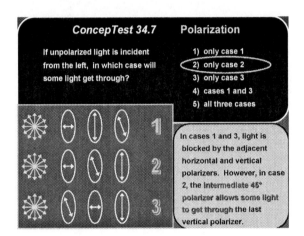

Conceptual Module 35.1
ConcepTest 35.1:   Reflection
Difficulty Level: 2
Suggested follow-up conceptual questions:
- **Where else does this occur?**

The reflection of light from water is such a common occurrence that we do not give it much thought. However, the difference between that case and the case of reflections from a planar mirror are striking. There are clear reflections from a very calm surface of water, which gives a mirror-like image, but more generally, the reflection is "shimmery" due to the undulation of the reflecting water surface.

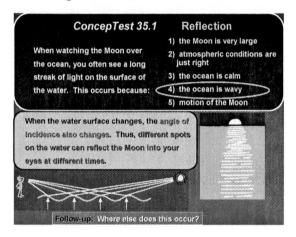

Conceptual Module 35.2 (three parts)
ConcepTest 35.2a: Mirror I
Difficulty Level: 3
Suggested follow-up numerical problem: Problem 35.12
Suggested follow-up conceptual questions:
- **What happens when the observer starts moving toward the mirror?**

This question gives students a chance to utilize the law of reflection to reconstruct the position of an image from a planar mirror. The ray reaching the observer on the left side appears to emanate directly from the (virtual) image located behind the mirror (right side).

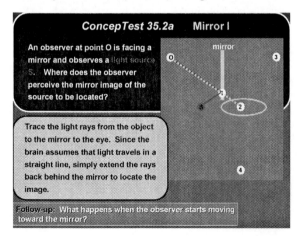

ConcepTest 35.2b: Mirror II
Difficulty Level: 3
Suggested follow-up numerical problem: Problem 36.4

Students can use the law of reflection to prove that a "full-length" mirror does not have to be as tall as the viewing object. In fact, students can convince themselves that if the mirror extended lower than the one shown, it would only serve to provide an image of the floor!

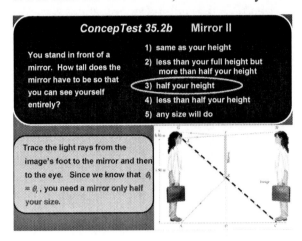

ConcepTest 35.2c: Mirror III
Difficulty Level: 2

The previous result, regarding the minimum size of a "full-length" mirror, is entirely dependent on the law of reflection, and has nothing to do with the object distance from the reflecting surface. The bottom ray, which is the one providing an image of the feet, will still be illuminating the same object, regardless of the position of that object.

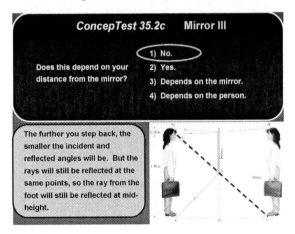

Conceptual Module 35.3
ConcepTest 35.3:   All Smoke and Mirrors
Difficulty Level: 4
Suggested follow-up numerical problem: Problem 36.2

This is a multi-step problem in reflection that requires the students to understand the nature of object and image. In this case, the object of the full-length mirror is actually the image in the hand mirror. A careful accounting of object and image distance for each reflection stage is needed in order to arrive at the answer.

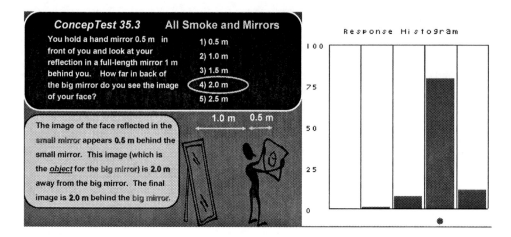

Conceptual Module 35.4 (two parts)
ConcepTest 35.4a: Refraction I
Difficulty Level: 2
Suggested follow-up conceptual questions:

   • **How does the speed in air compare to that of 1 or 2?**

The angle of refraction is related to the ratio of indices of refraction for the two media. Using this fact, and the knowledge that the light is moving at its maximum speed in the air, the students should be able to infer that the higher speed is in the medium with the least amount of bending.

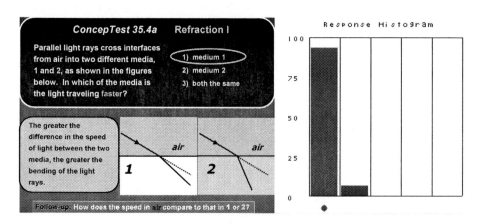

ConcepTest 35.4b: Refraction II
Difficulty Level: 3
Suggested follow-up numerical problem: Problem 35.38 and 35.22

The students have to use what they learned in the previous question to infer the ranking of the indices of refraction based on the bending of the light rays. They also need to remember that the ray will bend toward the normal when entering a medium of higher index of refraction (and vice versa).

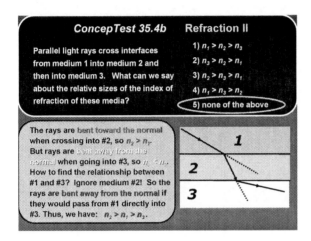

Conceptual Module 35.5 (two parts)
ConcepTest 35.5a: Gone Fishin' I
Difficulty Level: 4
Suggested follow-up numerical problem: Problem 35.57

This is a difficult question for students. They must first trace the path of a light ray *from* the object back *toward* the observer in order to establish the image position (which is higher, in this case). Then they must realize that a bullet will not refract, and so must be aimed lower than the image to account for the refraction of the light ray emanating from the object.

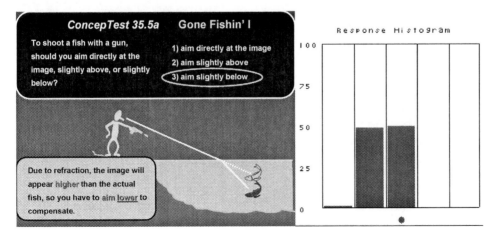

ConcepTest 35.5b: Gone Fishin' II
Difficulty Level: 2
Suggested follow-up numerical problem: Problem 35.18

This follow-up question should actually be easier. Students should realize that the laser beam will be affected in exactly the same way as the light ray from the object, so it should be fine to simply aim directly at the image and let the refraction process work for both rays.

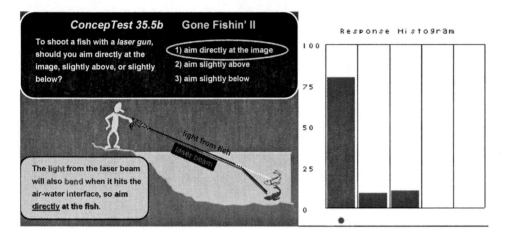

Conceptual Module 35.6
ConcepTest 35.6:   Parallel lines
Difficulty Level: 4
Suggested follow-up numerical problem: Problems 35.49 and 35.50
Suggested follow-up conceptual questions:
- **What happens when the top glass moves toward the bottom glass?**

The refraction of the two parallel rays occurs identically for both rays, so in the end, the angled piece of glass accomplishes nothing more than a lateral shift in the position of the lines on the paper. The shift occurs because of the angle imposed on the rays when they refract into the glass slab.

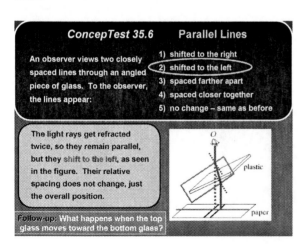

Conceptual Module 37.1
ConcepTest 37.1: **Superposition**
Difficulty Level: **2**

Students have encountered superposition in terms of vectors, but the general notion of superposition as "adding" of quantities may not have been driven home. The superposition of two waves is simply the addition of the amplitudes at each point along the wave. This is easily illustrated in this question, where the wave forms involve simple square pulses.

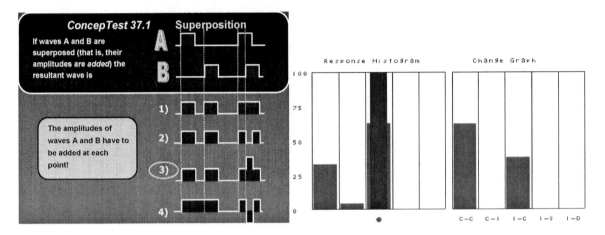

Conceptual Module 37.2 (two parts)
ConcepTest 37.2a: **Phase Difference I**
Difficulty Level: **2**
Suggested follow-up conceptual questions:
- **What would the wave look like for no. 4 to be correct?**

This question examines the phase difference between two waves. An understanding of phase is needed for the upcoming work on interference. The notion that a half-wavelength corresponds to a phase difference of 180° and a quarter-wavelength is 90° is important for the students to get straight.

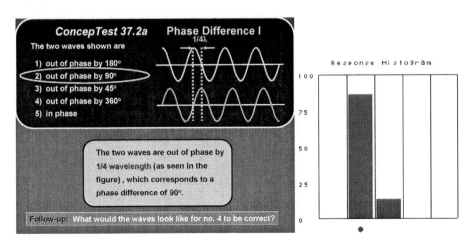

ConcepTest 37.2b: Phase Difference II
Difficulty Level: 2

This is a simple interference problem where the students must realize that waves displaced by an integral number of wavelengths will still be in phase. The periodic nature of the waves guarantees that each successive wavelength is identical to its predecessors, so that such a shift alters nothing.

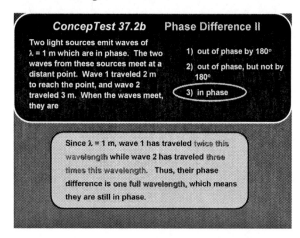

Conceptual Module 37.3 (two parts)
ConcepTest 37.3a: Double Slits I
Difficulty Level: 3
Suggested follow-up numerical problem: Problems 37.1, 37.9 and 37.14

This question examines the basic formula governing double-slit interference. The general idea is to give the students a feeling for the interplay of the slit spacing, the wavelength and the position of the fringes on the screen (as determined by the angle θ and the distance of the screen to the slits). In this case, with the slit spacing fixed, the pattern spreads out (θ increases) as the wavelength increases.

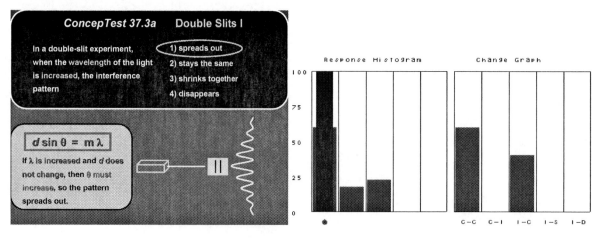

ConcepTest 37.3b: Double Slits II
Difficulty Level: 3
Suggested follow-up numerical problem: Problems 37.2, 37.4 and 37.7
Suggested follow-up conceptual questions:
- **When would the interference pattern disappear?**

This follow-up question continues to explore the double-slit interference relation. In this case, with the wavelength fixed, the pattern gets tighter (θ decreases) as the slit spacing increases.

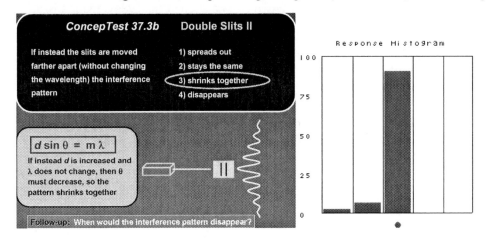

Conceptual Module 37.4
ConcepTest 37.4:   Path Difference
Difficulty Level: 2

One of the central ideas of interference relates to the path difference between two different waves. This is essentially what determines whether the waves will be in phase or out of phase when they arrive at the observer. In the double-slit interference pattern, each successive fringe corresponds to an additional phase shift of a full wavelength. It is important for students to understand this relationship.

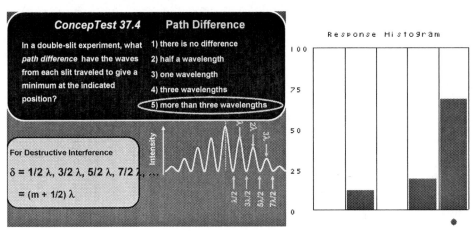

Conceptual Module 37.5
ConcepTest 37.5:   Interference Pattern
Difficulty Level: 4
Suggested follow-up numerical problem: Problems 37.10, 37.11 and 37.12
Suggested follow-up conceptual questions:
   • **What happens when the phase difference is 90°?**

This question is asking students to examine the phase relationship between interfering waves more carefully. While they have learned that the phase difference at the observer depends largely on the path-length difference, this question purposely alters the *initial* phase relationship of the waves to see if students can realize that this will simply "flip" the pattern on the screen.

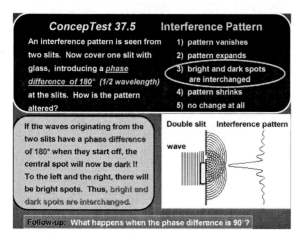

Conceptual Module 37.6 (four parts)
ConcepTest 37.6a: Parallel Slides I
Difficulty Level: 2
Suggested follow-up numerical problem: Problem 37.32

This question emphasizes the path-length difference in interference. For a given slide position, the interference is uniformly dark or light across the entire slide. As the slide positions change, the path-length difference between interfering waves is constantly changing, so the pattern changes as well.

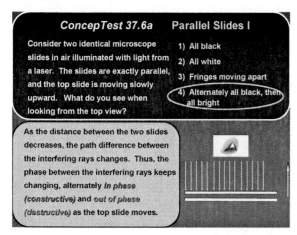

ConcepTest 37.6b: Parallel Slides II
Difficulty Level: 1
Suggested follow-up numerical problem: Problems 37.36 and 37.37

In this case, the slides are fixed, but the path-length difference arises from the angle between the slides, leading to a variable separation across the slide. The interference at point A might be expected to be constructive, due to the a path-length difference of zero, but due to the additional phase shift that occurs at the interface, point A in fact indicates destructive interference. This is the same issue that gives a dark spot in the center of Newton's rings.

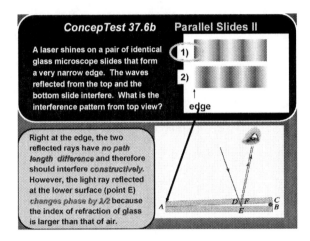

ConcepTest 37.6c: Parallel Slides III
Difficulty Level: 4
Suggested follow-up numerical problem: Problems 37.38 and 37.39

Extending the previous question, the angled slides are now brought closer together. This reduces the path-length difference and causes the interference pattern to spread out (assuming fixed wavelength). That is, the ith fringe (which corresponds to a specific path-length difference) will now move to a new position farther out on the slide in order to maintain that same path-length difference (since the slides have now moved closer).

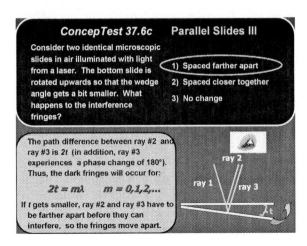

ConcepTest 37.6d: Parallel Slides IV
Difficulty Level: 4
Suggested follow-up numerical problem: Problem 37.40

This variation of the question alters the wavelength of the waves by having them travel in water. The decrease in wavelength that occurs in water (where $n > 1$) leads to a tighter interference pattern.

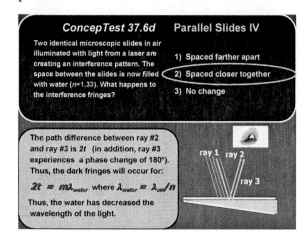

Conceptual Module 38.1 (two parts)
ConcepTest 38.1a: Diffraction I
Difficulty Level: 3
Suggested follow-up numerical problem: Problems 38.20 and 38.24

This question examines the expression for diffraction maxima and minima, which relates the wavelength and slit width to the position of interference fringes on the screen. Based on this relation, the wider the slit, the narrower the diffraction pattern.

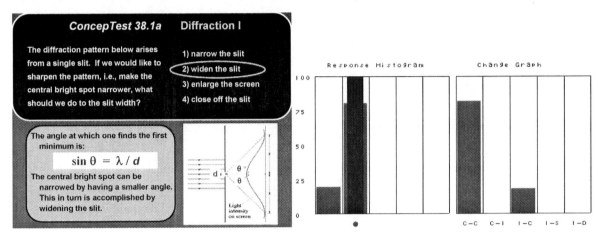

ConcepTest 38.1b: Diffraction II
Difficulty Level: 4
Suggested follow-up numerical problem: Problems 38.23 and 38.26

This two-step question requires students to recognize the shift in the diffraction pattern that will occur when the wavelength is changed, and then to deduce what must be done to another parameter (slit width) in order to recover the original pattern. Both of these steps must be performed with the same diffraction formula utilized in the previous question.

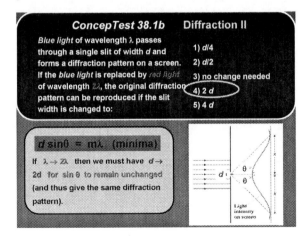

Conceptual Module 38.2
ConcepTest 38.2:   **Diffraction Disk**
Difficulty Level: **2**
Suggested follow-up conceptual questions:
- **What if the disk is oval and not circular?**

This question emphasizes the relevance of the path-length difference. At the center of the shadow, the waves emanating from the edge of the disk have all traveled the same distance, therefore they will all be in phase and should give a maximum intensity at that point.

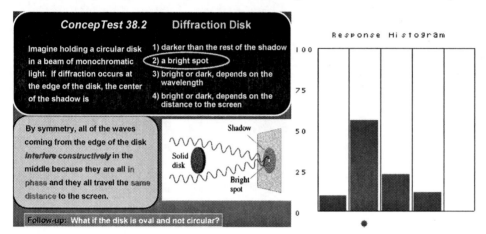

Conceptual Module 39.1
ConcepTest 39.1: Playing Ball on the Train
Difficulty Level: 2
Suggested follow-up conceptual questions:
- **What velocity does the ball have, as measured by an observer at rest on the station platform?**

A basic concept to understand before embarking on special relativity is the notion of reference frames. Students have a lot of experience with reference frames (sitting in class vs. driving in a car) but have probably not given this much consideration. This question tries to get them to relate their experience to the physical quantities in the respective frames.

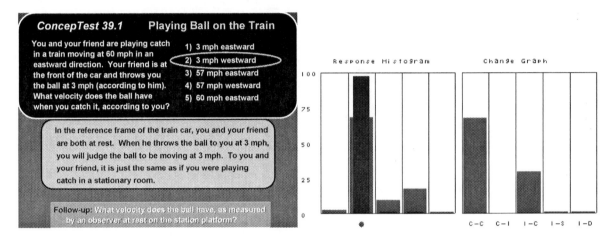

Conceptual Module 39.2
ConcepTest 39.2: Running with an Electron
Difficulty Level: 2

The students know that magnetic fields are generated by moving charges. However, that motion is relative, and it can in fact be the observer who is moving relative to a fixed charge. The idea that the presence of a magnetic field is frame-dependent will probably come as a surprise to students.

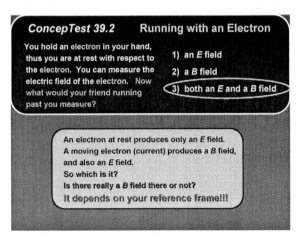

Conceptual Module 39.3
ConcepTest 39.3:   Inertial Reference Frames
Difficulty Level: 1

The definition of an inertial reference frame is one that is not accelerating. This question asks students to make this distinction for several choices, keeping in mind that uniform circular motion does indeed involve an acceleration.

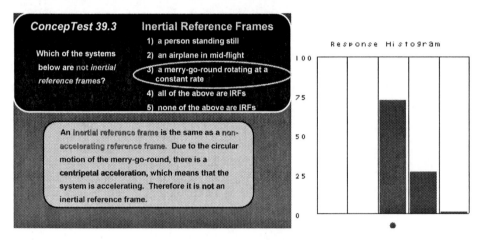

Conceptual Module 39.4 (two parts)
ConcepTest 39.4a: Changing Reference Frames I
Difficulty Level: 2

Certain quantities are frame-dependent but other quantities are invariant. The students are asked to examine several kinematic quantities to deduce whether they depend on the reference frame or not. For example, velocity is obviously dependent on the frame, as evidenced by riding in a car.

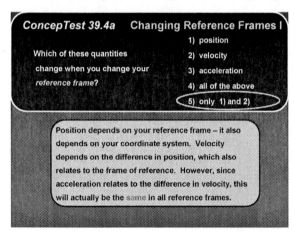

ConcepTest 39.4b: Changing Reference Frames II
Difficulty Level: 2

This question continues to examine the frame dependence of various physical quantities.

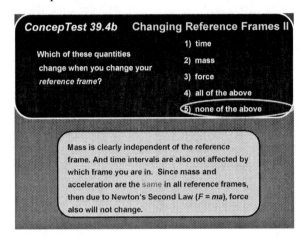

Conceptual Module 39.5
ConcepTest 39.5:   Windowless Spaceship
Difficulty Level: 2

Since the physics of inertial reference frames is the same in all such frames, it is therefore impossible to distinguish a frame at rest from a frame moving at constant velocity. Any kinematics experiment that would be performed in either frame would yield the same result.

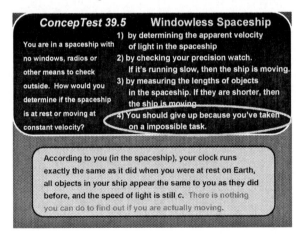

Conceptual Module 39.6 (three parts)
ConcepTest 39.6a: Borg Ship I
Difficulty Level: 2

This initial question ignores special relativity (for the moment) and asks students to identify the relative speed of two approaching objects. This is essentially an exercise in the "classical" addition of velocities, mainly to establish the meaning of the concept of relative velocity.

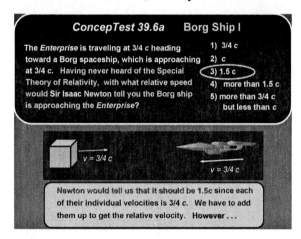

ConcepTest 39.6b: Borg Ship II
Difficulty Level: 2
Suggested follow-up numerical problem: Problem 39.39

Now taking special relativity into account, the students must assert that the speed of light is the ultimate speed. In this case, while the relative velocity will certainly be greater than $0.75c$, it cannot exceed c, which is the speed of light.

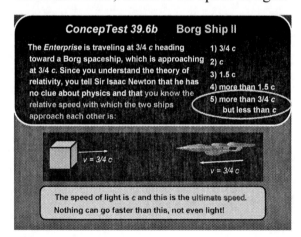

ConcepTest 39.6c: Borg Ship III
Difficulty Level: 1

Here, again, the fact that the speed of light is the ultimate speed is re-emphasized. Even though the speed of the source is non-zero, the speed of light does not change, for neither the source nor the observer.

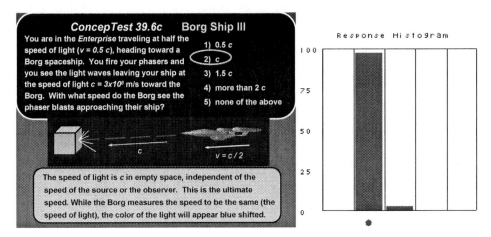

Conceptual Module 39.7 (two parts)
ConcepTest 39.7a: Speed of Light I
Difficulty Level: 2

This classic statement illustrates the postulate that the speed of light c is the same in all inertial reference frames. Thus, even though the observer is moving rapidly, the speed of light in that observer's frame is still c.

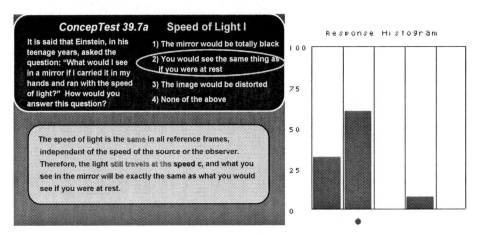

ConcepTest 39.7b: Speed of Light II
Difficulty Level: 2

Since the speed of light is reduced in a medium with index of refraction $n > 1$, it is indeed possible for a highly relativistic particle to move faster than light (in that medium!). This leads to a shock wave called Cherenkov radiation (see Section 14-9 of the textbook). However, it must be understood that no particle can travel faster than c (where this is the speed of light in vacuum).

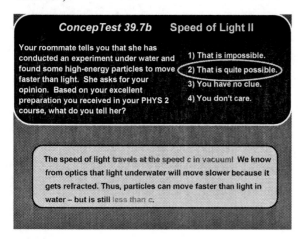

Conceptual Module 39.8
ConcepTest 39.8:   Foghorns
Difficulty Level: 2

This is a "warmup" to the discussion of simultaneity. In this case, while the observer hears the sounds at the same time, the fact that one is softer than the other allows the observer to extrapolate that this sound must have originated farther away and thus must have sounded first.

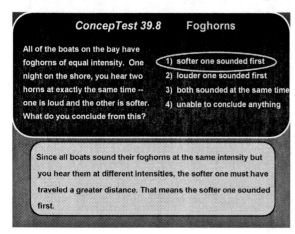

Conceptual Module 39.9
ConcepTest 39.9:   **Balls in Boxcar**
Difficulty Level: 3
Suggested follow-up numerical problem: **Problem 39.1**

In this case, the classical understanding of relative velocity applies. According to the ground observer, the green ball has a higher initial speed, but the far end of the car is receding from it. The blue ball has a lower initial speed, but the near end of the car is approaching it. Thus, the travel times in both cases will end up being the same, and the balls strike the respective walls *simultaneously*.

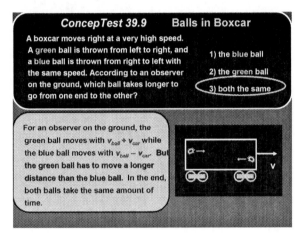

Conceptual Module 39.10 (two parts)
ConcepTest 39.10a: **Light Flashes in Boxcar I**
Difficulty Level: 2

In the reference frame of the boxcar, the light flashes traverse the same distance at the same velocity, so the travel times in both cases will be the same, and the flashes will arrive at the respective walls *simultaneously*.

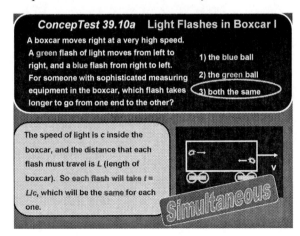

ConcepTest 39.10b: Light Flashes in Boxcar II
Difficulty Level: 4

This question considers the same situation from the perspective of the ground observer, but the result is different from ConcepTest 39.9 above. The key point here is that the light flashes *still travel at the speed of light*, independent of the motion of the boxcar (which is quite different from the case of the two balls). Since the distance traveled is different as the boxcar moves, but the speed of the flashes is the same, therefore the hits *will not be simultaneous*, according to the ground observer.

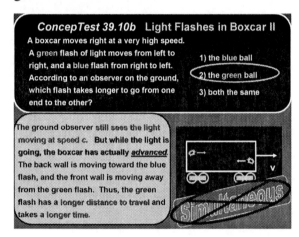

Conceptual Module 39.11
ConcepTest 39.11:   Causality
Difficulty Level: 2

Seeing the result of the previous ConcepTest, students realize that as the boxcar speeds up, the blue flash will hit earlier and earlier before the green flash, and the time interval between the emission of the blue flash and its contact with the wall decreases. However, the contact can never actually *precede* the emission of the flash, since that would require the boxcar to move faster than *c*!

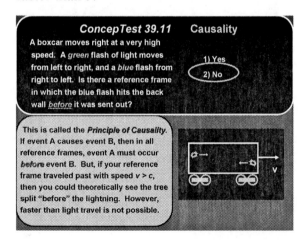

Conceptual Module 39.12 (two parts)
ConcepTest 39.12a: Boxcar I
Difficulty Level: 3

In this case, the classical understanding of relative velocity applies. According to the ground observer, the soccer ball has a higher initial speed, but the far end of the car is receding from it. Since the difference in each case is simply due to the speed of the boxcar, the higher speed and longer distance end up giving the same travel time for the soccer ball.

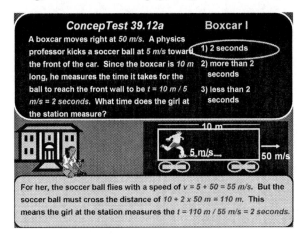

ConcepTest 39.12b: Boxcar II
Difficulty Level: 3
Suggested follow-up numerical problem: Problems 39.7, 39.9 and 39.74

This case is similar to above, except that a light flash is involved (instead of a soccer ball). Since both the ground and boxcar observers see the light move at the same speed, the ground observer will measure a longer transit time because the far end of the car is receding from the flash. This is the first glimpse of the effect of time dilation for the students.

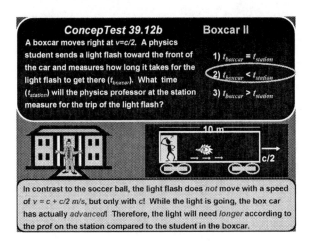

Conceptual Module 39.13 (three parts)
ConcepTest 39.13a: Time Dilation I
Difficulty Level: 3
Suggested follow-up numerical problem: Problems 39.13 and 39.14

The time dilation effect ("moving clocks run slow") implies that an observer who is *not* in the frame of the event will measure a longer time interval. Thus, the astronaut's pulse rate would appear to be slower, as determined by the Earth-bound observer. It can be very confusing for students to identify which frame is the "rest" frame and which frame is the "moving" frame. This is especially difficult since the concept of motion is all relative!

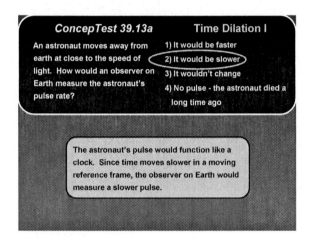

ConcepTest 39.13b: Time Dilation II
Difficulty Level: 3
Suggested follow-up conceptual questions:
- **What would the astronaut in the spaceship measure?**

This follow-up question on time dilation is very similar to the previous one. Here again, since the observer is *not* in the rest frame of the pendulum, that observer will measure the period to be slower than the proper period (measured when an observer is at rest with respect to the pendulum).

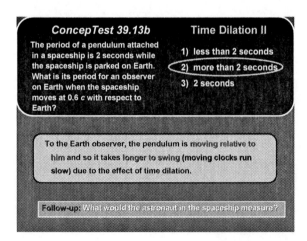

ConcepTest 39.13c: Time Dilation III
Difficulty Level: 2

This question is intended to dispel any notion that the time dilation effect is related to the direction of motion. By the logic posed in this question, if moving away from a clock means that time runs slower, then moving towards the clock will make time speed up (which is untrue!).

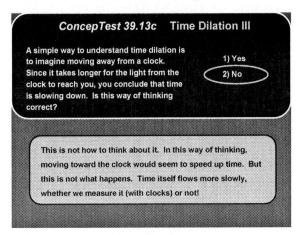

Conceptual Module 39.14

ConcepTest 39.14:   Length Contraction
Difficulty Level: 3
Suggested follow-up numerical problem: Problems 39.6, 39.10, 39.11 and 39.70
Suggested follow-up conceptual questions:
*   **What would the astronaut measure about his spaceship?**

In length contraction, an observer *not* in the rest frame of the object will see it to be shorter than its proper length. In this case, the Earth-bound observer is clearly not in the rest frame of the moving spaceship, so the length will be contracted. Since the length contraction effect is related to the speed of the moving object, the contraction will become more pronounced as the speed increases.

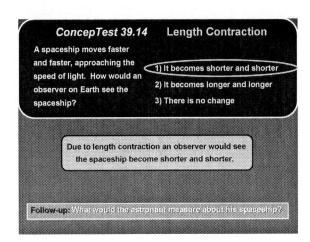

Conceptual Module 39.15
ConcepTest 39.15: Pancake or Cigar?
Difficulty Level: 3
Suggested follow-up numerical problem: Problem 39.12 and 39.75

Students must realize that the length contraction affects the dimension *along the direction of motion*, and not the other dimensions that are perpendicular to the motion. Thus, the spherical spaceship in this case will appear contracted in the horizontal direction of motion, but unaffected vertically – this will lead to a pancake-like shape.

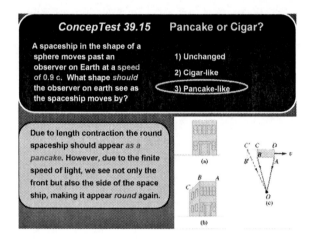

Conceptual Module 39.16 (two parts)
ConcepTest 39.16a: The Tunnel I
Difficulty Level: 4

This is a classic paradox that the students are asked to resolve. In this first part, the spacecraft is readily seen to be length contracted according to the lady (ground observer), so it will fit inside the tunnel when both doors are closed simultaneously (in the lady's frame!). Generally, there is little difficulty with this part of the two-part series of questions.

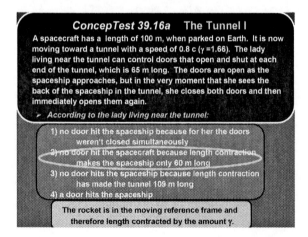

ConcepTest 39.16b: The Tunnel II
Difficulty Level: 5

This second part often causes conceptual difficulties. According to the spacecraft observers, the tunnel is now length contracted, so the situation is even worse for them! However, it must be agreed that if the spacecraft is not destroyed according to the lady (previous question), then that result must also hold as viewed in the moving frame. The resolution to the paradox lies in the fact that the people in the spacecraft *do not see the doors closed simultaneously*, and this is how they explain their safe passage.

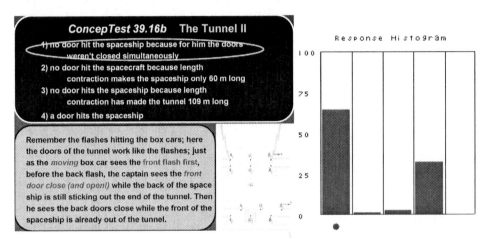

Conceptual Module 39.17
ConcepTest 39.17:   Relativistic Mass
Difficulty Level: 3
Suggested follow-up numerical problem: Problems 39.46, 39.54, and 39.55

This is a straightforward two-step question. The students must use the length information to infer the relativistic factor (sometimes called γ), which must then be applied to obtain the relativistic mass. In this case, the factor is 2.0, which leads to a doubling of the mass. Note that some choices can be eliminated immediately, since the mass can never decrease.

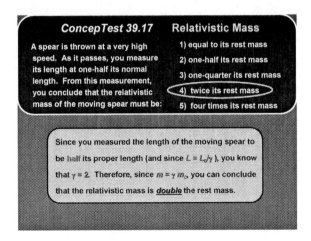

Conceptual Module 39.18
ConcepTest 39.18:   Muon Decay
Difficulty Level: 4
Suggested follow-up numerical problem: Problems 39.4 and 39.81

It is important for the students to realize that the outcome of two events must be agreed upon by observers in different frames. In this case, the muons reach Earth in both cases. From the frame of reference of an Earth-bound observer, we say that time dilation made the muon lifetime exceed the proper lifetime, which enabled the muons to travel farther and therefore reach Earth's surface. However, from the muon's frame, the story is different (even though the result is the same!). The muons say that the distance from the upper atmosphere to the surface was length contracted, and that is how they could reach the surface during their proper lifetime.

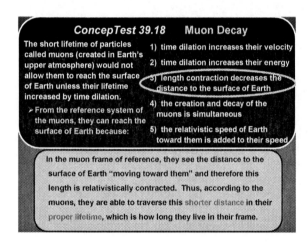

Conceptual Module 40.1
ConcepTest 40.1: Photons
Difficulty Level: 2
Suggested follow-up numerical problem: Problems 40.2 and 40.3

It is useful for the students to make a close association between the Planck relation and the visible spectrum. Generally, the visible spectrum is characterized by wavelength and color, whereas the students learn the Planck relation as $E = hf$. This question allows the students to connect color to wavelength, and then wavelength to energy.

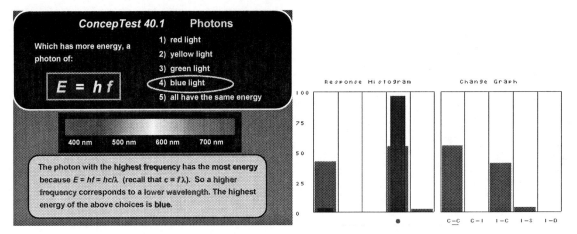

Conceptual Module 40.2 (five parts)
ConcepTest 40.2a: Photoelectric Effect I
Difficulty Level: 3
Suggested follow-up numerical problem: Problems 40.7 and 40.8
Suggested follow-up conceptual questions:

- **What do you expect to happen to the work function of a metal if the metal was heated up?**

The work function is what gives rise to a particular cutoff in energy for the photoelectric effect. This characteristic energy can be represented by a frequency, which is a direct result of the Planck relation ($E = hf$). This question emphasizes (again) this connection between energy and frequency.

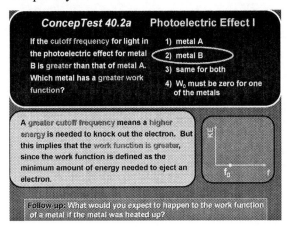

ConcepTest 40.2b: Photoelectric Effect II
Difficulty Level: 4
Suggested follow-up numerical problem: Problems 40.5 and 40.9

This question comes back to the relation between color, wavelength and energy. In this case, red light has a longer wavelength, which means it has lower energy. In fact, as an additional twist, the energy is actually *below* the cutoff energy, so no electrons can be emitted. Another way to look at this is that the wavelength of red light is *longer than the cutoff wavelength*, which again implies a lower energy.

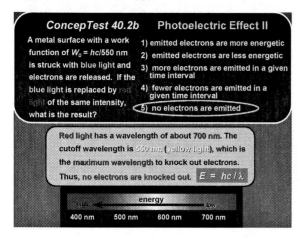

ConcepTest 40.2c: Photoelectric Effect III
Difficulty Level: 2

In this case, the wavelength is decreased, which means that the energy of the incident light has increased.   The issue here is what is the effect of the increased energy. This does not affect the number of electrons emitted, but does increase the individual energies of the electrons emitted.

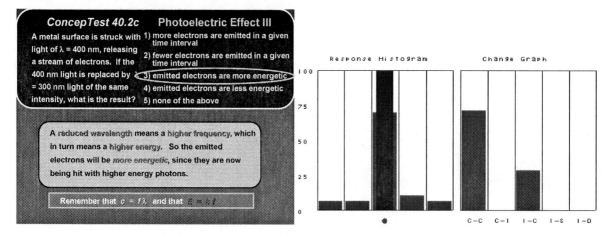

ConcepTest 40.2d: Photoelectric Effect IV
Difficulty Level: 2
Suggested follow-up numerical problem: Problems 40.4, 40.6 and 40.12

In this follow-up question, the wavelength is held fixed, but the intensity of the light has increased. This means that more photons are impinging on the metal surface, which results in the release of more electrons. However, the electron energies do not change, since the energy of the photons has not changed (there are just more photons). This emphasizes the difference between the energy and the intensity of the incident light.

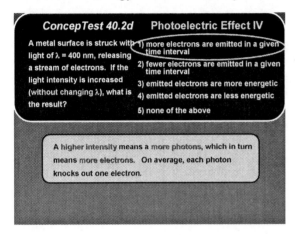

ConcepTest 40.2e: Photoelectric Effect V
Difficulty Level: 2

The measured current is related to the amount of charge flowing, which relates directly to the number of electrons (and not their energies). The students have just seen that this quantity is proportional to the intensity of the light (and not its energy, which is related to frequency or wavelength).

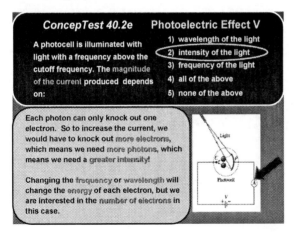

Conceptual Module 40.3 (four parts)
ConcepTest 40.3a: Wave-Particle Duality I
Difficulty Level: 2
Suggested follow-up numerical problem: Problem 40.31

The wave-particle duality of nature specifies that both photons and matter can have wave-like and particle-like properties. The wavelength of a matter wave is inversely proportional to its momentum, so the proton with the lower momentum (in this case, the lower speed, because both have the same mass) will have the longer wavelength.

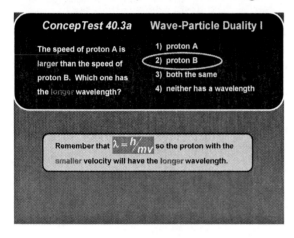

ConcepTest 40.3b: Wave-Particle Duality II
Difficulty Level: 2

The wavelength of a matter wave is inversely proportional to its momentum, so the particle with the lower momentum (in this case, the smaller mass, because both have the same speed) will have the longer wavelength. Here it is the electron with the longer wavelength (rather than the proton).

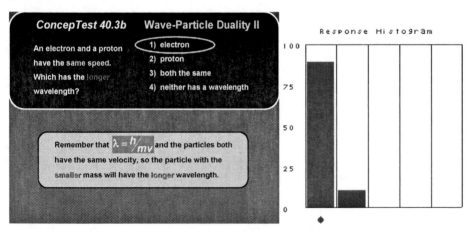

ConcepTest 40.3c: Wave-Particle Duality III
Difficulty Level: 4
Suggested follow-up numerical problem: Problems 40.28, 40.29 and 40.30

This question sets up the same type of problem, but where the proton and electron have the same kinetic energy. This must be related to the momentum of the particle, in order to draw a conclusion about the wavelength. Rewriting the kinetic energy as $KE = p^2/2m$ indicates that the lighter particle (electron) will also have the smaller momentum (and hence, the longer wavelength).

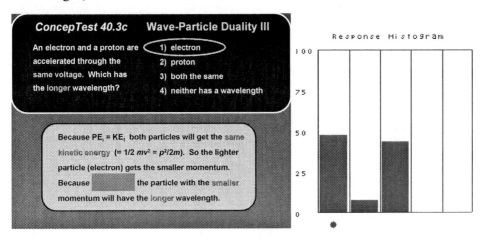

ConcepTest 40.3d: Wave-Particle Duality IV
Difficulty Level: 1

This question directly addresses the relation between the wavelength of a matter wave and the momentum of the particle.

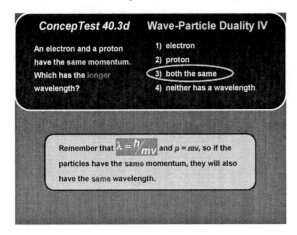

Conceptual Module 41.1
ConcepTest 41.1:   **Ionization**
Difficulty Level: **1**
Suggested follow-up numerical problem: Problem 41.1, 41.2
Suggested follow-up conceptual questions: How much energy does it take to change a He$^+$ ion into a He^{++} ion? Keep in mind that $Z = 2$ for helium.

This is a quick check to make sure that the students know the ground-state energy of the hydrogen atom and also that they understand what is meant by ionization. Discrete transitions to higher bound levels is something they will also deal with, but they need to realize that transitions to the continuum (unbound) states are possible as well (*i.e.*, ionization).

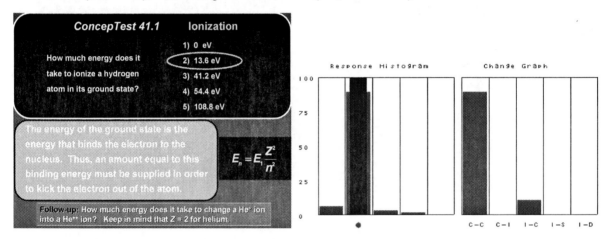

Conceptual Module 41.2 (two parts)
ConcepTest 41.2a: **Atomic Transitions I**
Difficulty Level: **3**
Suggested follow-up numerical problem: Problem 41.3
Suggested follow-up conceptual questions:
- **Which transition will emit the shortest wavelength photon?**

Students must get accustomed to the energy level diagram, in terms of the spacing of the energy levels. They must also understand that electrons will gain energy when making upward transitions or lose energy when making downward transitions.

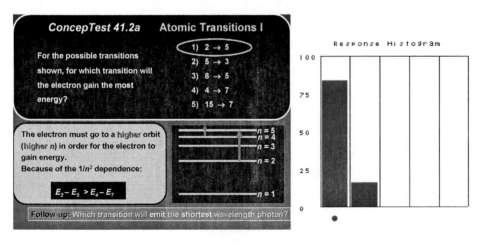

ConcepTest 41.2b: Atomic Transitions II
Difficulty Level: 3
Suggested follow-up numerical problem: Problem 41.7
Suggested follow-up conceptual questions:
- **Which transition leads to the shortest wavelength photon?**

Students should understand that the energy of an emitted photon is the same as the energy difference between the two levels in a transition. In this case, the "reddest" photon corresponds to a lower-energy transition, which would pertain to a transition between the most closely spaced levels.

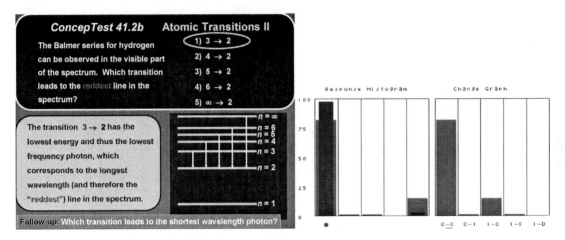

Conceptual Module 41.3
ConcepTest 41.3: Balmer Series
Difficulty Level: 2
Suggested follow-up numerical problem: Problem 41.8, 41.9, 41.10
Suggested follow-up conceptual questions:
- **From the diagram at right, where in the EM spectrum is the Lyman series located?**

This is more of a question of common sense. The Balmer series is the only series that involves visible light, so none of the other transitions that are occurring can be observed in the visible range.

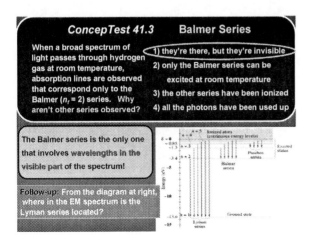

Conceptual Module 41.4 (two parts)
ConcepTest 41.4a: Energy Levels I
Difficulty Level: 2

This is an exercise in counting transitions. The students must systematically consider each initial state and add up the number of transitions possible, and then add up the total.

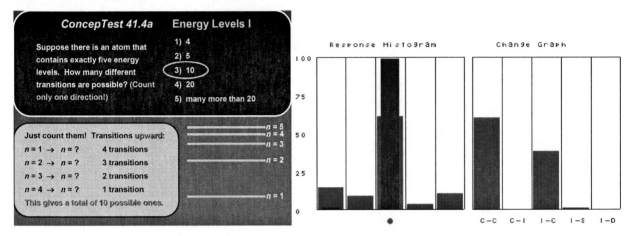

ConcepTest 41.4b: Energy Levels II
Difficulty Level: 4
Suggested follow-up numerical problem: Problem 41.4

This is a more challenging question, in which students must infer 4 high-energy transitions (from the blue and violet lines) and 2 lower-energy transitions (from the yellow and orange lines). Then they must search the available energy level diagrams to match this pattern (which is satisfied by #2).

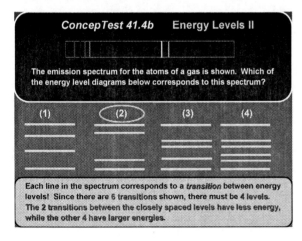

Conceptual Module 41.5
ConcepTest 41.5: Rutherford Model
Difficulty Level: 2

The Rutherford atom was characterized by a continuum of levels (not discrete levels, as in the Bohr atom). Since this would allow any energy transition to be possible, then all energies of light incident on the atom could potentially be absorbed and the spectrum would appear totally dark.

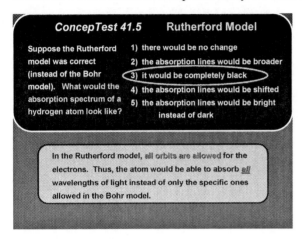

Conceptual Module 41.6
ConcepTest 41.6: Ionic Bonding
Difficulty Level: 2

The likely partners in an ionic bond are atoms that can either readily give up a valence electron (to leave behind a closed shell) or readily accept one in a vacant valence orbital (to fill a shell).

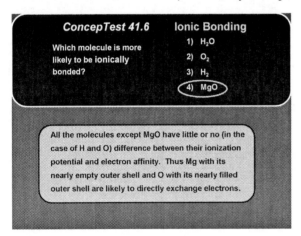

Conceptual Module 41.7 (two parts)
ConcepTest 41.7a: Electron Spin I
Difficulty Level: 1
Suggested follow-up numerical problem: Problem 41.26

This is a simple question about the Pauli Exclusion Principle. Students need to remember the definition of an antisymmetric wave function.

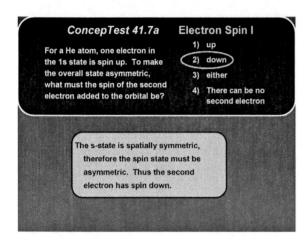

ConcepTest 41.7b: Electron Spin II
Difficulty Level: 3

Students need to recognize how the Pauli Principle works in the combination of several quantum numbers. The above answer in the previous ConcepTest does not apply since the electron now enters a *p*-orbital.

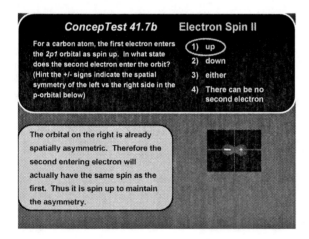

Conceptual Module 41.8
ConcepTest 41.8: Vibrational Levels
Difficulty Level: 2
Suggested follow-up numerical problem: Problem 41.40, 41.41

Students need to remember the angular momentum selection rule for vibrational levels.

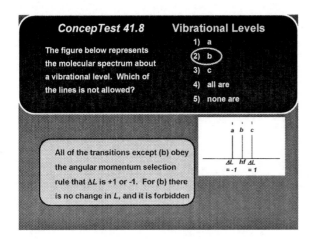

Conceptual Module 41.9
ConcepTest 41.9: More Bonding
Difficulty Level: 1

Students need to remember the definition of ionic bonding.

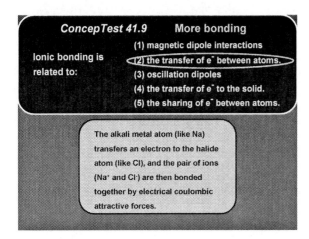

Conceptual Module 43.1
ConcepTest 43.1: Solid H and He
Difficulty Level: 2

This is a simple question where students learn how to translate their knowledge from atomic levels to band structure in solids.

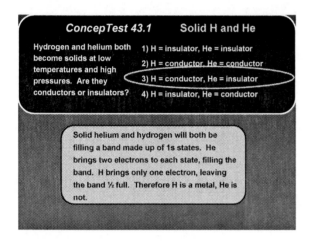

Conceptual Module 43.2
ConcepTest 43.2: Metallic Conduction
Difficulty Level: 2
Suggested follow-up numerical problem: Problem 43.5, 43.9, 43.10

This question tests students' understanding of an energy gap in the band structure of solids and its relationship to conduction.

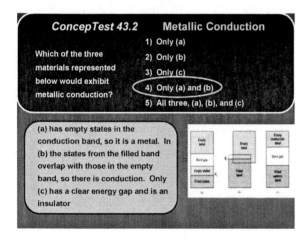

Conceptual Module 44.1
ConcepTest 44.1:   **The Nucleus**
Difficulty Level: 1

Regarding the four fundamental forces of nature, the nuclear interaction is the strongest. It is much stronger than the Coulomb force that causes like charges to repel. This introductory question is intended to highlight this point.

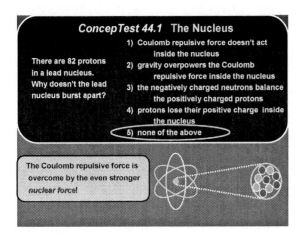

Conceptual Module 44.2 (three parts)
ConcepTest 44.2a: **Binding Energy I**
Difficulty Level: 2

The concept of binding energy is often confusing for students. The notion that there is more energy in a free proton and electron than in a bound hydrogen atom (due to the binding energy!) means that the former combination weighs more than the latter. The equivalency of mass and energy (by $E = mc^2$) allows us to talk about mass and energy interchangeably. This example of an atomic system is meant to serve as a gentle introduction to the concept of binding energy, since the students should be quite familiar with the hydrogen atom.

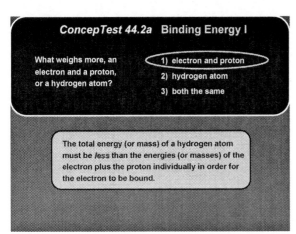

ConcepTest 44.2b: Binding Energy II
Difficulty Level: 2

This follow-up question emphasizes the mass difference alluded to in the previous question. Since the binding energy is negative for a bound system, the mass (or energy) of a hydrogen atom is actually less than that of a free proton and electron by 13.6 eV.

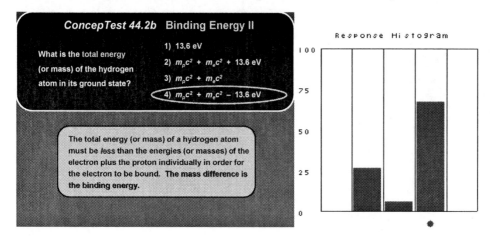

ConcepTest 44.2c: Binding Energy III
Difficulty Level: 2
Suggested follow-up numerical problem: Problems 44.2, 44.54, 44.17 and 44.8

Now we switch gears to a nuclear system, but the concept of binding energy remains the same. In this case, the bound tritium nucleus has a lower total energy (weighs less) than the separate constituents. The difference in energy is simply the binding energy, which in this case is 8.5 MeV.

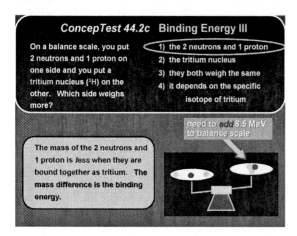

Conceptual Module 44.3
ConcepTest 44.3:   **Separation Energy**
Difficulty Level: **2**
Suggested follow-up numerical problem: Problems 44.20 and 44.56

The proton will tend to be repelled by the other protons in the nucleus, so in fact the removal of a proton is aided by the Coulomb repulsion. The uncharged neutron does not have this advantage, and so it will take more energy to remove a neutron (15.7 MeV) than to remove a proton (12.1 MeV).

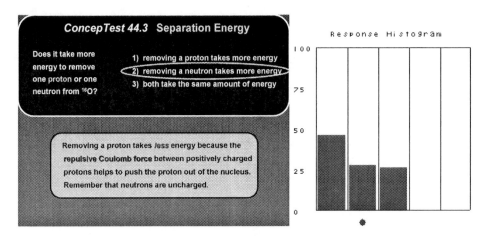

Conceptual Module 44.4
ConcepTest 44.4:   **Nuclear Reaction Products**
Difficulty Level: **3**
Suggested follow-up numerical problem: Problems 44.1, 44.23, 44.25 and 44.30
Suggested follow-up conceptual questions:
- **What would you get if you started with $p + {}^{16}O$ instead?**

For this question, it is a matter of counting the neutrons and protons on both sides and then requiring a balance. In the nuclear reaction, constituents are exchanged, but the total number of nucleons (neutrons and protons) is conserved.

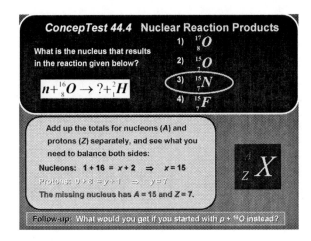

Conceptual Module 44.5
ConcepTest 44.5:   **Nuclear Reactions**
Difficulty Level: **2**
Suggested follow-up numerical problem: Problem 44.39
Suggested follow-up conceptual questions:
- **Is radioactive decay an endothermic or exothermic reaction?**

Some reactions give off energy when they occur (exothermic) and therefore can occur spontaneously, whereas other reactions require some input energy in order to occur (endothermic). Radioactive decay occurs spontaneously with a corresponding release of energy, so the reaction is exothermic and therefore the Q-value must be positive.

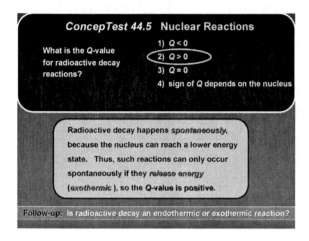

Conceptual Module 44.6 (two parts)
ConcepTest 44.6a: **Particle Emission I**
Difficulty Level: **2**

Alpha particles are positively charged. The students will have to remember the right-hand rule in order to determine the direction of the magnetic force on a moving positively charged particle.

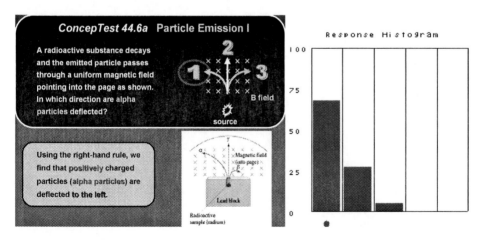

ConcepTest 44.6b: Particle Emission II
Difficulty Level: 2
Suggested follow-up conceptual questions:
   • **What particles are bent to the right?**

Gamma rays are uncharged – they are essentially photons – and uncharged particles are not deflected in a magnetic field.

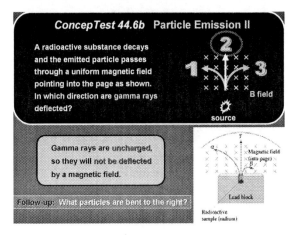

Conceptual Module 44.7
ConcepTest 44.7:   Radioactive Decay Energy
Difficulty Level: 2
Suggested follow-up numerical problem: Problem 44.14
Suggested follow-up conceptual questions:
   • **What process could release a photon with billions of eV?**

The students have already seen that energies of a few eV pertain to atomic systems. Binding energy of nuclear systems has already been discussed, and so the students should be familiar with the fact that in nuclear systems, we are talking about energies of several MeV (millions of eV). The energy scale is determined largely by the strength of the interaction (nuclear force vs. Coulomb force).

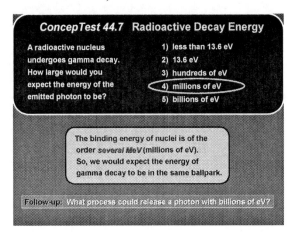

Conceptual Module 44.8 (three parts)
ConcepTest 44.8a: Alpha Decay I
Difficulty Level: 2
Suggested follow-up conceptual questions:
- **In what directions are the two products emitted?**

This question relates back to the conservation of momentum. Since the initial system has zero momentum, then momentum conservation dictates that the final system will have zero momentum, so that the momenta of the reaction products must be equal and opposite.

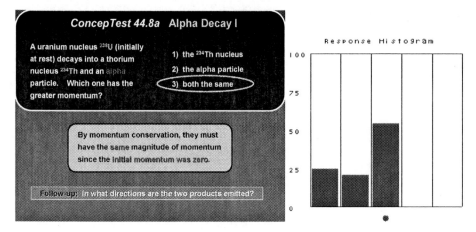

ConcepTest 44.8b: Alpha Decay II
Difficulty Level: 3

Since the momenta have the same magnitude, then the particle with the smaller mass must have the greater velocity. In this case, the alpha particle is moving faster than the ^{234}Th nucleus.

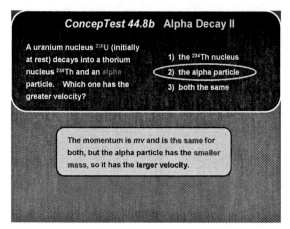

ConcepTest 44.8c: Alpha Decay III
Difficulty Level: 4
Suggested follow-up numerical problem: Problem 44.38

For this question, the students must recall that kinetic energy can be rewritten as $KE = p^2/2m$. With the momenta of the two particles being equal, then the lighter mass particle (the alpha particle) will have the greater kinetic energy.

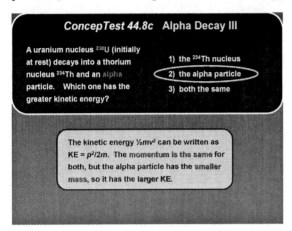

Conceptual Module 44.9
ConcepTest 44.9:   Beta Decay
Difficulty Level: 3
Suggested follow-up numerical problem: Problem 44.32, 44.32 and 44.43
Suggested follow-up conceptual questions:
   • **How would you turn ^{14}C into ^{15}N?**

In beta decay, a neutron turns into a proton and emits a beta particle (and a neutrino). In this type of reaction, the number of nucleons (A) does not change, but the number of protons (Z) does change. Thus, a new element is formed (Z+1) with the same atomic mass (A) as the original nucleus.

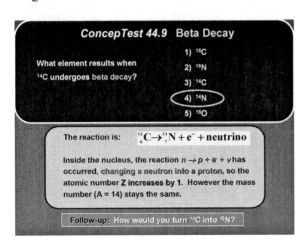

Conceptual Module 44.10 (four parts)
ConcepTest 44.10a: Radioactive Decay Law I
Difficulty Level: 3
Suggested follow-up numerical problem: Problem 44.35
Suggested follow-up conceptual questions:
   • **When will the sample be reduced to nothing?**

In this question, the students must simply count the number of half-lives that have passed, with a reduction by a factor of two in mass for each passing half-life. In this case, 3 half-lives have gone by, leading to a reduction factor of $2^3 = 8$ in mass.

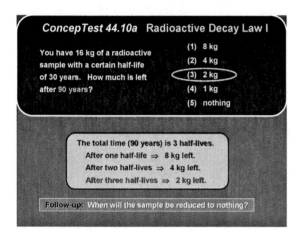

ConcepTest 44.10b: Radioactive Decay Law II
Difficulty Level: 3
Suggested follow-up numerical problem: Problem 44.37
Suggested follow-up conceptual questions:
   • **How much of the sample is left after another 10 years?**

In this case, the initial and final masses are given, and the students are asked to infer the half-life from the total time (10 years) that has passed. In this case, the mass is reduced by a factor of $2^2 = 4$, which means that two half-lives have gone by. Thus, each half-life must be 5 years.

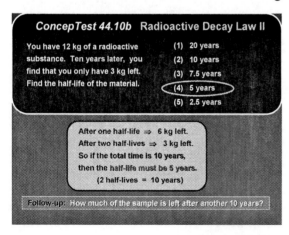

ConcepTest 44.10c: Radioactive Decay Law III
Difficulty Level: 4

Radioactive decay is not a linear process – it follows an exponential decay law. The time involved in this problem is not an integral number of half-lives. The students will probably realize that 40 years (two half-lives) would leave 100 g and that 60 years (three half-lives) would leave 50 g. But the fact that 50 years is in between these choices *does not mean* that 75 g will be left over! In fact, there will be less than 75 g, due to the rate of decay governed by the exponential law.

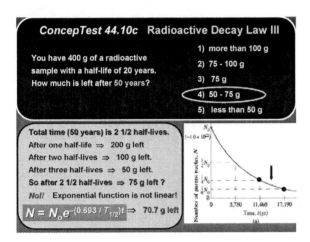

ConcepTest 44.10d: Radioactive Decay Law IV
Difficulty Level: 4
Suggested follow-up numerical problem: Problems 44.41, 44.42 and 44.58
Suggested follow-up conceptual questions
   •   **When will the samples again have equal amounts?**

This is a multi-step problem in which the students must relate what they know about one sample and the decay time given to the other sample. First, the final amount of the known sample must be found, and then, working backwards from there, the initial amount of the unknown can be determined.

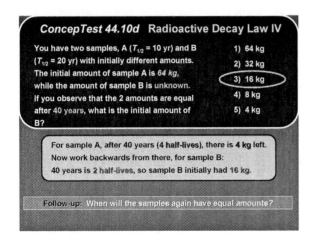

Conceptual Module 44.11 (two parts)
ConcepTest 44.11a: Activity and Half-Life I
Difficulty Level: 1
Suggested follow-up conceptual questions
- **What is the ratio of activities for the two samples?**

The activity is inversely related to the half-life (for samples of equal size). That is, a sample with a high activity will decay quickly and therefore have a shorter half-life.

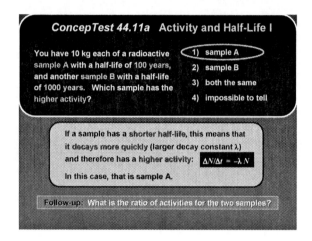

ConcepTest 44.11b: Activity and Half-Life II
Difficulty Level: 2
Suggested follow-up numerical problem: Problem 44.36

This question is quite similar to the previous one, except for the quantitative feature added. In this case, the factor of 5 in activity (for equal size samples) must be appropriately applied to the half-life.

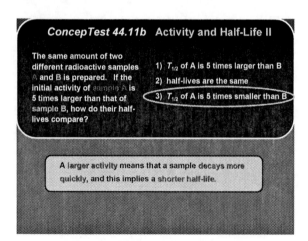

Conceptual Module 44.12

ConcepTest 44.12:   Nuclear Fission
Difficulty Level: 2
Suggested follow-up numerical problem: Problems 44.48, 44.50, and 44.51
Suggested follow-up conceptual questions

- **Where are the fission fragments located relative to the original nucleus on the curve of binding energy per nucleon?**

This is essentially a binding energy question. The nucleus undergoes fission because it can reach a lower energy (mass) state by splitting apart. Thus, the fragments must have less mass than the original nucleus when it was intact. This is the opposite of what was seen for light nuclei (such as tritium), but it is all related to the position of the components on the curve of binding energy per nucleon.

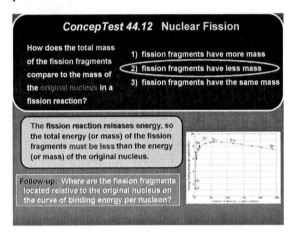

Conceptual Module 44.13

ConcepTest 44.13:   Nuclear Fusion
Difficulty Level: 2
Suggested follow-up numerical problem: Problems 44.49, 44.52 and 44.53
Suggested follow-up conceptual questions

- **Which weighs more: the fusion products or the pieces?**

This question gets to the heart of why light nuclei prefer to undergo fusion and heavy nuclei prefer to undergo fission. Increasing the binding energy per nucleon makes the result more stable.

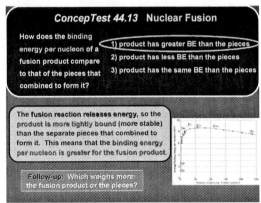

Conceptual Module 44.14
ConcepTest 44.14:   Radiation Shielding
Difficulty Level: 2

Gamma rays are the least interacting of the three types of radioactive decay because they are not charged. Alpha particles are doubly charged, so they lose the most energy. Betas are lighter and singly charged, so they lose less energy. But gamma rays are the hardest to stop.

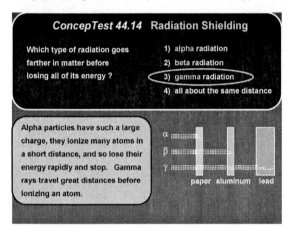

Conceptual Module 44.15 (two parts)
ConcepTest 44.15a: Radiation Exposure I
Difficulty Level: 3

The intensity of radiation follows an inverse square law, so that the intensity drops as the square of the distance. Thus, an increase in distance by a factor of 2 will result in a drop of intensity by a factor of 4.

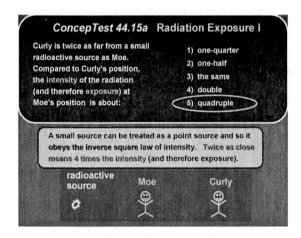

ConcepTest 44.15b: Radiation Exposure II
Difficulty Level: 3

In this question, the reduction factor is specified and the students must determine the safe distance. An estimate is required in this case because the required factor of 10 is not a perfect square. Thus, a factor of 3 in distance (15 m) is *not* enough and the next choice (20 m) must be selected.

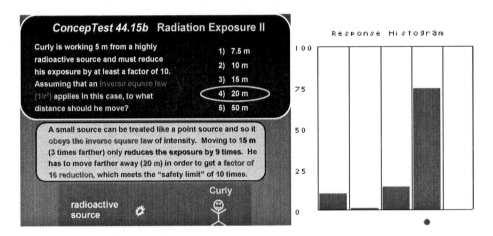

Conceptual Module 44.16
ConcepTest 44.16:   Radiation Damage
Difficulty Level: 1
Suggested follow-up conceptual questions
  • **What type of radiation will tend to do the most damage?**

This question addresses the issue of the mechanism of radiation damage to materials (biological or inorganic). The damage occurs due to ionization of the materials.

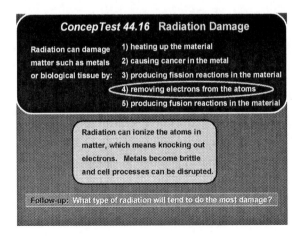